Table of Contents

Chapter 8: Cellular Energy & Organism Complexity

Chapter 9: Evolution

Chapter 11: Humans and the Environment   211

Practice Test 1   223

Practice Test 2   249

Index   273

PREFACE

Passing the Georgia End of Course Test in Biology will help students who are learning or reviewing material for the EOC Test. The materials in this book are based on the testing standards as published by the Georgia Department of Education.

This book contains several sections. These sections are as follows: 1) General information about the book; 2) A Diagnostic Test; 3) An Evaluation Chart; 4) Chapters that teach the concepts and skills that improve graduation readiness; 5) Two Practice Tests. Answers to the tests and exercises are in a separate answer manual. The answer manual also contains a Chart of Standards for teachers to make a more precise diagnosis of student needs and assignments.

We welcome comments and suggestions about the book. Please contact the author at

American Book Company
PO Box 2638
Woodstock, GA 30188-1383

Toll Free: 1 (888) 264-5877
Phone: (770) 928-2834
Fax: (770) 928-7483
Web site: www.americanbookcompany.com

ABOUT THE AUTHORS

Michelle Gunter graduated from Kennesaw State University in Kennesaw, Georgia with a B.S. in Secondary Biology Education. She is a certified teacher in the field of Biology in the state of Georgia. She has three years experience in high school science classrooms. She has nine years experience in biology and biological systems. She has won awards for her research in the field of aquatic toxicology. Mrs. Gunter enjoys teaching students of all ages the wonders of the natural world.

Liz A. Thompson holds a B.S. in Chemistry and an M.S. in Analytical Chemistry, both from the Georgia Institute of Technology. Research conducted as both an undergraduate and graduate student focused on the creation and fabrication of sensors based on conducting polymers and biomolecules. Post graduate experience includes work in radioanalytical and sensor chemistry. Her publications include several articles in respected scientific journals, as well as partial authorship of the textbook *Radioanalytical Chemistry* (2007). At every educational level, Mrs. Thompson has enjoyed teaching, tutoring and mentoring students in the study of science.

TEST-TAKING TIPS

1   Complete the chapters and practice tests in this book. This text will help you review the skills for English/Language Arts: Reading. The book also contains materials for reviewing skills under the Research standards.

2   Be prepared. Get a good night's sleep the day before your exam. Eat a well-balanced meal, one that contains plenty of proteins and carbohydrates, prior to your exam.

3   Arrive early. Allow yourself at least 15–20 minutes to find your room and get settled. Then you can relax before the exam, so you won't feel rushed.

4   Think success. Keep your thoughts positive. Turn negative thoughts into positive ones. Tell yourself you will do well on the exam.

5   Practice relaxation techniques. Some students become overly worried about exams. Before or during the test, they may perspire heavily, experience an upset stomach, or have shortness of breath. If you feel any of these symptoms, talk to a close friend or see a counselor. They will suggest ways to deal with test anxiety. Here are some quick ways to relieve test anxiety:

   • Imagine yourself in your most favorite place. Let yourself sit there and relax.

   • Do a body scan. Tense and relax each part of your body starting with your toes and ending with your forehead.

   • Use the 3-12-6 method of relaxation when you feel stress. Inhale slowly for 3 seconds. Hold your breath for 12 seconds, and then exhale slowly for 6 seconds.

6   Read directions carefully. If you don't understand them, ask the proctor for further explanation before the exam starts.

7   Use your best approach for answering the questions. Some test-takers like to skim the questions and answers before reading the problem or passage. Others prefer to work the problem or read the passage before looking at the answers. Decide which approach works best for you.

8   Answer each question on the exam. Unless you are instructed not to, make sure you answer every question. If you are not sure of an answer, take an educated guess. Eliminate choices that are definitely wrong, and then choose from the remaining answers.

9   Use your answer sheet correctly. Make sure the number on your question matches the number on your answer sheet. In this way, you will record your answers correctly. If you need to change your answer, erase it completely. Smudges or stray marks may affect the grading of your exams, particularly if they are scored by a computer. If your answers are on a computerized grading sheet, make sure the answers are dark. The computerized scanner may skip over answers that are too light.

10 Check your answers. Review your exam to make sure you have chosen the best responses. Change answers only if you are sure they are wrong.

Biology Diagnostic Test

Directions:

Today you will be taking the Biology End-of-Course Test. Read each question carefully and then choose the *best* answer.

Be sure that the question number on the answer sheet matches the number on the test. Then mark your answer by filling in the circle on your answer sheet. Do not write your answer in the test booklet. If you do not know the answer to a question, skip it an go on. You may return to it later if time permits.

If you need to change an answer on your answer sheet, be sure to erase your first mark completely. Do not make any stray marks on the answer sheet.

Do not turn the page until instructed to do so.

Section I

1   José wanted to determine if the amount of food he fed his fish affected the size of fish in his tank. Examine the experimental setup below.   SCSh3e, SCSh3f, SCSh5b

• José fed the fish in Tank One 2.5 grams of food each day.

• José fed the fish in Tank Two 5.0 grams of food each day.

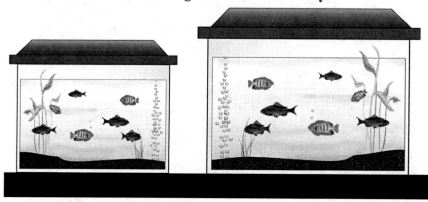

Tank One   Tank Two

José found that the fish in Tank One were smaller than the fish in Tank Two. José decided that feeding his fish more food will increase their mass and length.

Is José's conclusion valid? Why or why not?

A   Yes, it is valid because the fish in Tank One are smaller than the fish in Tank Two.

B   No, it is not valid because José failed to control the size of the fish tanks.

C   Yes, it is valid because the two fish tanks were given different amounts of food.

D   No, it is not valid because the two fish tanks have different numbers of fish in them.

2   **Many types of interactions exist between species. Which of the diagrams below represents commensalism?**   SB4a

Leech

A   Diagram W

B   Diagram X

C   Diagram Y

D   Diagram Z

3   **What is the correct procedure for determining the smell of a chemical in a test tube?**   SCSh2b

A   Securely hold the tube, place your nose two inches over the tube and sniff.

B   Holding the test tube and avoiding the airborne molecules, place your nose directly over the tube and sniff.

C   With the test tube angled away from your face, use one hand to fan the airborne molecules toward your nose.

D   Never attempt to smell the airborne molecules of a liquid chemical.

Go On

Use the image below to answer question 4.

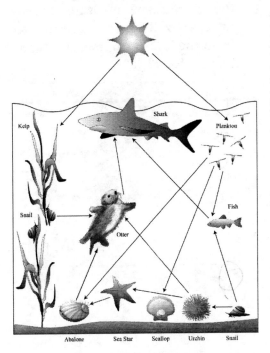

4 Which statement best describes the SB4b relationship between an urchin and the other members of the food web?

A The urchin is prey to the snail and to the otter.

B The urchin is a competitor to the sea star and the otter.

C The urchin is a predator to the snail and a competitor to the fish.

D The urchin is a predator to the sea star and the snail.

5 An abandoned home site SCSh3e, SB4d from the 1950s is discovered on a rural road in the southeastern United States. The entire front of the building is covered with a type of clinging vine. The uncontrolled growth of this plant has resulted in the destruction of the front of the home. This plant does not seem bothered by any natural predators. It was later discovered the scientific name for this plant is *Lonicera japonica*. Based on these facts, which of the following is a reasonable inference?

A All clinging vines will destroy property.

B The home was made of cheap materials.

C With human guidance, the vine would be beautiful.

D The vine is an invasive plant brought from Japan.

6 Using the SI system, what unit of SCSh3c measurement would be used to determine mass?

A meters

B liters

C grams

D millimeters

Go On

7 In the lab, which piece of equipment would you use to measure 250 ml of glucose solution? SCSh2a

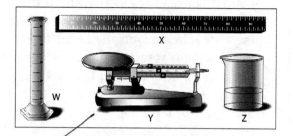

A equipment piece X, meter stick

B equipment piece W, graduated cylinder

C equipment piece Y, triple beam balance

D equipment piece Z, beaker

8 Upon hatching from the egg, sea turtles are attracted to the brightest light in the night sky, usually provided by the moon. This light guides the baby turtles out to sea. What type of behavior does this illustrate? SB4f

A learned behavior

B innate behavior

C convergent behavior

D predatory behavior

9 Which term below best describes the paramecium shown below? SB1a

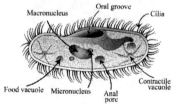

A unicellular

B multicellular

C noncellular

D bicellular

10 Consider an energy pyramid that has four trophic levels, as shown in the figure below. What is the correct ordering of the four organisms pictured from the lowest trophic level to the top trophic level? SB4b

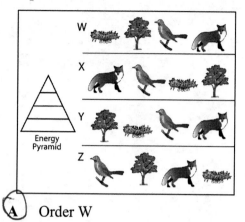

A Order W

B Order X

C Order Y

D Order Z

11 Proteins are made in the ribosomes of a cell, whereas DNA is found only in SB1a

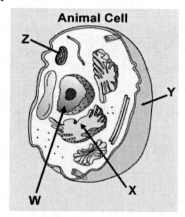

A organelle W.

B organelle X.

C organelle Y.

D organelle Z.

4

Go On

12 Which organelle is directly involved in cellular transport?   SB1a

    A   endoplasmic reticulum (ER)

    B   mitochondria

    C   Golgi apparatus

    D   cell membrane

13 During strenuous exercise, animals cannot take in enough oxygen for all of their cells to carry out aerobic respiration. When this happens, the cells carry out lactic acid fermentation. Lactic acid fermentation is a type of respiration that produces what valuable cellular commodity?   SB3a

    A   oxygen

    B   carbon dioxide

    C   energy

    D   protein

To learn how species are related, scientists can compare structures found in the species to find similarities. The skulls shown below are from four different animals.

Reptile A   Reptile B

Reptile C   Reptile D

14 Which two animals are the MOST closely related?   SB3c, SB5c, SB5b

    A   Reptiles A & B

    B   Reptiles B & C

    C   Reptiles A & D

    D   Reptiles C & D

15 A DNA double helix has two complementary strands. The sequence below is the base sequence of one strand. During replication, this strand experiences an inversion mutation. Identify the correct results.   SB2d

    TTA AGC CCA GCT TAA

    A   TTA AGC ACC GCT TAA

    B   TTA AGC CCA GCT TAA

    C   UUA UGC CCA GCU UAA

    D   TTA AGC CC GCT AAT

Go On

16 **Which of the following accurately illustrates active transport?**

SBa1

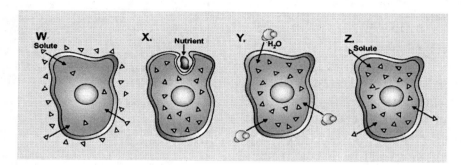

A   images X & Z

B   only image Z

C   images W & Y

D   only image Y

Go On

Use the information and table below to answer question 17.

Genes direct the manufacture of proteins, so a common genetic profile will generally produce similar protein production and activity. An experiment is conducted to discover the effect of a protein (F_1) being inactivated in chicks, prior to hatching. The procedure developed involves administering an inhibiting virus to a chick during its incubation. It is important that the inhibiting virus be administrated at the time that the protein is activated in the developing chick. Therefore, the virus is administered on day 23 of the experiment. The resulting qualitative data is then compared with the observation made on normally hatching chicks, in which the F_1 protein remains active. Four different species of bird chicks (A-D) are used. The results are shown below.

	Webbed feet?	Feathers on feet?
Experimental Bird A	yes	no
Normal Bird A	yes	no
Experimental Bird B	yes	yes
Normal Bird B	no	no
Experimental Bird C	no	yes
Normal Bird C	no	yes
Experimental Bird D	yes	yes
Normal Bird D	no	no

17 **Which of the following questions identifies a source of possible error in the experiment?**   SCSh5b

    A   Do any of the bird species tested have webbed feet when the F_1 protein is active?

    B   Do the eggs of the four bird species incubate for the same amount of time before hatching?

    C   Are all of the bird species tested approximately the same size?

    D   Do all of the bird species normally have feathers on their feet?

Go On

18 A liquor store is burglarized at twilight. A witness across the street sees the burglar force his way in by breaking a window. After the police arrive, they find blood on the broken glass and send it to the laboratory for DNA analysis. Down at the precinct, the witness looks over a lineup of suspects, but admits that all three of the suspects look very much like the man he saw breaking into the store. A DNA analysis of the three suspects produces the fingerprints shown here. Which suspect was the burglar? SB2f

Police Sample   Suspect 1   Suspect 2   Suspect 3

A   Suspect 1

B   Suspect 2

C   Suspect 3

D   All suspects have some of the DNA markers from the police sample, so the test is inconclusive.

19 Which of the following represents RNA in the figure shown here? SB2a

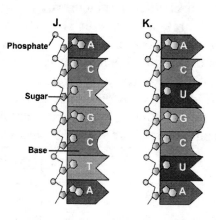

A   J only   **C**   K only

B   both J and K   **D**   neither J nor K

20 During meiosis, crossing over may occur with pairs of homologous chromosomes. What is the result of crossing over? SB2c

A   genetic variation

B   genetic mutations

C   fertilization

D   evolution

8

Go On

Predators and prey interact in the environment in very complex ways. Scientists often select traits in prey populations and observe the effects of predators and environmental change over many generations. A type of African cichlid is observed having a variety of colors. The average wild type fish is brown (see graph below). Over several years, a new water pollutant is released into water systems, causing the plants in the environment to become more red in color.

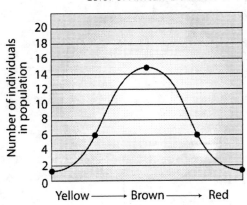

21 Which graph below would you expect to correctly reflect the effect of the pollutant on the African cichlid population?

SCSh4b,
SCSh6c,
SB5d

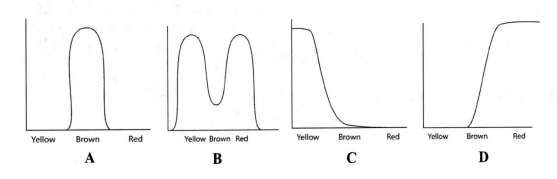

Go On

The pedigree below shows the occurrence of a certain genetic disorder in three generations of a canine family. Use the pedigree to answer question 22.

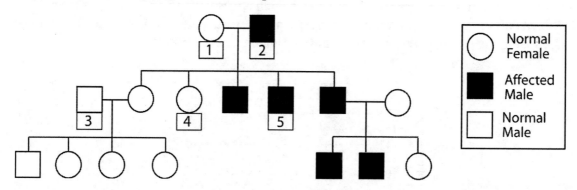

22 The disorder is caused by a dominant allele (Y^F), while the allele for the normal condition is recessive (Y^f). Based on the diagram, which individual has the genotype XY^f?

SB2d

A   individual 1

B   individual 2

C   individual 3

D   individual 5

23 Which of the following statements is NOT true?

SB3a

A   In plants, the products of photosynthesis are used as reactants in respiration, and the products of respiration are used to fuel photosynthesis.

B   Plants carrying out photosynthesis provide a source of oxygen for animals, and respiration provides a source of carbon dioxide for plants.

C   Photosynthesis and respiration convert energy from one form to another.

D   Plant and animal cells perform both respiration and photosynthesis.

24 The tundra is located near the north and south poles and experiences light rainfall. Summer temperatures average only 1 degree Celsius. The subsoil of the tundra is permanently frozen. Grasses, mosses and lichens are present. Animals such as polar bears, caribou, hares, arctic wolves and birds live in the tundra. What type of factors are the amount of rainfall and temperature?

SB4a

A   biotic factors

B   abiotic factors

C   rainfall is biotic and temperature is abiotic

D   temperature is biotic and rainfall is abiotic

Go On

25 The chemical energy supply for all living cells is contained in a particular molecule. When this molecule breaks down, it releases energy that may be used for activities such as muscle contractions, photosynthesis and locomotion. What is the molecule that is the storehouse of cellular energy? SB1a, SB1b

A DNA

B RNA

C ATP

D ADP

26 If a body cell of a human contains 46 chromosomes, how many chromosomes would a human egg cell contain? SB2e

A 46

B 92

C 23

D 0

27 A child is diagnosed with a rare genetic disease. Neither parent has the disease. How might the child have inherited the disorder? SB2b, SB2c

A The disorder is dominant and was carried by one parent.

B The disorder is recessive and carried by both parents.

C The disorder is sex-linked and carried by the father.

D The disorder could only be caused by a mutation during mitosis because neither parent had the disorder.

28 In mice, brown hair is dominant to white. Cross a heterozygous female with a heterozygous male. The genotypic ratio will yield SB2b, SB2c

A 3 brown: 1 white.

B 3 white: 1 brown.

C 1 brown: 2 tan: 1 white.

D 100% brown hair.

Go On

The diagram below shows the classification of four organisms. Use this information to answer question 29.

Common Name	Heart worm	Hookworm	Tapeworm	Roundworm
Organism	1	2	3	4
Class	Secernentea	Secernentea	Secernentea	Secernentea
Order	Spirurida	Spirurida	Ascaridida	Spirurida
Family	Filariidae	Uncinariidae	Ascarididae	Filariidae
Genus	*Dirofilaria*	*Necator*	*Ascaris*	*Loa*

29 According to the diagram, which two organisms are the MOST related?   SB3c

A   Organisms 1 & 4

B   Organisms 1 & 2

C   Organisms 2 & 4

D   Organisms 2 & 3

30 Consider the food web shown below. Which of the following organisms represents the trophic level at which the least amount of energy is present?   SB4a

A   grass   C   frog

B   mouse   D   snake

31 Observed evidence for evolution includes   SB5c

A   fossils, DNA sequences and homologous structures.

B   tropisms, genetic drift and speciation.

C   gene flow, mutations and tropisms.

D   phenotypes, food preferences and fossils.

32 Which of the following characteristics is common to both bacteria and viruses?   SB3d

A   contain genetic material

B   can be killed using antibiotics

C   have a cell membrane

D   have a protein coat

Go On

Use the following passage to answer question 33.

The peppered moth is often used as a case study to illustrate natural selection. The peppered moth is found in two speckled colorations: light-colored and dark-colored. The allele for dark-colored moths is dominant, while the allele for light-colored moths is recessive. In 1850s England, most of the peppered moth population was light in color and blended in with the birch trees they commonly landed on. Their light coloration, or camouflage, makes it hard for birds and other predators to spot and capture them. Dark-colored peppered moths were also present but were fewer in number because they were more susceptible to predation. By the early 1900s, industrial air pollution had covered the birch trees with soot, generally darkening the appearance of the bark. The dark-colored moths now blended in with the trees more effectively than the light-colored moths, and as a result were less easily spotted by predators. Correspondingly, the dark colored moths became greater in number than the light-colored moths.

33 Which of the following statements accurately represents the evolutionary trend demonstrated by the peppered moths?   SB5d

A   A smaller percentage of light-colored moths survive to reproduce, shrinking the gene pool and causing mutations.

B   More and more dark-colored moths survive to reproduce, which shifted the allele frequency towards the dark-colored allele.

C   Over time, the light-colored moths will become homozygous for the light allele and become extinct.

D   Over time, the birds will get used to eating the light-colored moths and stop eating the dark-colored moths.

34 A landscaper crossed two heterozygous junipers. She noticed that of the offspring junipers, 73% were short and 27% were tall. These results indicate that the allele for shortness is   SB2c

A   dominant.

B   recessive.

C   co-dominant.

D   incompletely dominant.

35 Which of the following statements accurately describes the difference between the way bacteria cause disease and the way that viruses cause disease?   SB3d

A   Both bacteria and viruses use host cells to reproduce, but viruses kill the host cell immediately, while bacteria maintain life within the host cell indefinitely.

B   Bacteria only cause disease by entering the body through the bloodstream and infecting a host cell, and viruses only cause disease by entering the body through air passages and infecting a host cell.

C   Bacteria cause disease by incorporating their DNA into the host's DNA, and viruses cause disease by incorporating their RNA in the host's RNA.

D   Bacteria are living cells that grow and reproduce in the body and produce toxins or damage tissues they grow in. Viruses use host cells to reproduce, and these host cells usually die when newly produced virus particles are released.

Go On

36 Which plant organelle is the site of photosynthesis?   SB1a

    A   chloroplast

    B   centriole

    C   cell wall

    D   mitochondria

37 Angiosperms, the flowering plants, are the most successful plants on Earth and have dominated the Earth's plant life for the past 65 million years. They can live almost anywhere on land and do not need to be near standing water to reproduce. Which of the following adaptations of angiosperms has allowed them to become fully adapted to life on land?   SB4e, SB5d

    A   seeds contained within protective fruits

    B   male and female parts contained in separate flowers

    C   less specialized xylem and phloem that require less energy from the plant to maintain

    D   very small leaves that reduce water loss in the plant

38 The graph below shows changes in two populations, the rabbit and the fox. After analyzing the data displayed in the graph, decide which of the following statements is a valid conclusion.   SCSh3f

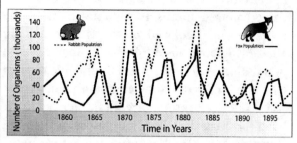

    A   The fox and rabbit have a predator-prey relationship.

    B   There is no correlation between the rabbit and the fox populations.

    C   The size of the rabbit population is a function of average daily temperatures.

    D   The presence of foxes stimulates reproduction in the rabbit population.

39 Which organelle listed and described below is common in both plant and animal cells?   SB1a

    A   mitochondria for cellular respiration

    B   a cell wall for protection

    C   centrioles used during mitosis

    D   chloroplasts for photosynthesis

Section II

40 In the United States, plastic products are considered to be disposable. In other words, as soon as a plastic container is emptied, a diaper is soiled, or a toy is broken, it goes to a landfill. Plastics are composed of long chains of molecules linked tightly together. Saprophytes cannot penetrate these molecules easily. Therefore, some plastics take nearly 200 years to completely break down. Also plastics are manufactured from oil, coal and natural gas, all of which are non-renewable resources. What is a reasonable solution to the plastic problem that takes into account ecological, social and economic factors?   SB4d

A   Immediately stop the manufacture of all plastic products.

B   Pull all of the plastic out of existing landfills, recycle it, and make no more plastic from raw materials.

C   Develop plastics using renewable resources, such as plant products, that decomposers can penetrate and break down.

D   Encourage consumers to stop purchasing any products made from or packaged in plastic until all plastic manufacturers are forced out of business.

41 Trilobites are a class of extinct arthropods that flourished during the Cambrian period of the Paleozoic era. The Carboniferous period left behind huge fields of coal beds in Europe. During the Devonian period, the first fish evolved legs and started to walk on land as amphibians. The beginning of the Silurian period was marked by a mass extinction that destroyed nearly 60% of marine species. Given the following diagram, place these periods in order from oldest to most recent.   SB5c

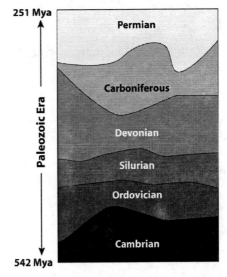

A   Carboniferous, Devonian, Silurian, Cambrian

B   Cambrian, Devonian, Silurian, Carboniferous

C   Cambrian, Silurian, Devonian, Carboniferous

D   Carboniferous, Silurian, Devonian, Cambrian

Go On

42 The use of windmills to pro- SB4d
duce power is encouraged by
many environmental proponents and by
the US government, which subsidizes
this power technology at a compara-
tively high rate. Windmills do not pol-
lute, produce a great deal of clean
energy and their use does not deplete
any natural resource. Wind power is a
good example of technology that har-
nesses which kind of resource?

A   a non-renewable resource

B   a renewable resource

C   a natural resource

D   renewable and natural resources

43 Which two groups of organ- SB3b
isms listed below are responsible for recycling decomposing organic
matter within the ecosystem?

A   plants and animals

B   animals and invertebrates

C   bacteria and fungi

D   animals and fungi

44 Which cycle of matter does the SB4b
illustration shown below best
represent?

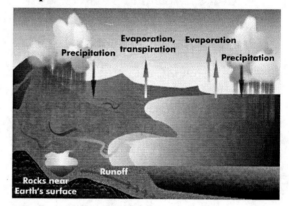

A   the water cycle

B   the carbon cycle

C   the nitrogen cycle

D   the phosphorus cycle

Go On

45 What does the carrying capacity represent? SB4a

   A the amount of mass in the entire population

   B the life expectancy of each organism

   C the largest number of individuals a given environment can support

   D the number of resources needed by each population in an ecosystem

46 In some fruit flies, the allele for having black eyes **(B)** is dominant to the allele for having red eyes **(b)**. A scientist mated a batch of fruit flies with genotypes as shown in the Punnett Square. What is the probability that the offspring will be born with red eyes? SB2c

	B	b
B	BB	Bb
b	Bb	bb

   A 25%

   B 75%

   C 50%

   D 100%

47 A biologist discovers a new organism. It lives on land, cannot move and makes all of its food from sunlight. How would he describe this organism? SB3b

   A producer

   B primary consumer

   C secondary consumer

   D decomposer

48 Possible effects of global warming would include all of the following except SB4d

   A an increase in ultraviolet radiation penetrating the Earth's atmosphere.

   B an increase in average temperature of the biosphere.

   C an increase in sea level.

   D climate changes.

49 Similar organisms that can interbreed and produce fertile offspring in a natural environment make up a(n) SB4a

   A species.

   B population.

   C community.

   D ecosystem.

Go On

50 Blackberry bushes require warm temperatures to sprout shoots and begin growing foliage. After a period of warm temperatures, most blackberry bushes require a period of cool temperatures for proper formation of the fruit and seed. However, several types of blackberry bushes are more tolerant of variable temperatures and can develop seeds and fruit in warmer temperatures. If global warming becomes a permanent trend, which scenario is most likely to occur?   SB5d

   A   Cold weather blackberry bushes will become extinct.

   B   Blackberry bushes that are tolerant of warm weather will become more numerous.

   C   All species of blackberry bushes will adapt and evolve into warm weather bushes.

   D   The blackberry bushes will evolve to no longer produce fruits.

Use the following diagram to answer number 51.

51 An owl and a salamander are both found in the same forest ecosystem. What is the BEST way to describe their role?   SB4a, SB4b

   A   They are abiotic factors.

   B   They are biotic factors.

   C   They are competitors.

   D   They are prey.

52 In what type of environment would you expect to find a non-vascular plant?   SB3b

   A   sand dune of a desert

   B   death valley salt flats

   C   rocky intertidal coastline

   D   bank of a freshwater stream

53 The movement of water across a selectively permeable membrane is   SB1d

   A   active transport.

   B   osmosis.

   C   mitosis.

   D   meiosis.

54 Which of the following statements correctly represents a negative impact of fossil fuel usage?   SB4d

   A   The burning of fossil fuels disrupts the water cycle by adding hydrogen to the atmosphere.

   B   Drilling for fossil fuels disrupts the carbon cycle by adding hydrogen to the atmosphere.

   C   The burning of fossil fuels releases carbon and carbon-based greenhouse gases to the atmosphere in excess volume.

   D   Mining for fossil fuels has irreversibly changed the ecological biomes of the Earth.

Go On

55 Consider the two plants shown. Based on their root structures, which plant is better adapted to life in a desert environment? *SB4e*

A Plant A is better adapted to life in a desert environment because its long thick roots reach deep into the earth to absorb water from the water table.

B Plant B is better adapted to life in a desert environment because its short shallow roots absorb water near the surface after rains.

C Root structure is NOT a factor in determining the degree of adaptation. Leaf structure is the only determining factor as to whether or not a plant is adapted to a desert environment.

D Neither plant A nor plant B are adapted to a desert environment because desert plants don't have roots.

56 The ancestors of polar bears became separated from brown bears when they moved from the mainland to the Arctic ice. Since they were in different environments, the traits selected in the Arctic ice population were different than the traits selected in the land population. Eventually, the two populations could no longer interbreed. Today, we call the descendants of the Arctic ice population polar bears and the descendants of the mainland population brown bears. This phenomenon of one group of organisms separating and forming two reproductively isolated groups is known as *SB5b, SB5d*

A extinction.

B parasitism.

C speciation.

D convergent evolution.

57 DNA is a large molecule composed of two strands of nucleotides. Each nucleotide contains a 5-carbon sugar, a phosphate group and one nitrogen base. There are only four nitrogen bases associated with DNA: cytosine, guanine, thymine and adenine. These nucleotides encode hereditary information, and these segments of information are commonly called genes. If all 30,000 genes are made up of the same twenty nucleotides, how does one gene differ from another? *SB2b*

A the size of the nitrogen bases

B the type of bonds between the nucleotides

C the sequence of the nitrogen bases

D the phenotypes of the nitrogen bases

Go On

58 Carbon is a common element found in living things. Carbon atoms tend to share electrons with other atoms forming   SB1c

   A covalent bonds.

   B hydrogen bonds.

   C ionic bonds.

   D proton bonds.

59 Which of the following Web addresses is MOST likely to contain reliable information on cleaning up a hazardous waste site?   SCSh1a, SCSh6c

   A www.stopmanufacturing.org

   B www.epa.gov/

   C www.lets-clean-up.com/

   D www.bobspage.com/

60 The African savanna has a large range of highly specialized plants and animals, which depend on each other to keep the environment in balance. The African people have begun to graze their livestock in many parts of the savanna grassland. What is the likely outcome of this activity?   SB4a, SB4c

   A The savanna grasses will grow more quickly as they are eaten, so the area of the savanna will increase.

   B The top consumers will leave the area, as there are no more animals to eat.

   C The grasses will be diminished and will cease to hold water into the soil, so the savanna will convert to a desert biome.

   D The loss of vegetation will cause groundwater to overflow, so the savanna biome will convert to a flooded grassland.

61 Which of the following characteristics is not common to all vertebrates?   SB3b

   A mammary glands

   B notochord

   C gill slits

   D endoskeleton

62 Mushrooms, Penicillium and black bread mold all belong to what kingdom?   SB3b

   A Protista

   B Fungi

   C Eubacteria

   D Plantae

63 The majority of the energy in the ATP molecule is   SB3a

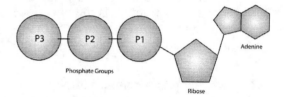

   A stored chemically in the P_1 - ribose bond.

   B stored chemically in the $P_2 - P_3$ bond.

   C stored chemically in the phosphate molecules.

   D stored chemically in the ribose sugar molecule.

Go On

64 Charles Darwin's ideas form the basis of the modern theory of evolution. Although he was not the first to propose that organisms changed over time, he was the first to propose a valid mechanism by which this happened. Central to his theory was the importance given to natural variation and its place in the context of natural selection. Which of the following statements most accurately describes Darwin's proposal on the nature of inherited variations?   SB5a, SB5b

A   Variations are ONLY inherited if they have proven to have a positive adaptive value in the previous generation.

B   Variations that have a negative adaptive value are LESS likely to be passed from parent to offspring.

C   Inherited variations occur by chance, and have a variable degree of adaptive value to the individual organism during its lifetime.

D   Inherited variations occur because of environmental conditions, and have a variable degree of adaptive value to the individual organism during its lifetime.

65 Water is an excellent solvent because   SB1d

A   it is a polar molecule.

B   it is an organic molecule.

C   it is always acidic.

D   it is a renewable resource.

66 The cycle shown is important to cells because   SB3a

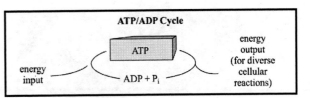

ATP/ADP Cycle

energy input

ATP

ADP + P_i

energy output (for diverse cellular reactions)

A   ATP is responsible for making energy within the cell.

B   ATP is the molecule used for energy storage within the cell.

C   ADP is the molecule used for energy storage within the cell.

D   ADP is responsible for making and regulating energy within the cell.

Go On

67 This diagram shows which process?

SB2e

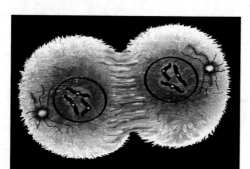

A   anaphase

B   metaphase

C   cytokinesis

D   interphase

68 Identify the main difference between plants and animals as listed below.

SB3b

A   Plants are made of cells while animals are not.

B   Plants are producers while animals are consumers.

C   Plants are green while animals are multicolored.

D   Plants have roots while animals do not.

Go On

Use the classification key to answer number 69.

1. a. Fur is marked with stripes and spots................ go to 2.
   b. Fur is primarily solid-colored…..…................ go to 3.

2. a. Dwells primarily in trees………....................…… *Leopardus wiedii* (margay)
   b. Dwells primarily on the ground…....................… *Leopardus pardalis* (ocelot)

3. a. Ears and tail are tipped with short, black fur …... *Puma concolor* (puma)
   b. Ears are tufted with long, black fur …................. *Caracal caracal* (caracal)

69 According to the classification key, to which genus and species does this cat belong?   SB3c

   A *Leopardus wiedii*

   B *Leopardus pardalis*

   C *Puma concolor*

   D *Caracal caracal*

Go On

70 What is the process shown in the diagram below?

SB2b

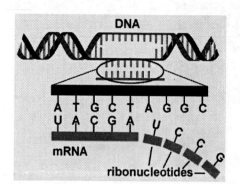

A   transcription

B   translation

C   replication

D   cytokinesis

71 An amateur horticulturist crossed a pink orchid flower with a purple orchid flower. The resulting offspring flowers were pink with purple stripes. How would you characterize the allele for color in this orchid flower?

SB2b

A   dominant

B   recessive

C   co-dominant

D   polygenetic

72 In some fruit flies the allele for having long bristles (B) is dominant to the allele for having short bristles (b). A scientist mated a batch of fruit flies with genotypes as shown in the Punnett square below. What is the probability that the off-spring will be born with short bristles?

SB2b, SB2c

	B	b
B	BB	Bb
b	Bb	bb

A   25%   C   50%

B   75%   D   100%

73 A biome in Australia is described as having many insects, lizards, snakes and succulent plants. This biome regularly experiences high temperatures and little rainfall. Identify the correct biome from the choices below.

SB4a

A   grassland

B   deciduous forest

C   desert

D   jungle

74 A new type of organism is found living in an extremely cold environment. This organism is unicellular and has a cell wall that lacks peptidoglycan (protein-carbohydrate molecule). To which kingdom does this organism belong?

SB3b

A   Archaebacteria

B   Eubacteria

C   Protista

D   fungi

Go On

75 Examine the cladogram below and determine the most closely related organisms.

SB3c

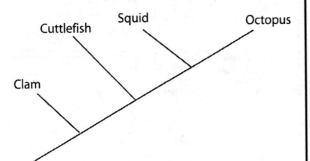

A   clam and octopus

B   cuttlefish and octopus

C   clam and squid

D   squid and octopus

76 The Florida panther (*Puma concolor coryi*) was once thought to be extinct, until it was found living in the Florida Everglades. Today, there are about 80 breeding members of this critically endangered subspecies of cougar.

SCSh9a,
SCSh1b,
SCSh3a,
SB4d

It is currently thought that the Georgia Eastern cougar (*Puma concolor cougar*) is extinct. In spite of this, its name remains on the Georgia State endangered species list, rather than being labeled an extinct species. Which statement is the MOST reasonable explanation for the continued presence of the Eastern cougar on the endangered species list?

A   The Eastern cougar remains on the list because environmentalists are sentimental about its loss.

B   The fact that Eastern cougars have not been seen recently does not mean that they are not there; they remain on the list to protect those animals that might still be living.

C   The Eastern cougar remains on the list to remind the public that animals can become extinct as a result of human exploitation of the environment.

D   No one has considered the status of the Eastern cougar because the endangered species lists are only updated occasionally.

Go On

77 The brown thrasher is the Geor- SB4a, gia state bird. This bird eats SB4b mainly small invertebrates, like cater- pillars, snails and grasshoppers. To what trophic level does this animal belong?

A   primary producer

B   primary consumer

C   secondary consumer

D   tertiary consumer

78 Identify the physical feature SB4f below that makes sea turtles adapted to life in the ocean.

A   large protective shell

B   flipper-like legs

C   amniotic egg

D   short tail

79 A man in rural south Georgia SB4c dies and wills his farm to his son that lives in Atlanta. The son does not plant or harvest on the land. Instead, he allows the land to return to a more nat- ural state. After 25 years, what type of plant life do you MOST expect to find growing on the land?

A   grasses and herbs only

B   lichens and moss

C   pine and hardwood trees

D   shrubs and grasses only

80 The pie chart below summa- SCSh2c, rizes laboratory injuries SCSh3d reported in 2006. How would you prevent the third most common laboratory injury?

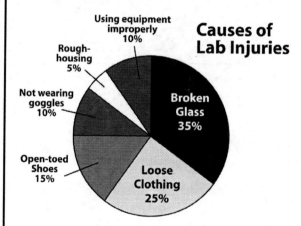

Causes of Lab Injuries

Using equipment improperly 10%
Rough-housing 5%
Not wearing goggles 10%
Open-toed Shoes 15%
Broken Glass 35%
Loose Clothing 25%

A   Dispose of broken glass correctly.

B   Don't wear loose-fitting clothing.

C   Don't wear open-toed shoes.

D   Always wear safety goggles.

EVALUATION CHART FOR GEORGIA BIOLOGY EOCT DIAGNOSTIC TEST

Directions: On the following chart, circle the question numbers that you answered incorrectly, and evaluate the results. These questions are based on the Georgia standards for biology. Then turn to the appropriate topics (listed by chapters), read the explanations, and complete the exercises. Review other chapters as needed. Finally, complete the practice test(s) to assess your progress and further prepare you for the End of Course Test.

*Note:Some question numbers will appear under multiple chapters because those questions require demonstration of multiple skills.

Chapters	Diagnostic Test Question
Chapter 1: Safety Procedures and Behavior	3, 7, 80
Chapter 2: Units and Measurements	1, 6, 7
Chapter 3: A Scientific Method	17, 59
Chapter 4: Applying Science	17
Chapter 5: Cells and Cellular Transport	9, 12, 16, 36, 39, 53, 58, 65, 67
Chapter 6: Nucleic Acids and Cell Division	11, 15, 19, 20, 70
Chapter 7: Genetics, Heredity and Biotechnology	18, 22, 26, 27, 28, 34, 46, 57, 71, 72
Chapter 8: Cellular Energy and Organism Complexity	9, 13, 23, 25, 29, 32, 35, 37, 39, 43, 47, 52, 61, 62, 63, 66, 68, 69, 74
Chapter 9: Evolution	8, 14, 21, 31, 33, 41, 50, 55, 56, 64, 75, 78
Chapter 10: Interaction in the Environment	2, 4, 5, 10, 24, 30, 38, 44, 45, 49, 51, 73, 77, 79
Chapter 11: Humans and the Environment	40, 42, 48, 54, 60, 76

Chapter 1
Safe Procedures and Behavior

GEORGIA PERFORMANCE SCIENCE STANDARDS COVERED IN THIS CHAPTER INCLUDE:

SCSh2 a – c	Students will use standard safety practices for all classroom laboratory and field investigations.

SAFETY PROCEDURES IN THE LABORATORY

Safety procedures are designed to protect you and others from injury. The most important safety rule is to always follow your teacher's instructions. Before working in the laboratory, fully read all of the directions for the experiment. Laboratory accidents can be easily avoided if safety procedures are followed. Be sure that you wear appropriate clothing for the lab, and remove any dangling jewelry. Know where eyewash stations are located. Decide what personal protective equipment, like aprons, goggles or gloves, are necessary. If there is an accident, spill or breakage in the laboratory, report it to your instructor immediately.

Glassware Safety

- To avoid being cut, never use broken or chipped glassware. Broken or chipped glassware should be properly disposed of in an appropriate labeled container.

- Only heat glassware that is thoroughly dry.

- Never pick up any glassware unless you are sure it is not hot. Remember, hot glass looks the same as cold glass. If glassware is hot, use heat-resistant gloves or tongs to handle it to avoid burns.

- To prevent glassware from cracking, do not bring glassware that is hot into contact with anything cold, especially cold water.

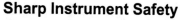

Sharp Instrument Safety

- Always use single-edged razors.
- Handle any sharp instrument with extreme care.
- Never cut any material toward you. Always cut away from you. Immediately notify your teacher if you receive a cut.
- Dispose of used or ruined sharp instruments in an appropriately labeled container.

Fire and Heat Safety

- Always wear safety glasses or goggles when working with an open flame.
- Never reach across a flame.
- Never heat anything (particularly chemicals) unless instructed to do so.
- Never heat anything in a closed container.
- Always use a clamp, tongs or heat-resistant gloves to handle hot objects.
- When using a Bunsen burner to heat a substance in a test tube, move the test tube in and out of the flame. Never leave the test tube directly in the flame for extended periods of time.
- Fire extinguishers should be located in or near the lab in case of a fire. Do not tamper with the extinguishers in any way. Only use an extinguisher if you have received proper training. Do not remove an extinguisher from its mounting unless instructed to by your teacher and/or during a fire.

Animal Safety

- Do not cause pain, discomfort or injury to a live animal.
- Follow your teacher's directions when handling animals.
- Wash your hands thoroughly after handling animals or their cages.

Electrical Safety

- If an extension cord is needed to plug in an electrical device, use the shortest extension cord possible. Never use an extension cord that is frayed or worn.
- Do not use socket multipliers to overload an electrical outlet.
- Never touch an electrical appliance or outlet with wet hands.
- Always be sure to keep electrical cords away from standing water

Chemical Safety

- Always wear a safety apron or lab coat and protective gloves when handling chemicals. This provides protection from chemical spills. If a chemical comes into contact with your skin, rinse immediately, for a minimum of 15 minutes and notify your instructor.

- If instructed by your teacher to smell a chemical, never smell the chemical directly. Instead, hold the container with the chemical away from your face and use your hand to waft the chemical odor toward your nose.

- Use proper ventilation in the lab. If chemicals (particularly organic solvents) are handled in the lab, a chemical fume hood should be available.

- When not in use, keep all chemicals properly stored in the appropriately labeled containers.

- Ensure that all chemicals are properly disposed of as instructed by your teacher.

Eye and Face Safety

- Wear safety goggles when handling chemicals.

- When you are heating a test tube or bottle, always point it away from you and others.

- Remember, chemicals can splash or boil out of a heated test tube, beaker or other container.

- If a chemical comes into contact with your eyes, rinse immediately at an eyewash station for a minimum of 15 minutes and notify your instructor.

Proper Dress

- When working in a laboratory setting, wear clothes that cover as much of your skin as possible. This means long-sleeved shirts and long pants rather than tank tops or shorts.

- Wear shoes that completely cover the toes.

- Tie back long hair to prevent it from coming into contact with chemicals or an open flame.

- Remove or tie back any dangling jewelry or loose clothing to prevent them from getting caught on any equipment or causing unsafe situations.

Through the Department of Labor, the United States Government runs the **Occupational Safety and Health Administration, (OSHA)**. The goal of OSHA is to protect the health and safety of America's workers. OSHA publishes regulations and procedures that help maintain safe work environments. It also has a great deal of guidance for workers and employers from all industries. The national OSHA website is at www.osha.gov.

Manufacturers of chemicals are required to produce, update and maintain a safety data sheet for each chemical they produce. This document is called a **material safety data sheet**, or **MSDS**. An MSDS lists information on chemical structure, chemical appearance, chemical properties and personal safety. It also contains information on safe storage and disposal of chemicals.

MSDS documents come with any chemical that is purchased. They are not discarded, but kept on file. If you want to see the MSDS for a chemical that you are working with, ask your teacher.

Official Safety Information

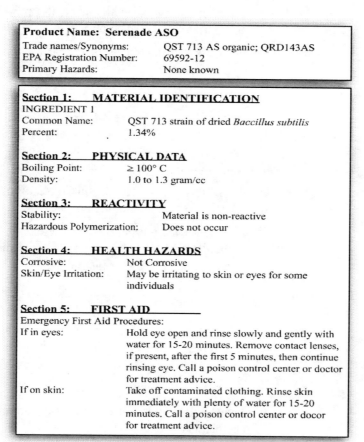

Source: http://www.agraquest.com/products/serenade/pdfs/Serenade_ASO-MSDS.pdf

Figure 1.1 Example of an MSDS

Section Review 1: Safety Procedures in the Laboratory

A. List several rules for ensuring the various safety concerns below are met.

glassware safety   animal safety   chemical safety
sharp instrument safety   electrical safety   eye and face safety
fire and heat safety

B. Choose the best answer.

1. How should you pick up a piece of hot glassware?

   A. with bare hands   C. with the sleeve of your shirt

   B. with heat-resistant gloves   D. with a spatula

2. How should you hold a test tube containing a chemical?

   A. pointed away from your face   C. held right up to your nose

   B. pointed at your eye   D. very close to your partner's face

3. You should report a cut in your skin, glass breakage or a chemical spill

   A. after the problem is handled.   C. immediately.

   B. never.   D. after you write down what happened.

4. Why shouldn't you wear dangling jewelry and baggy clothing to the laboratory?

   A. The baggier the clothes, the more chemical fumes are absorbed.

   B. The metal in the jewelry changes the expected reaction.

   C. Lab coats don't fit over baggy clothes.

   D. Jewelry and clothing could get caught on equipment, and clothes can catch on fire.

5. When you are done with an experiment, how should you dispose of any chemicals used?

   A. Mix them all up in a waste container and dump them in the trash.

   B. Pour them all down the sink.

   C. Follow the instructions given to properly dispose of the particular chemical(s).

   D. Mix the chemicals in a flask and heat the mixture until it evaporates into the air.

6. Your microscope needs to be plugged in to an electrical outlet. What is the best way to do this?

   A. with a plug that has two bent prongs

   B. with a plug that has straight prongs and a short power cord

   C. with a plug that has straight prongs and a long extension cord

   D. with a plug that has straight prongs and a frayed extension cord

EQUIPMENT AND MATERIALS

Laboratory equipment and materials are tools used in scientific investigations. Each piece of equipment in the lab has a specific purpose. Part of behaving safely is the ability to identify lab equipment and recognize its use. Inappropriate use of equipment and material causes accidents. If you don't know the purpose of a piece of equipment, ask your teacher. Instruments are used to enhance the ability of our senses to observe the world around us.

Glassware for handling liquids:

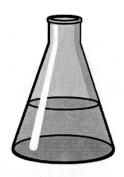

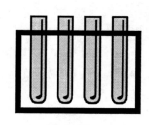

An **Erlenmeyer flask** is used to mix liquids; its narrow mouth prevents splashing and lessens the dispersion of noxious fumes. Although sometimes it is marked to make volume measurements, they are only approximate values.

Test tubes are used to mix, measure or heat liquids. Test tubes are not usually marked with measurements, so they are only used to make approximate measurements.

Beakers are used to mix and heat liquids. Like the Erlenmeyer flask, they are not intended for accurate volume measurement.

An **eyedropper** is used to dispense small measurements of a liquid.

Equipment for heating:

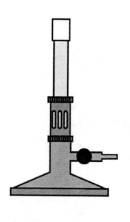

A **Bunsen burner** is a source of gas heat.

A **hot plate** is a source of electrical heat.

Tongs are used to grasp heated material.

A **tripod** holds glassware above a Bunsen burner.

Wire gauze usually goes on top of a tripod to hold the glassware being heated.

Equipment for measuring mass:

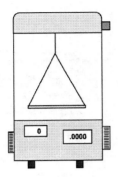

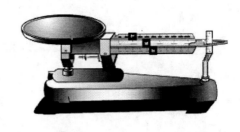

A **mechanical pan balance** is used to accurately determine mass to the nearest ten thousandth of a gram. The balance above is tared (zeroed out).

A **triple-beam balance** is used to determine the mass of heavier materials to the nearest gram.

Equipment for measuring volume:

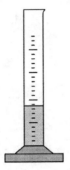

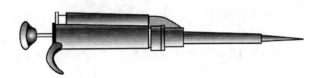

Graduated cylinders are "graduated" or marked with a scale for measurement. They are used to accurately measure liquid volume.

Pipets are used to accurately measure small liquid volumes. Pipets are usually marked TD (to deliver). When using a TD glass pipet with a bulb dispenser, do not "blow out" excess liquid left in the tip as you dispense. The pipet is designed to deliver the exact volume marked on the side.

Equipment for measuring length:

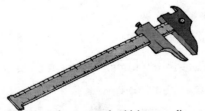

A **meter stick** measures length or width.

A **caliper** is used to accurately measure the thickness or diameter of an object, on smaller scale than a ruler. The jaws of the caliper are closed on the object to be measured, then the distance between the jaws is read. Calipers work best on firm, solid objects.

Observation equipment:

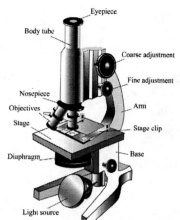

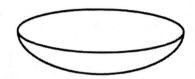

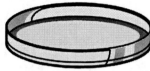

A **microscope** enables us to see things too small to see with the unaided eye. The three components are (1) the arm, which is used to lift and carry the microscope (2) the objectives, which magnify the sample (3) the two adjustment knobs, which focus the view.

A **watch glass** is a holding container or covering device.

A **Petri dish** is a glass or plastic dish used to culture cells. Cell culture is a method of growing microscopic organisms. Petri dishes have covers to enclose the cultured sample.

Section Review 2: Equipment

1. Which of the following is used as a source of heat in the laboratory?

   A. thermometer   B. Bunsen burner   C. gasoline   D. thermostat

2. Which has specific markings for measurement and is used to accurately measure liquid volume?

   A. test tube   C. ruler
   B. beaker   D. graduated cylinder

3. Which of the following pieces of equipment is used to handle liquids but is not intended for accurate measurement?

   A. beaker   C. Erlenmeyer flask
   B. test tube   D. all of the above

4. If you were instructed to heat something on the Bunsen burner, what would you use to hold your container over the burner?

   A. a watch glass   C. a piece of wire gauze held by a tripod
   B. gloved hands   D. a Petri dish

5. What of the following should be measured with a caliper, rather than a meter stick or ruler?

   A. length of a worm   C. length of a shark
   B. width of a snail shell   D. width of a worm

SITUATIONAL SAFETY

Laboratory safety is much more than a set of rules that define what you should and shouldn't do. It is a set of practices that should accompany a serious attitude and focus on your work. Many accidents can be avoided if you simply pay attention to the task at hand. In the following figure, we see a class that has mostly abandoned its focus on work.

Figure 1.2 A Classroom in Chaos

Let's see if you can pick out the things that are going wrong and the students that are behaving correctly:

1. What are two unsafe activities shown in the illustration? Why are they unsafe?

2. List two correct lab procedures depicted in the illustration.

3. What should Bob do after the accident?

4. What should Sue do to avoid an accident?

5. Find three things shown in the lab that should not be there.

6. Compare Joe's and Carl's lab techniques. Who is doing it the correct way?

7. List three items in the illustration that are there for the safety of the students in the lab.

Before reading on, please take some time to examine the picture and answer the questions for yourself. Then we'll give you our perspective.

1.   What are two unsafe activities shown in the illustration? Why are they unsafe?

There is SO much to choose from! Let's take the activities of Tim and Ray first. Tim is hitting Ray over the head with a book. This is a DEFINITE no-no. First, Ray could get hurt. Additionally, other people could get hurt, even if they are not fooling around. *No horseplay is allowed in the lab; accidents happen when people are not paying attention.*

Next, take a look at what Joe and Jim are about to do: they are about to drink their experiment. That is EXTREMELY unsafe. *When in the laboratory, you should never put anything to your nose or mouth, unless specifically directed by your teacher to do so.*

2. List two correct lab procedures depicted in the illustration.

Tina is doing a great job holding the test tube over the flame with the proper tool (called tongs). Carl and Tina are both wearing proper safety goggles and are focused on their work.

3. What should Bob do after the accident?

The first thing Bob should do is *let the teacher know the accident has occurred!* In fact, that is what all students should do ANY time there is an accident in the lab. Next he should (carefully) clean up the glass with a glass collection broom and dustpan. He should make sure to *follow his teacher's directions* on whether to put the broken glass in the trash can or into another receptacle that might be designated specifically for glass.

4. What should Sue do to avoid an accident?

Never leave long hair loose in the lab. Sue may not like this, but if she doesn't do something to pin down her beautiful golden locks of hair they are going to catch on fire! Given the choice between securing her hair and having it singed, she'll choose to find a hair clip or hair band!

5. What are three things shown in the lab that should not be there?

Some of these are obvious, and some are not. Well, first, there is a rabbit loose in class. If you look closely, you'll see a pair of scissors that definitely should not be in the electric socket. Third, there should not be a beaker and spill on the floor next to Tim. Now it's your turn: name three more unsafe situations.

_____

_____

_____

_____

6. Compare Joe's and Carl's lab techniques. Who is doing it the correct way?

Way to go Carl! Just say NO to Joe! *Never put anything in the lab in your mouth, especially not a liquid that is labeled with the symbol for poison!*

7. List three items in the illustration that are there for the safety of the students in the lab.

If you look in the upper right hand corner you should see the *fire extinguisher, safety blanket and first aid box*. It's important to know where all three of these items are located at all times. They are there for your safety and the safety of others. Of course, in our picture, the first aid kit is flapping open and the fire extinguisher is missing. *Let your teacher know if laboratory safety equipment is damaged or missing.*

It's also important to note that some of the students are *wearing safety glasses*. You should know where these are and make sure to wear them during lab.

The most important safety precautions you can take in a science lab is to *always follow instructions*, and when something happens that shouldn't make sure to *inform your teacher as soon as possible*.

THINK WHILE YOU WORK

The student lab is a place where accidents are more likely to happen. This is true for two reasons.

1. Students are learning to investigate through experimentation. Because they are learning, they may be more likely to make mistakes.

2. Experimentation itself is the investigation of the unknown. As such, it carries risk.

It is up to the student to be alert and focused. The student must also use common sense when making decisions in the laboratory. Finally, the student must learn to infer and predict.

Inference means using your existing body of knowledge to determine causes and appropriate actions. **Predicting** involves using your knowledge to foretell the outcome of an action. These skills should be applied to the data that you obtain in lab. They should also be used to guide your behavior in the laboratory. The following activities are designed to show how to use data to make appropriate decisions.

Activity

Rodrigo fills a glass beaker with distilled water and places it on a hotplate. He heats the water, measuring the temperature every three minutes. His results are shown below.

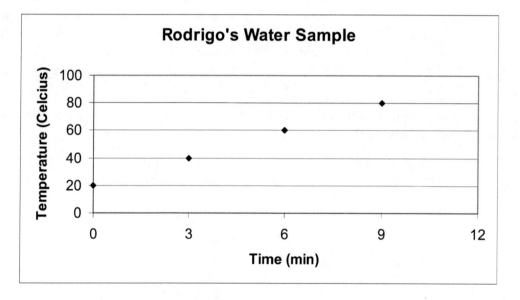

1. What temperature did the water sample start at? Was it warm or cold?
2. What do you predict the temperature will be at 12 minutes?
3. When the experiment is over, should Rodrigo remove the beaker from the hot plate with his bare hands?
4. Is it safe to breathe around the boiling sample, or should Rodrigo wear a face mask?

Activity

Marita places a beaker containing chemical A on a triple beam balance. She records the mass. She adds chemical B to the beaker and records the mass. As the chemicals begin to react, fumes are produced, and mass is lost. Marita records the mass of the beaker every 10 seconds. Her results are shown below.

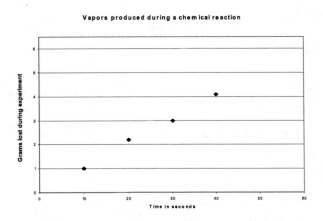

1. Where should this experiment be performed?
2. Predict how many grams will be lost at the 60-second mark?
3. Where has the mass gone?

Activity

A national study reveals the most common causes of laboratory injuries. The results are shown below.

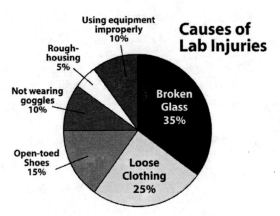

1. Based on this graph, what can you infer to be the greatest threat to student safety?
2. Look back at Figure 1.2. Which of the students in that figure are practicing the unsafe behaviors shown in this circle graph?
3. Make a circle graph of your own. How many students in Figure 1.2 are practicing each unsafe behavior?
4. Does your circle graph show the same patterns as the national study above? Why do you think there are differences?

Section Review 3:   Situational Safety

1.   Various safety rules apply in the laboratory. In order to protect your clothing, you should

   A.   wear an apron.
   B.   wear clothing treated with Teflon.
   C.   wear clothing treated with Scotchgard™.
   D.   wear as many layers as possible.

2.   Reaching across a flame is

   A.   never acceptable.   C.   sometimes acceptable.
   B.   always acceptable.   D.   seldom acceptable.

3.   Identify when you should report a chemical spill to your teacher.

   A.   immediately
   B.   after you've cleaned up the spill
   C.   only if you think the spill is dangerous
   D.   after you've finished the experiment so your results are not ruined

4.   Identify the lab activity that should be conducted under a fume hood.

   A.   measuring very high velocities
   B.   using high voltage sources of laser light
   C.   mixing chemicals that produce dangerous vapors
   D.   massing a series of objects

5.   What is the BEST way to avoid eye damage from chemical splashes in the laboratory?

   A.   Wear your eyeglasses.
   B.   Wear your contact lenses.
   C.   Wear your safety glasses or goggles over your eyeglasses.
   D.   Stay near the eyewash station and first aid kit throughout class.

6.   Who is the primary person responsible for your safety in the laboratory?

   A.   you   C.   your classmates
   B.   your teacher   D.   your parents

CHAPTER 1 REVIEW

Use the following scenario to answer questions 1 – 2.

A student sitting at a lab computer was surprised by the explosion of a chemical waste bottle. Nitric acid and shards of glass were sprayed all over the lab. The day before, 2L of nitric acid waste had been added to a chemical waste bottle, which originally contained methanol. Nitric acid reacts violently with most organics, like methanol. Over the course of 12 – 16 hours, it is likely that some leftover methanol reacted with the nitric acid waste and created enough carbon dioxide to over pressurize the container.

1. Which of the following actions would have been a reasonable way to PREVENT the accident?

   A. Chemical containers should be triple-rinsed and completely dry before being used for waste accumulation.

   B. Safety glasses should always be worn while in the laboratory, even while performing non-laboratory work.

   C. Nitric acid waste should have been flushed down the drain.

   D. A cap should never be placed on waste bottles, so they do not become pressurized.

2. What does this scenario emphasize?

   A. the need to eliminate waste

   B. the need to wear safety goggles

   C. the need to need to dispose of waste properly

   D. both B and C

3. Graduated cylinders are marked in units of

   A. grams.　　　　B. meters.　　　　C. millimeters.　　　　D. milliliters.

4. Select the BEST piece of equipment for observing whether or not different solids float in a given liquid.

   A. watch glass

   B. beaker

   C. Erlenmeyer flask

   D. Petri dish

5. How is a broken glass beaker discarded?

   A. Wrap it in paper towels and throw it in the trash.

   B. Wrap it in a plastic bag and throw it in the trash.

   C. Gently dropping it into the labeled broken glass container.

   D. Slam-dunking it into the labeled broken glass container.

6. Anthony draws 2 mL of a water sample into a glass pipet. If he wants to culture the growth of microorganisms in the water, what basic piece(s) of equipment does he need?

   A. a Petri dish
   B. a watch glass and a Petri dish
   C. a watch glass and a microscope
   D. a Petri dish and a microscope

7. What is the reason for NOT wearing sandals in the lab?

   A. to protect your toes from electrical shock
   B. to trample your sense of style
   C. to eliminate stinky feet
   D. to avoid injury to your feet from chemical spills or broken glass

8. The following figure shows a compound light microscope.

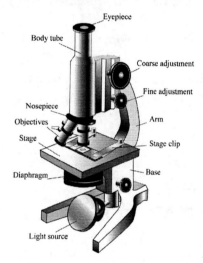

   • Which named part of the microscope is primarily responsible for magnification of a sample?

   _____

   • What is the purpose of the course adjustment knob?

   _____

   _____

Chapter 2
Units and Measurements

GEORGIA PERFORMANCE SCIENCE STANDARDS COVERED IN THIS CHAPTER INCLUDE:

SCSh5 c – e	Student will demonstrate the computation and estimation skills necessary for analyzing data and developing reasonable scientific explanations.

SCIENTIFIC MEASUREMENT

In order to describe the world around them, scientists often take measurements. This allows them to quantify the phenomenon. But *how* one measures is just as important as *what* one measures. To illustrate this, let's use an example, Andrew's teacher has asked him to measure the length of the classroom.

There are a few things that Andrew must remember when making his measurement:

- All measurements must have a unit. If Andrew measures the length of his classroom and announces that it is 16.7, it doesn't mean much. Yards, meters, feet? We need a unit.
- All units must be common. What if Andrew tells us that the room is 16.7 lengths of *his* feet? Great. Now we have to measure Andrew's feet in order to derive the length of the room.
- All units must be common *everywhere*. Andrew finally gets it together and tells us that the room measures 16.7 standard feet. Well, now *we* know the length of the room, but no one in Japan or Germany will understand the measurement because the rest of the world uses the metric system.

The United States has been a bit slow to comply, but metric units are now increasingly used in this country. In the following sections, we will discuss the units appropriate to various measurements and the conversion of those units.

INTRODUCTION TO SI UNITS

The **SI units** of measurement are used throughout the world when performing calculations related to scientific investigations. It stands for *Le Système International d'Unites* and was established in France about 200 years ago. SI units were adapted from the metric system, and the base units are meter (m), gram (g) and second (s) to measure length, mass and time, respectively. In addition, volume, density and temperature are measurements frequently used in the laboratory.

The **English system** of measurement, also called the **U.S. Customary System**, is used in the United States. In this system, the foot (ft) is the standard length, the pound (lb) is the standard weight and the second (s) is the standard for time. Although you are probably more familiar with the English system, the SI units are used in the scientific community and throughout the world. Therefore, SI units will be the standard system of measurement used in this book. Some units and conversions are listed in Table 2.1 and Table 2.2.

Table 2.1 - English and Metric Systems (with abbreviations)

English			Metric		
Length					
12 inches (in)	=	1 foot (ft)	1000 millimeters (mm)	=	1 meter (m)
3 ft	=	1 yard (yd)	100 centimeters (cm)	=	1 m
5,280 feet (ft)	=	1 mile (mi)	1000 m	=	1 kilometer (km)
Mass					
16 ounces (oz)	=	1 pound (lb)	1000 milligrams (mg)	=	1 gram (g)
2000 lbs	=	1 ton	1000 g	=	1 kilogram (kg)
Volume					
16 fluid ounces (fl oz)	=	1 pint (pt)	1 cubic centimeter cm^3	=	1 milliliter (mL)
2 pts	=	1 quart (qt)	1000 mL	=	1 liter (L)
4 qts	=	1 gallon (gal)			

Table 2.2 English-Metric Conversions

English		Metric
Length		
1 inch (in)	=	2.54 cm
3.281 ft	=	1 m
Mass		
0.035 oz	=	1 g
1 lb	=	0.453 kg
Volume		
33.8 fl oz	=	1 L
1 gal	=	3.78 L

STANDARD SI MEASUREMENTS

The standard SI unit of measurement to determine **length** is the **meter (m)**. To better visualize a meter, it is helpful to know that 1 meter is equal to 3.2 feet. Length measures the distance from one point to another and can be used to determine a person's height in meters, the distance between your home and your school in kilometers, the length of a leaf in centimeters, or the thickness of a dime in millimeters. A ruler or **meter stick** is commonly used to measure length, as seen in Figure 2.1 below.

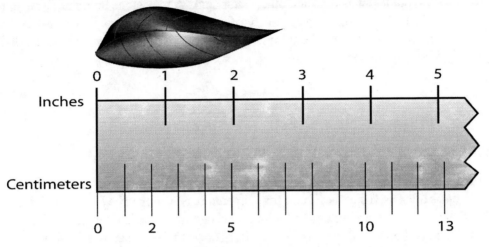

Figure 2.1 Metric Ruler

Mass is the measure of the amount of matter in an object. Its standard SI unit is the **gram (g)**, and its tool of measurement is the balance. The mass of a needle, a rock and a person would be expressed in milligrams, grams and kilograms, respectively.

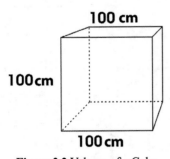

Figure 2.2 Volume of a Cube

Volume is the amount of space occupied by an object. Volume is determined in different ways depending on the shape (i.e. cube, sphere, irregular) and state of matter (i.e. solid, liquid, gas) of the object. For a regularly shaped object, like a cube, volume is determined by multiplying the length times the height times the width of the object ($V = l \times h \times w$). The units used for volume are cubic centimeters (cm^3 or cc) or milliliters (mL). Figure 2.2 shows this relationship. One cubic centimeter is equal to one milliliter, which is equal to one thousandth of a liter. An eyedropper usually holds about 1 mL of liquid.

A **graduated cylinder** is used to measure the volume of liquids. When liquids are placed in a graduated cylinder, a meniscus will form. A **meniscus** is the curve of liquid at its surface. The meniscus may curve down or up, depending on the liquid. To read the volume of the liquid, get eye level with the meniscus and measure from the bottom of the curve of the meniscus if it curves downward or the top of the meniscus if it curves upward. Figure 2.3 shows how to read a meniscus by getting eye level with it and measuring at the center point.

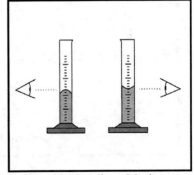

Figure 2.3 Reading a Meniscus

Density, D, is the mass (m) of an object divided by its volume (V), $(D = m/V)$. The standard SI unit for density is kg/m^3, but it is also commonly expressed in units of grams per cubic centimeter (g/cm^3). Density is a characteristic material property. That means the density of two objects of the same material is always the same even if the objects have different masses. For example, a gold ring and a gold brick both have the same density, because they are both made of gold. However, because the gold brick contains more matter than the gold ring, it has a greater mass.

Density explains why some things float and other things sink. A rock at the bottom of a stream is denser than water, so it sinks to the bottom. A piece of styrofoam is less dense than the water, so it floats. If an object sinks, it is more dense than the liquid it is placed in. If an object floats, it is less dense than the liquid it is placed in. The same is true of gases.

$$D = \frac{m}{V}$$

Temperature measures how hot or cold something is. All measurements for temperature are taken in degrees. **Celsius** is often used, but the SI unit for temperature is **Kelvin**. The English unit is **Fahrenheit**. Both Celsius and Fahrenheit are written in their abbreviated forms with a degree symbol, as in °C and °F, whereas Kelvin is abbreviated as K. To convert from one unit to another, use the following formulas:

$$C = \frac{(F - 32)}{1.8} \qquad F = 1.8\,C + 32 \qquad C = K - 273.15 \qquad K = C + 273.15$$

C is degrees Celsius; **F** is degrees Fahrenheit; **K** is Kelvin.

Figure 2.4 Temperature Conversion Formulas

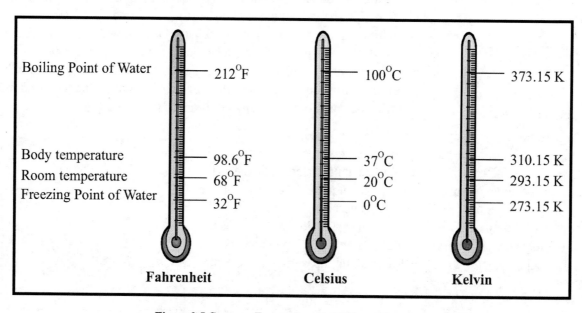

Figure 2.5 Common Temperatures in Different Temperature Scales

METRIC UNIT CONVERSIONS

The units in the metric system are defined in multiples of 10 from the standard unit. The metric prefixes indicate which multiple of 10 the standard unit should be multiplied or divided by. Multiply when changing from a greater unit to a smaller one: divide when changing from a smaller unit to a larger one. The chart below is set up to help you know how far and which direction to move a decimal point when making conversions from one unit to another. Each space on the chart stands for a multiplication factor of 10. To convert a kilometer (km) to a meter (m), move 3 spaces to the right. So, multiply (km) (10^3) = (km) ($10 \times 10 \times 10$)= (km) (1000) = m. To convert m to km, divide the meter value by 1000.

Prefix	kilo (k)	hecto (h)	deka (da)	unit (m, L, g)	deci (d)	centi (c)	milli (m)
Meaning	1000	100	10	1	0.1	0.01	0.001

DIMENSIONAL ANALYSIS

Now that we have covered the units themselves and talked about adjusting their magnitude, we need to discuss converting the identity of the units. This is important because you will often encounter measurements in common units (remember Sergio's thumb?) which must be converted to SI units. This is done by the process of dimensional analysis. **Dimensional analysis** is a structured method of helping you to convert units by using conversion factors. A dimension is a property that can be measured, such as length, time, mass or temperature. It may also be derived by multiplying or dividing other dimensions. Some examples of derived dimensions include length/time (velocity), length^3 (volume) or mass/length^3 (density). Dimensions are *not* the same as units. The dimensions of a physical quantity can be measured in any appropriate unit. For instance, velocity can be measured in mph, m/s, etc., but it will always be a measure of length divided by time. Therefore, the dimensions of velocity are length/time.

A **conversion factor** is a defined relationship between two units. They are similar to the expressions shown in Tables 2.1 and 2.2, but they are written as fractions that are always equal to 1. For instance, the conversion from ounces to pounds is 16 oz = 1 lb. We can write two conversion factors using this information:

$$\frac{16 \text{ oz}}{1 \text{ lb}} \quad \textbf{and} \quad \frac{1 \text{ lb}}{16 \text{ oz}}$$

Ratios of equivalent values expressed in different units like these are known as conversion factors. To convert given quantities in one set of units to their equivalent values in another set of units, we set up dimensional equations. We will write our dimensional equations so that the old units cancel and we are left with only the new units. So you will have to choose which form of the conversion factor you need to use. How will you know? In order to eliminate a unit in the numerator, you will need to cancel it out by choosing a conversion factor that places that unit in the denominator. Likewise, if you want to eliminate a unit that is in the denominator, you will choose a conversion factor that places that unit in the numerator. Because any factor divided by itself is equal to 1, this process will eliminate factors that you do not need.

Example 1: How many cubic centimeters are in 2 liters?

Step 1. Begin by writing the term that needs to be converted:

$$2 \text{ L}$$

Step 2. Identify the unit that the term needs to be converted into:

$$2 \text{ L} = \underline{\quad} \text{ cm}^3$$

Step 3. Next, identify the conversion formulas that will be needed:

$$1 \text{ cm}^3 = 1 \text{ mL} \textbf{ and } 1000 \text{ mL} = 1 \text{ L}$$

Step 4. Write both forms of the conversion factors as fractions:

$$\frac{1 \text{ cm}^3}{1 \text{ mL}} \text{ or } \frac{1 \text{ mL}}{1 \text{ cm}^3} \quad \textbf{and} \quad \frac{1000 \text{ mL}}{1 \text{ L}} \text{ or } \frac{1 \text{ L}}{1000 \text{ mL}}$$

Step 5. Select the correct conversion factors that will eliminate unwanted units:

$$2 \text{ L} \times \frac{1000 \text{ mL}}{1 \text{ L}} \times \frac{1 \text{ cm}^3}{1 \text{ mL}} = \underline{\quad} \text{ cm}^3$$

Step 6. Cross out the units that cancel and multiply the rest together:

$$2\,\cancel{\text{L}} \times \frac{1000\,\cancel{\text{mL}}}{1\,\cancel{\text{L}}} \times \frac{1 \text{ cm}^3}{1\,\cancel{\text{mL}}} = 2000 \text{ cm}^3$$

Notice that the units of "mL" and "L" cancel, leaving you with cm^3.

WRONG: If you had used the conversion factors incorrectly, this is what you would have:

$$2\text{L} \times \frac{1\text{L}}{1000\text{mL}} \times \frac{1\text{mL}}{1\text{cm}^3} = \frac{2\text{L}^2}{1000\text{cm}^3}$$

Notice, liters multiplied by liters are liters squared (L^2). None of the units cancel, so you know right away that this is a wrong approach.

A grid-like format is a different way to represent multiplying several conversion factors together. Each column contains a conversion factor that is needed to convert your units. Let's try to convert a rate of speed and see how this works for you.

Example 2: 36 kilometers per hour is how many meters/sec?

$$\frac{36\,\cancel{\text{km}}}{1\,\cancel{\text{hour}}} \left| \frac{1\,\cancel{\text{hour}}}{60\,\cancel{\text{min}}} \right| \frac{1\,\cancel{\text{min}}}{60 \text{ s}} \left| \frac{1000 \text{ m}}{1\,\cancel{\text{km}}} \right. = \frac{36 \times 1000 \text{ m}}{60 \times 60 \text{ s}} = \frac{36000 \text{ m}}{3600 \text{ s}} = 10 \text{ m/s}$$

Section Review: 1: Units and Conversions

A. Define the following terms.

SI Units	kilogram	graduated cylinder	Celsius
U.S. Customary System	weight	meniscus	Kelvin
length	volume	water displacement	Fahrenheit
meter	cubic centimeter	density	
mass	milliliter	temperature	

B. Choose the best answer.

1. The volume of liquid held in an eyedropper is BEST measured in

   A.   millimeters.   B.   milligrams.   C.   milliseconds.   D.   milliliters.

2. The amount of matter in an object is its

   A.   weight.   B.   mass.   C.   volume.   D.   density.

3. Identify the correct conversion of 2.5 L to units of mL.

   A. 0.0025 mL   B. 250 mL   C. 2,500 mL   D. 25,000 mL

4. Density is a good way to identify materials because

   A.   different masses of the same object will always have different densities.
   B.   different masses of the same object will always have the same density.
   C.   the same volume of the same object will always have different densities.
   D.   the same mass of two different objects will have the same density.

5. What is the best way to read the volume of a liquid in a graduated cylinder?

   A.   Read the level of the liquid going up the side of the cylinder.
   B.   Make sure five people in the laboratory read it before you write it down.
   C.   Glance at the cylinder and write down the first number you see.
   D.   Read the level of liquid at the middle of the meniscus, at eye level.

6. What are the most appropriate units to use when describing the length of a caterpillar?

   A. meters   B. milliliters   C. centimeters   D. nanometers

PRECISION AND ACCURACY

Science is not built on single results but the collection of large amounts of data from many experiments. In fact, one of the tests for something being scientifically correct is whether it can be repeated anywhere and still produce similar results. But experiments do not always produce the exact *same* result every time. This happens because there are many factors that can affect the experiment, and it is difficult to control all of them. Typically, a set of experiments will produce a range of results. But how can a scientist tell the difference between acceptable and an unacceptable range of data?

Scientists must analyze their data for precision and accuracy. **Precision** is the degree of closeness within a range of results. If you were throwing a ball repeatedly against a wall and hit the same spot every time, your aim would be very precise. **Accuracy** is the degree of agreement between a measured result and an accepted value. For example, let's say your family has a garage sale. You estimate that you will make $1000 but instead only made $150. Clearly, your estimate was very inaccurate. If, on the other hand, you sold $975, your estimate would be much more accurate. A helpful way to think of the difference between precision and accuracy is to consider a dart game with a target as in Figure 2.6. The bull's eye in the center is the "accepted value" that you want to hit. The first instance shows random hits that are far from the center. So the precision and accuracy are both poor. The precision is good when the darts all hit the same location. The dart throws are accurate when they hit close to the bull's eye. But only when the darts hit close together and hit the center are the throws both precise <u>and</u> accurate.

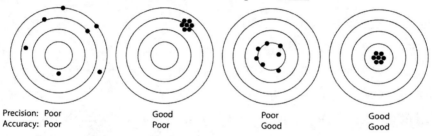

| Precision: | Poor | Good | Poor | Good |
| Accuracy: | Poor | Poor | Good | Good |

Figure 2.6 Precision and Accuracy

Precision can also be defined in terms of scale. The smaller the scale on which a measurement is made, the more distinct the measurements can be. Let's think of an example to illustrate this.

Three small water samples are collected by Adam and Trisha. Adam uses a 100 mL graduated cylinder; Trisha uses a 10 mL graduated cylinder. Their data is shown below.

Sample	Adam's Volume Measurement	Trisha's Volume Measurement
1	8 mL	8.27 mL
2	8 mL	8.54 mL
3	8 mL	8.31 mL

Adam cannot make a good assessment of the volume of his sample, because his instrument is not precise enough. Trisha can clearly see, with her more precise glassware, that she collected three water samples with distinctly different volumes.

It is important to note that measurements can be made very precisely, but not accurately. They can also be made accurately, but not precisely.

ERROR

Measurements have varying degrees of accuracy. When there is disagreement between a measured value and an exact or accepted value, then **error** is present. There are many reasons for error when taking measurements. It's easy to see how the quality of the instrument can affect the measured value. There are also factors that are difficult to control, such as maintaining a constant wind speed on a spring day. Human error, commonly called operator error, can occur because of poor technique or just simple mistakes. Certain amounts of error are common and expected, having little impact on the values obtained. Other error can be chronic, making the data completely useless. In general, a scientist using a high-quality instrument and good measurement technique will produce more reliable results.

Activity

Use the two thermometers below to answer the following questions.

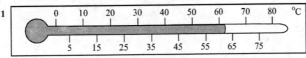

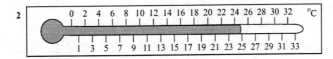

1. Which thermometer will give you a more precise temperature reading?

2. What temperatures do thermometer A and B show?

3. Ask 10 classmates what temperature reading they recorded for thermometers A and B. Prepare a bar graph that displays your data.

4. What is your best estimate of the error associated with each of these thermometers? (Hint: The range of answers shown in your bar graph should help you estimate the amount of error in the reading.)

CALCULATING USING SIGNIFICANT FIGURES

Maintaining the appropriate number of significant figures preserves the accuracy of results even after the measurements have been used in calculations. When doing calculations with measurements, the accuracy of the calculated result is dependent on the least accurate measurement.

Addition and Subtraction

When adding or subtracting, the result is rounded off to the digit farthest to the right in <u>all</u> components. In other words, the number of decimal places in the answer should equal the smallest number of decimal places of any addend (number to be added).

Example 1:	3345.23	This number is accurate to the hundredths place.
	+ 1.178	This number is accurate to the thousandths place.
	3346.408	

The least accurate measurement in this problem has its final digit in the hundredths place. Therefore, the answer must also be rounded to the hundredths place. The 8 will round the zero up to 1. The answer, then, is 3346.41.

Example 2:	83.5	This number is accurate to the tenths place.
	− 45.012	This number is accurate to the thousandths place.
	38.488	

The least accurate measurement in this problem has its final digit in the tenths place. Therefore, the answer must also be rounded to the tenths place. The 8 in the hundredths place will round the 4 up to 5. The answer, then, is 38.5.

Multiplication and Division

When multiplying and dividing, the result is rounded off so that it has the same number of significant figures as the factor with the least number of significant figures.

Example 1:	70.54	This number has 4 significant figures.
	× 406	This number has 3 significant figures.
	28,639.24	

The factor that has the least number of significant figures is 406, which has 3 significant figures. The result, then, must also have 3 significant figures. The final significant digit will be in the hundredths place. The number 3 does not round 6 up. Therefore, the result is 28,600.

Example 2:	100.02	This number has 5 significant figures.
	÷ 0.012	This number has 2 significant figures.
	8,335	

The factor 0.012 has only 2 significant figures. Therefore, the result can have only 2 significant figures. The final significant digit will be in the hundredths place. The number 3 does not round 3 up. The result, then, is 8300.

Practice Exercise 1: Adding and Subtracting with Significant Figures

Do the following calculations. Round your answers to the correct number of significant figures.

1. 0.300
    + 2.678

2. 67.540
    − 1.093

3. 1,089.000
    + 34.023

4. 3,500
    + 6,713

5. 76.10
    − 0.05

6. 101.00
    − 7.32

7. 900.010
    + 68.020

8. 897.76
    − 0.06

9. 10,657
    + 13,000

Practice Exercise 2: Multiplying and Dividing with Significant Figures

Do the following calculations. Round your answers to the correct number of significant figures.

1. 456.1
    × 0.032

2. 7,400
    × 0.09

3. 703
    × 0.290

4. 20.03
    ÷ 7.13

5. 813.0
    ÷ 1.005

6. 5.02
    ÷ 0.02

7. 700.03
    × 1.40

8. 0.0004
    ÷ 0.79

9. 34,567
    ÷ 11,000

Section Review: 2:   Judging Measurements

A. Define the following terms.

significant figures   accuracy   precision

error

B. Choose the best answer.

1.   Which of the following measurements is the MOST precise?

A.   2.90 L   B.   2.7 L   C.   24 L   D.   24.32 L

2.   Mandy and Jessica test the pH of <u>a water sample</u> six times each. The data they collected is shown in the following table.

Measurement	Mandy's pH Data	Jessica's pH Data
1	5.71	5.6
2	5.72	5.7
3	5.81	5.8
4	5.74	5.2
5	5.80	5.7
6	5.83	4.9

Which of the following statements correctly describes the precision of these measurements?

A.   Both data sets are equally precise.

B.   Neither set is precise.

C.   Mandy's data is more precise.

D.   Jessica's data set is more precise.

3.   Which of the following pieces of lab equipment would give you the MOST precise measurement?

A.   a 10 mL graduated cylinder   C.   a 10 mL test tube

B.   a 100 mL graduated cylinder   D.   a 100 mL Erlenmeyer flask

4.   Samuel measures the volume of a liquid sample. He estimates its volume to be about 20 mL. Which of the following pieces of glassware will allow him to make the most accurate and precise measurement?

A.   a 10 mL graduated cylinder

B.   a 25 mL graduated cylinder

C.   a 250 mL graduated cylinder

D.   a 25 mL beaker

CHAPTER 2 REVIEW

1. What is the ratio of kiloliters to milliliters?

   A. 1000:1

   B. 1:1000

   C. 1,000,000:1

   D. 1:1,000,000

2. Which of the following volume measurements is the LEAST precise?

   A. a 2 liter bottle of soda

   B. a 255 gram box of cookies

   C. a 500 milligram antacid tablet

   D. a 473 milliliter bottle of salad dressing

3. A doctor shouts out "Give her 20 ccs of epinephrine!" during a TV drama. What does this mean?

   A. Give the patient 20 liters of epinephrine.

   B. Give the patient 20 fluid ounces of epinephrine.

   C. Give the patient 20 milliliters of epinephrine.

   D. Give the patient 20 test tubes full of epinephrine.

4. Mandy and Jessica measured the pH of a <u>nearby stream</u> on 6 consecutive days. The data they collected is shown in the following table.

Measurement	Mandy's pH Data	Jessica's pH Data
1	5.6	5.4
2	5.7	5.7
3	5.8	5.8
4	5.8	5.6
5	5.8	5.7
6	5.5	5.0

Which of the following statements correctly describes the accuracy of these measurements?

   A. Both data sets are equally accurate, since they are measured to the same decimal place.

   B. Neither set is accurate, because the data was collected for only a few days.

   C. Mandy's data is more accurate, because the measurements are closer together.

   D. The accuracy of the data cannot be assessed, since the sample conditions could not have been the same for each measurement.

5. Jeff and Manish are playing darts. Each throws four darts, aimed at the center of the dartboard. The results are shown below.

Jeff   Manish

Which statement best describes the results of their competition?

A. Manish is more accurate.
B. Jeff and Manish are equally accurate.
C. Jeff is more accurate.
D. Jeff is more precise.

6. Which piece of glassware gives the most precise measurement?

A. a 3 mL glass pipet
B. a 3 L Erlenmeyer flask
C. a 10 mL graduated cylinder
D. a 10 mL beaker

7. Identify the correct conversion of 4.2 grams (g) to kilograms (kg).

A. 4.2 g = 0.0042 kg
B. 4.2 g = 0.042 kg
C. 4.2 g = 42 kg
D. 4.2 g = 4,200 kg

8. The temperature outside is 309K. What qualitative description would fit the day?

A. Whew, is it HOT!
B. Brrr, I am freezing!
C. Kinda nice out, huh?
D. I could use a light jacket.

9. A meniscus sometimes causes error in the measurement of which dimension?

A. time   B. volume   C. length   D. mass

10. Identify the conversion factor that would convert grams per milliliter (g/mL) to kilograms per liter (kg/L).

A. $\dfrac{g}{mL} \times \dfrac{1kg}{1000g} \times \dfrac{1000mL}{1L}$

B. $\dfrac{g}{mL} \times \dfrac{1kg}{1000g} \times \dfrac{1L}{1000mL}$

C. $\dfrac{g}{mL} \times \dfrac{1000g}{1kg} \times \dfrac{1000mL}{1L}$

D. $\dfrac{g}{mL} \times \dfrac{1000g}{1kg} \times \dfrac{1L}{1000mL}$

Chapter 3
A Scientific Method

GEORGIA PERFORMANCE SCIENCE STANDARDS COVERED IN THIS CHAPTER INCLUDE:

SCSh3 a – f	Students will identify and investigate problems scientifically.
SCSh4 a	Students use tools and instruments for observing, measuring, and manipulating scientific equipment and materials.
SCSh8 a and c	Students will understand important features of the process of scientific inquiry.

In Chapters 1 and 2, we looked at some of the skills you would need to be a scientist. In this chapter, we are going to look at another important skill: knowing how to **inquire**.

Let's say that you are sitting in your backyard. Your mom told you to weed the garden, but you'd rather be doing almost anything than that. So, you are just sitting there… daydreaming…WHOA! What is that? A brightly-colored hot air balloon is floating in the sky, way above you. Now that is something that you don't see every day. You wonder, how high up is that?

In fact, you might think of a number of questions, which is great. Instead of hunting for answers right away, let's look first at the questions themselves. What are you doing when you ask questions like this? You are being human, for one thing. Humans, as a species, have a strong drive to observe situations, ask questions and discover answers. After all, your pet cat or dog is very unlikely to even notice the balloon. Even if they did, they do not have the thought processes necessary to wonder how it works.

You are also operating as an amateur scientist. You may not have thought about it, but that is what all scientists are: just people like you, thinking about the world we all live in, and trying to solve its mysteries, one situation at a time.

A functional definition of science is: the observation, identification, description and explanation of **natural phenomena**. Natural phenomena are observable facts or events in the world around us, like the clouds. Scientific processes help explain natural phenomena. Scientists believe all natural phenomena have logical, verifiable explanations — sometimes it just takes some thought, effort and time to find them!

Through the study of science, we ask questions, develop **hypotheses** (educated guesses), and design and carry out experiments to gain a better understanding of the universe. Then, we must try to make sense of the results from the experiments through analysis. Only then can we arrive at some conclusion about our hypothesis. Take a look at the graphic below and you'll see how scientific thinking can be represented as a system.

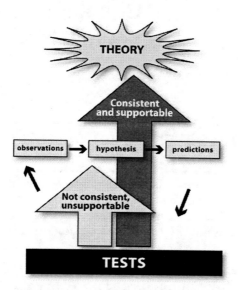

Figure 3.1 The System of Scientific Thought

To "do" science, you must have some way of thinking through the possible solutions to a problem and testing each possibility to find the best solution. There are many valid scientific processes, and an entire book could be written about how thought is translated into questions, experiments and conclusions. But since our space for this topic is limited, we'll provide you with one of the most common "scientific processes." Our scientific process will have the following steps:

Observations are made by using the **five senses** — sight, touch, smell, sound and taste — so, let's start there. Step one is to observe some aspect of the world around you.

1. Identify a problem to solve based on your observations. How can you state the problem as a question for investigation?

2. Do a little research to find out what is already known about your question.

3. State a hypothesis — that is another way of saying "an educated guess at the solution to your problem."

4. Conduct an experiment or set of experiments that aim to produce results that will support or contradict your hypothesis.

5. Collect and organize your data. What does it tell you?

6. Analyze the data and summarize the results as a conclusion in terms of the original hypothesis.

Remember, this is just one way to organize your thoughts; things don't always happen this way. Sometimes you might have a hypothesis and only later on realize a problem for which it is applicable. It's also possible that you might actually have a test and conclusion in search of a problem. Finally, your experiment may generate unexpected data which is hard to interpret and doesn't answer your question as clearly as you were hoping. What do you do then? Well, that's up to you. There are several paths you could take. Let's look at each step more closely. After that, we will see what the options are.

1. MAKING OBSERVATIONS AND DEFINING THE PROBLEM

You may have noticed a natural phenomena many times before, like the wind blowing on your face, but never really thought much about it. Then a family vacation finds you standing on the beach, with the wind gusting so hard off the ocean that it is taking the foam from waves' tops and hurling it toward shore. Where is that wind coming from? Why is the water so rough? Is the wind stirring up the water, or is it the other way around?

On the other hand, some observations catch your attention the first time, like seeing a hot air balloon move across the sky. That should generate some questions. How did the balloon get up there? How does a hot air balloon fly? Why is it called a *hot air* balloon? How do you steer it? How do you get down?

Figure 3.2 Hot Air Balloon

Think about those two different observations. Both are made using the five senses. How are they different? The first is an observation of a natural phenomenon — the wind. The second is an observation of a man-made object, a technological innovation — the hot air balloon. Although we can see the hot air balloon, we only see the effect of the wind on other objects and not the wind itself. At the same time, we know that the balloon is subject to gravity so the balloon is being affected by natural phenomena. So, how does a balloon rise? The hot air balloon makes use of heated gas to lift itself up enough to overcome gravity; otherwise, it wouldn't be in the air! It needs air through which to move and it needs wind to move it. Ultimately, there are many cause and effect relationships in the universe, but we need to focus our study of hot air balloons on a specific problem. Given these requirements, let's ask this question: how high can a hot air balloon go?

Asking questions helps you to define a problem. By asking questions, we can search for logical explanations for what we observe and find ways to solve problems.

2. PERFORMING RESEARCH

Research can be done on many levels — how much you need to do and where you need to look depends on the problem that you are investigating. For an explanation to a phenomenon that you feel fairly certain has already been explored, you may only have to noodle around on the Internet to find your answer. But beware! While the Internet has become a pervasively-used information resource in our society, it transmits information *of all kinds*. Some sites may contain correct information, while others are nothing more than a collection of opinions or outright falsehoods. You must learn to judge which sites, or types of sites, contain information that you can rely on to be factual. Table 3.1 is a good start.

Table 3.1 Reliability of Internet Resources

Generally More Reliable	Generally Less Reliable
Sites that are updated daily	Sites that are rarely updated
News outlet sites	"Viewpoint" sites that seek to persuade
Government agency or University sites .gov or .edu	Individual home pages .com or .org

To address a more complicated scientific question, research into peer reviewed journals will be necessary. This is referred to as "going to the literature" by scientists. A **journal** is a specialized publication. It differs from a magazine in a few important ways. First, the authors of journals are not paid journalists; they are scientists who want to distribute their research to other scientists. Their goal is to broaden the current body of knowledge. Second, authors who write articles for journals must follow a set of rules that define the kind of research that will be accepted, and the scientific methodology that produced it. Third, the submitted article is **peer-reviewed**. That means that it is scrutinized (reviewed) by anonymous scientists in a similar field (peers). If the peer reviewers disagree with a method used or conclusion reached, they will send the article back for re-investigation or revision. The goal is to be certain that published material is as trustworthy and useful as possible.

Figure 3.3 Journal Cover

There are thousands of journals, each of which focuses on a particular subject area, or specialty within an area of study. Two journals that address broad scientific issues are *Science* and *Nature*. You may have heard of these. Two journals that focus on more specialized topics are *Environmental Science and Technology* and the *Journal of Wind Engineering and Industrial Aerodynamics*. You probably have not heard of these, but they are widely read. Rest assured, there is a journal that applies to almost any scientific topic you can think of, as well as many that you did not know existed.

Let us close the topic by distinguishing what type of research can be done on the Internet versus through journal research. An Internet search will allow you to discover how a hot air balloon works, where you can go to get lessons or rides in one and where hot air balloon races and demonstrations will be held. Going to the literature will help you find out every type of meteorological research ever conducted by a weather balloon, along with statistical analysis of the data. It will enable you to find a comprehensive description of the Earth's atmosphere at every level, and thus learn how high a hot air balloon will fly. It will describe pollutants sampled in our atmosphere by balloons and the chemical interactions of those molecules. It will examine a wide variety of conclusions that can be drawn from that data on issues like global warming and ozone layer depletion. A journal search will show you recorded air currents, including the jet stream, for every area of the world.

In short, well-directed research can help you find almost any answer you want — except when there aren't any answers to your question yet. Then it is time to experiment. Look over your research, take a deep breath and make a hypothesis.

3. FORMING THE HYPOTHESIS

Remember, a hypothesis is not just any guess, like guessing how many jelly beans are in a jar at a carnival. A hypothesis is an educated guess. A hypothesis is a way of forming an opinion about how or why something happens, based on patterns that you have observed over time.

The hypothesis can be developed using either inductive or deductive reasoning. **Inductive reasoning** allows you to draw on your observations of specific events to hypothesize a general trend. **Deductive reasoning** requires you to use a general truth to hypothesize particular events. Here are two examples to illustrate:

- Taylor notices that every time she throws a ball up, it comes down. She inductively reasons that next time (and perhaps every time) she throws a ball up, it will come down. She mentions her hypothesis to Cory.
- Cory uses deductive reasoning when he says, "Well, of course. That is Newton's Theory of Gravitation. Basically, it says that what goes up, must come down. So next time you throw the ball up, it will certainly come down."

Now let's go back to the hot air balloon and see how you can use your reasoning skills to form a hypothesis.

During your research, you should have accumulated some knowledge about how hot air balloons work. But unless you are fairly adventurous, you probably don't have much experience with hot air balloons. It may seem to you that you cannot use inductive reasoning to develop your hypothesis. Let's broaden the field of necessary experience. Have you ever flown on an airplane? If you have, then that is part of your body of experience with objects that fly, and you should use that experience to make a reasonable assumption.

Figure 3.4 Airplane

You may also develop your hypothesis deductively. It is important that your hypothesis is not immediately apparent. For instance, you might say, "All things that fly have wings." Clearly, a hot air balloon doesn't have wings, so your starting point is inaccurate. Beginning with a correct principle is vital when coming up with a hypothesis through deductive reasoning.

You may find that your hypothesis is wrong, but that is OK. You have to start somewhere! Try it now. Just remember that your hypothesis must be testable, meaning that you can design an experiment that proves or disproves its supposition. For the sake of this discussion, we'll choose the flowing hypothesis: a hot air balloon can travel higher than a commercial airplane.

4. SETTING UP THE EXPERIMENT

A **scientific experiment** should be designed to give measurable results which either prove or disprove the hypothesis. To gather meaningful data, the experiment must be set up to examine only one condition (or **variable**) at a time.

There are three types of variables seen in an experiment:

- **independent variable** (sometimes called the **manipulated variable**) – The factors that are changed or manipulated during the experiment. They are the ones that the experiment is trying to test.

- **dependent variable** (sometimes called the **responding variable**) – This is usually the factor that the experimenter is measuring or counting. The dependent variable is the one that changes in response to the independent variable.

- **control variables** – All the other factors in the experiment. These are things that you attempt to control, and are kept constant during the course of the experiment.

How would you set up an experiment to see how high a hot air balloon could fly? Of course, you would have to purchase a balloon and all the extra equipment, learn to fly the balloon and make some very important decisions about where to fly and what to take with you. Taking all of those logistics for granted, though, you would probably start at a certain point, on a day with calm weather, and launch your balloon in such a way that it goes *up* more than it goes *over*. (Hopefully, you will have done a lot of research about wind and air currents before the launch.)

What are the independent, dependent and control variables in this experiment? You are trying to see how high the hot air balloon can fly versus the commercial airplane, so we can call the independent variable the mode of flight. Notice that it is the independent variable because it is not dependent on anything – it is a choice you made during the hypothesis. You could have chosen a hawk instead of a commercial airplane and the experiment is still the same. The dependent variable is the variable you will actually use to compare the two modes of flight. So, altitude is the dependent variable. You want the experiment to compare the altitude of a hot air balloon and a commercial airplane and nothing else. To ensure this, you would need to conduct the experiment with all other possible variables – such as beginning location, season of the year, the time of day – kept constant so that you are not actually comparing two events that are not actually comparable. These are the control variables.

Scientists typically conduct many experiments at once. When this happens, it is necessary to divide everything into groups. The **experimental group** is the group that will be tested, such as 10 different kinds of hot air balloons. The **control group** is the group that the experimental group will be tested against, such as 10 different kinds of commercial airplanes.

You go up, up, up, measuring your altitude at intervals. At this point you are collecting data.

5. COLLECTING AND PRESENTING DATA

Data is gathered from the observations and measurements taken during a scientific experiment. There are two types of data: qualitative and quantitative. **Qualitative data** are the observations made with your senses. This is information that cannot be assigned a numerical value. Examples of qualitative data can include shades of color, texture, taste or smell. **Quantitative data** are the measurements — anything that can be expressed as a number, or quantified. Quantitative data can include lengths, weights, masses, volumes, time, temperature or anything else expressed as a value. Because quantitative data is a measurement, the number that is recorded is an exact and accurate quantity of a measured amount. Furthermore, quantitative data usually has a unit of some kind, like 12 feet, 3 ounces or 5 hours. In these cases, the unit is as important as the value.

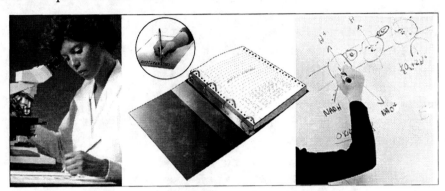

Figure 3.5 Qualitative Data

Qualitative data is **subjective,** meaning that its recording depends on the person. For instance, if you asked three people how warm it is outside, you might get three different answers, like "quite hot," "uncomfortably warm" and "very pleasant." None of these answers are measurements. They are describing qualities.

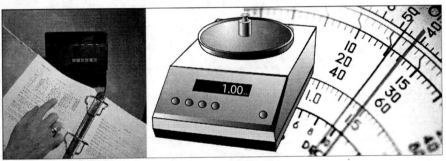

Figure 3.6 Quantitative Data

Quantitative data is more **objective**, meaning that it does not depend as much on the person making the measurement. For instance, if three people were asked to read a thermometer, they would all come up with similar temperatures, like 78.1°, 78.0° and 78.3° Fahrenheit. The differences in their measurements are the result of the slightly different ways that each person estimates. So, there is some subjectivity in quantitative data, but not nearly as much as that present in a qualitative observation.

All observations and measurements from the experiment must be recorded. If the data collected are organized in a logical manner, they can be more easily analyzed to determine the results of the experiment. Both qualitative and quantitative data can be organized in a data **table**. Diagrams, graphs and charts may also be used to present the data. The point is to present data in a form that makes its meaning clear. Often this means looking for **trends** or patterns in the data. Through careful evaluation, you can interpret the results of the experiment.

Up to this point, we have been considering a theoretical experiment. You will be pleased to know that it has actually been done! A *National Geographic* article tells the story. In 1961, two US Navy officers took an experimental high-altitude balloon to the outer edge of the stratosphere. The name of the balloon was the USN Stratolab V[1] and it rose to an altitude of 113,740 feet. One way to look at their flight is to view it in a **diagram**, which is a good way to show the relationship between things. The diagram in Figure 3.7 allows us to view the record altitude reached by Stratolab V[1] and compare it to other things, like the layers of the atmosphere or the cruising altitude of a commercial plane. During their ascent, the officers recorded data on their altitude, the barometric pressure and the air temperature in a table. They also noted the time that each set of measurements was taken. This data is more specific, and should be organized in a table, as shown in Table 3.2.

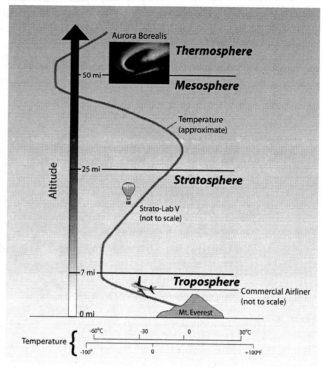

Figure 3.7 Diagram of Atmospheric Layers

Table 3.2 Stratolab Data

time	altitude (ft.)	temperature (°F)	pressure (psi)
7:08 am	0	74	14.7
7:34 am	26,000	−27	6.8
7:50 am	43,000	−73	2.4
8:10 am	53,000	−94	1.4
8:25 am	65,000	−80	0.74
9:05 am	95,000	−41	0.2
9:47 am	113,740	−29	0.09

1. See the website http://www.history.navy.mil/download/space-11.PDF for more on Stratolab.

Data recorded in a table can often be graphed to show the relationship between the data in a way that is easier to analyze. **Line graphs** are a great way to show how the dependent variable changes in response to the independent variable. The independent variable is plotted on the *x*-axis (horizontal axis), and the dependent variable is plotted on the *y*-axis (vertical axis). You can see this in Figure 3.8, where the change in pressure is noted at different altitudes.

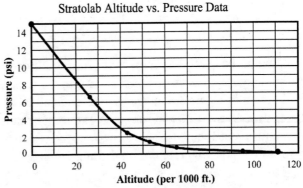

Figure 3.8 Line Graph of Stratolab Data

Line graphs are also used to compare multiple groups of data. These are called **multiple line graphs**, and could be used to compare the data from two or more balloon flights.

A **circle graph**, also known as a **pie chart**, is used to show parts of a whole. Many times, circle graphs show percentages of a total. Our hot air balloonists might use a pie chart to show the percentages of various gases that make up the atmosphere.

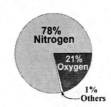

Figure 3.9 Circle Graph of Atmospheric Composition

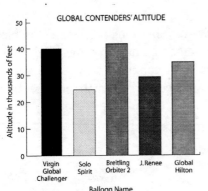

Figure 3.10 Bar Graph of Balloon Altitude

Notice that the circle graph conveys information about different things — in this case, different atmospheric gases. What if you want to compare different things that are not a part of a whole? A good way to do that is the **bar graph**. Figure 3.10 is a bar graph that indicates the maximum cruising altitude of the Global Contenders[1]. The Global Contenders were five hot air balloon teams who were competing to be the first to successfully conduct a non-stop circumnavigation of the globe in 1997. Their preparation and progress were reported on throughout the world, and examined in a Nova Special.

These are the three main types of graphs. They can be made very complicated (to show multiple pieces or groups of information) or very simple. Graphs can be a powerful tool in presenting your data, and great care should be taken in assembling them. The best graphs are lucid and clearly indicate trends. Poor graphs confuse the reader and fail to show any conclusive evidence.

6. DRAWING CONCLUSIONS

You now know a lot more about hot air ballooning history than you did when you started this chapter, but what can you get out of it? The point of every experiment is to support or disprove the initial hypothesis. Let's say that your initial hypothesis was that a hot air balloon could fly higher than an airplane. Look at the data and decide if this is true. In doing so, you are drawing a conclusion.

---

1. See the NOVA website http://www.pbs.org/wgbh/nova/balloon/ for more on the Global Contender

A **conclusion** is a judgment based on observation and experimentation. It should be a logical statement made from the results of the experiment. It is usually easier to see a conclusion when the data is well-organized, as described in the previous section.

You have to be careful about generalizing too broadly when drawing a conclusion. This often means examining your own conclusion for flaws, as well as reevaluating your original hypothesis. For instance, the diagram in Figure 3.7 indicates that the Stratolab flew much higher than a commercial airliner…but is that always the case? The bar graph of the flight altitudes of the Global Contenders indicates that they were cruising at about the same altitude as the commercial airliner, so the hypothesis may still hold. But there is an unknown here: does the commercial airliner always cruise at 30,000 feet? How high can a plane — any kind of plane — actually go?

In fact, the cruising altitudes of both the commercial airliner and the balloon are largely weather-dependent. The airline pilot wants to fly where there is the least turbulence, and that altitude varies depending on the air currents generated by storm systems. It cannot be too high, though, or there will not be enough air for the plane's jets to push against to keep it aloft. The balloon pilot also wants to stay away from bad weather, but must follow air currents because he has no jet engines to propel him. So, the available data indicates that a hot air balloon can fly higher than some airplanes, under some weather conditions. That is not a very concrete conclusion, but it is something. The bottom line is that through your investigation, you realize that this scientific investigation needs some work if you are to arrive at an accurate conclusion.

At this point, you have two choices: you can go back and design a new experiment to definitively prove (or disprove) your hypothesis or you can look over your data and use it to make a new hypothesis. Designing new experiments may mean ensuring that more variables are controlled, different variables are manipulated, or that more than one test flight is conducted. In developing a new hypothesis, you may arrive at a hypothesis that is totally different than your initial concept or you may just need to narrow the breadth of the statement. That is one of the great things about science: all information is valuable, including negative results, and can lead you in a variety of directions.

Regardless of the outcome of the results, it is important that the conclusion is well-written. Scientists exist all over the world and many do not speak English as their first language. In science, clear communication is crucial to ensure that others know exactly what you mean and are not left guessing about some aspect of your experiments or your conclusion. It is not enough to look smart by using big words and glossing over the particulars. *The point is to communicate, not to show off.*

Figure 3.11 Poor Communication Helps No One

Once you have a good hypothesis and have obtained evidence that conclusively supports or contradicts it, your conclusion opens the door to more scientific investigation. One door that opens is to use your conclusion to make inferences about the results. An **inference** involves using your conclusion as a starting point in inductive reasoning. For example, if your conclusion that hot air balloons can travel higher than commercial airplanes is true and some friends of yours have a hot air balloon, then you would infer that they could travel in it to a higher altitude than a commercial airplane.

Notice that the experiment hasn't been conducted and that there are a number of variables that are being ignored. Inferring from your conclusion means that you take it for granted that it is true and make generalizations from there.

Another possible use for your conclusion is in the development of a model. A **model** is mathematical description of an event. Models identify correlations and cause-and-effect relationships in the phenomena they describe. Models can be translated into computer simulations. These simulations are designed to describe the outcome of an experiment under a given set of conditions. For instance, the data in Table 3.2 could be used to develop a model. Altitude, pressure and temperature data from the experimental flight could be correlated to provide a mathematical framework. Multiple flights would generate more data and make the model more accurate. Adding more variables, like weather conditions or wind speeds, will make the model even more useful.

The result is a computer program that determines outcomes, given certain data. The model allows you to enter data like weather conditions and pressure, and then decides, based on the data that it was created from, what altitude your balloon can fly to. In other words, models make mathematical use of experimental data to make predictions.

GOING THE EXTRA MILE — MAKING A PREDICTION

A **prediction** is a forecast of the possible results of events. Knowledge we have gained from observation and experimentation can help us make predictions about seemingly unrelated events. Models can help, but are not always necessary. Whether or not a model is used, a great deal of extra thought must go into a prediction, for the simple reason that you are making a statement about something that you haven't tested yet. If we go back to the hot-air balloonists, we see that as the altitude increased over 110,000 feet, the pressure dropped nearly to zero. What predictions can we make? Here are three:

(a) A hot air balloon cannot fly higher because the pressure will drop to zero and the balloon will have nothing to push against.

(b) A hot air balloon cannot fly higher because the temperature will drop again to temperatures where the balloon cannot function.

(c) A hot air balloon can fly higher with a better design and more resilient materials.

Which statement do you think is correct? Based on the trend that you see in Figure 3.8, you would probably guess prediction (a) because there is more evidence for it. However, you may feel a little wary about your choice. Why? *Because you haven't tested it yet!* Ah, well that is OK! You should be wary when making predictions, but more important, you should be educated. Now, more than ever, it is important to see what research is out there. Information from other scientists can help reinforce your data, so that you can make the best prediction possible. But where to find this other information.....?

Activity
Make three predictions about the experiment described in this chapter.

Activity

Organize the data below into a table.

1. Diameter of pine cones collected on various nature hikes. Pine log Mountain: 19 cm; 19 cm; 17 cm; 21 cm; 15 cm. Brasstown Bald: 15 cm; 19 cm; 22 cm; 16 cm; 13 cm. Kennesaw Mountain: 10 cm; 15 cm; 11 cm; 8 cm; 7 cm; 12 cm.

2. Number of insects collected in traps over six days: Honey-194, 239, 158, 133, 186, 171 and 206; Sugar water- 115, 117, 112, 133, 122, 114 and 175; Apple Juice- 94, 72, 114, 146, 101, 135 and 230 and Vinegar-24, 22, 1, 34, 16, 19 and 19.

3. Amount of water collected each day: 112 L, 158 L, 186 L, 144 L, 146 L, 161 L, 189 L, 138 L, 171 L, 121 L, 173 L and 166 L.

4. Number of cars passing your house every week for fifteen weeks: 158, 239, 186, 140, 245, 201, 172, 192, 226, 230, 155, 164, 210, 219 and 189.

Now use the data tables you have created to make an appropriate graph of each data set.

Activity

Richard has a plant growth experiment to carry out. His goal is to compare the growth of one type of plant to that of another. He obtains two different species of plant from his teacher. He places them in equivalent conditions and records their growth every five days. His data is shown in the multiple line graph.

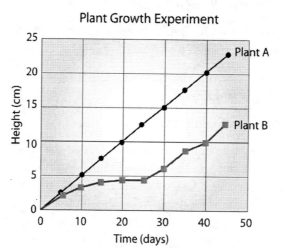

1. What ratio best describes the growth of Plant A?

2. Richard is excited. His experiment is complete and he has reached a conclusion. "Plant A grows at more than twice the rate of Plant B!" He sends his data and conclusion to the *Journal of Horticultural Mediocrity* for peer review. You are his peer reviewer. Write a response to Richard, critiquing his experimental methods and conclusions. What would you require Richard to do, in order to have his work published?

Section Review 1: A Scientific Method

A. Define the following terms.

natural phenomena	control group	diagram	variable
hypotheses	qualitative data	table	independent variable
five senses	research	graph	conclusion
observations	journal	chart	inference
dependent variable	peer review	deductive reasoning	model
control variable	inductive reasoning	scientific experiment	prediction
experimental group	quantitative data		

B. Choose the best answer.

1. The ability to draw from specific knowledge and experience to make a general explanation is
   - A. deductive reasoning.
   - B. inductive reasoning.
   - C. a reasonable explanation.
   - D. processing.

2. Something occurring in nature that is experienced through our senses is
   - A. a control group.
   - B. inductive reasoning.
   - C. an observation.
   - D. a hypothesis.

3. An educated guess is a/an
   - A. hypothesis.
   - B. theory.
   - C. question.
   - D. reason.

4. The variable that tests whether the hypothesis is valid or not is called the
   - A. independent variable.
   - B. dependent variable.
   - C. control variable.
   - D. observation.

Municipal Solid Waste (MSW) is what goes into landfills. Basically, it is the garbage we put out at the curb. It can be divided up by type as follows.

Category	Percentage
Rubber, Leather and Cloth	7.3
Yard Trimmings	13.1
Food Scraps	11.7
Wood	5.7
Other	3.4
Metals	7.6
Paper	34.2
Plastics	11.9
Glass	5.2

5. What is the BEST way to display this data?
   - A. circle graph
   - B. diagram
   - C. multiple line graph
   - D. single line graph

CHAPTER 3 REVIEW

1. Large amounts of petrified wood are found in northeast Arizona. Using inductive reasoning, four inferences are made. Which is the MOST reasonable?

   A. All wood becomes petrified.

   B. A living forest once stood there.

   C. No forests grew in other parts of Arizona.

   D. Wood only becomes petrified in northeast Arizona.

2. Which of the following is MOST likely to be a peer-reviewed journal?

   A. *National Geographic*

   B. *New England Journal of Medicine*

   C. *Scientific American*

   D. *Ladies Home Journal*

3. Andrika has learned that the hot water in her house is always gone by 6:30 am. She knows that this is because her sisters and mother always get to the shower before her. She decides to experiment with her morning routine to see if she can get a hot shower in the morning. Over the course of a week, she changes the time that she gets up, making it 10 minutes earlier each day. What is the dependent variable in this experiment?

   A. the time she gets up

   B. the volume of hot water her family uses

   C. the temperature of the water in the water heater

   D. the temperature of the water in Andrika's shower

4. Which of the following phrases contains quantitative data?

   A. Green leaves surround white flowers.

   B. Ricky's football jersey is number 85.

   C. Seeds sprout more quickly when it is warm.

   D. Water evaporates at a rate of 2 mL per minute.

5. Ryan noticed that his cola loses its carbonation as it warms. He knows that it is carbon dioxide that causes cola to fizz. Ryan decides to do a scientific experiment to research this phenomenon. What is the next step Ryan should take?

   A. graph his data

   B. draw a conclusion

   C. make an observation

   D. form a hypothesis

Chapter 4
Applying Science

© Copyright American Book Company. DO NOT DUPLICATE. 1-888-264-5877.

GEORGIA PERFORMANCE SCIENCE STANDARDS COVERED IN THIS CHAPTER INCLUDE:

SCSh1 a – c	Students will evaluate the importance of curiosity, honesty, openness and skepticism in science.
SCSh6 a – d	Students will communicate scientific investigation and information clearly.
SCSh7 a – e	Students analyze how scientific knowledge is developed.
SCSh8 b, d and e	Students will understand important features of the process of scientific inquiry.

In the past three chapters, you have learned a lot about scientific processes. But there is much more to being a scientist than knowing facts and investigation methods. Being a scientist places you in a group of people who value truth and accuracy.

But with all the scientific claims you see everyday, it may sometimes be difficult to tell which are truthful and accurate. That is, to tell the difference between science and sales. You can probably think of at least one situation where scientific research has been used to support one product or another. How do you know the information you see is correct?

As you know, one way scientists "monitor" themselves and their research is through the **peer-review** process. Peer review subjects the research (usually written in a specific format called a **research paper**) to independent "checks" by qualified experts in that area of science.

Another way is through a **clinical trial**. This is a kind of experiment where products (particularly medicines) are tested on animals or people. A clinical trial only occurs after the product has been well-researched and tested in the laboratory. The results of the trial are data that help the makers of the product decide if the product can be sold to the public. Often, these results are used in the advertisements that you see every day.

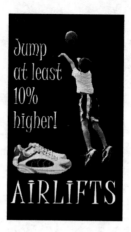

Figure 4.1 Advertisements

Who would want to publish false information anyway?

Well, scientific research is often connected with economic or political issues. These issues can influence the scientists performing the research by causing **bias** in their interpretation of the data. Biased data has been interpreted to suit the goals of the interpreter. Let's look at a two situations that involve bias.

Figure 4.2 Ghost Activity?

UNINTENTIONAL BIAS

People usually pay more attention to data that confirms their beliefs. If you believe in ghosts, you are more likely to interpret mysterious sights or sounds as GHOST ACTIVITY! Someone that does not believe in ghosts would probably interpret a ghostly figure in the corner as the work of a pesky sister. *This kind of bias is unintentional.*

INTENTIONAL BIAS

People may give more weight to data that will give them a reward. If good clinical trial results for a new acne treatment will advance the career of the researchers involved, they may be more likely to overlook the fact that the medicines make some of the study participants feel sick, sprout white nose hair, or have bad skin reactions. *This kind of bias may be intentional.*

Figure 4.3 Acne Treatment?

Whether intentional or unintentional, bias must be avoided when conducting a scientific investigation. This is usually accomplished by conducting **blind trials**, where the researchers do not know who has received the real medicine and who has received a **placebo** (this would be the control group).

Is bias the only reason that false information is published?

When a few different researchers all interpret the data differently, bias could be a factor. On the other hand, sometimes people just naturally look at things in different ways. It could also be that the experiment was poorly designed, giving unclear data.

There is a final complicating factor that is exceptionally important to consider. There might be factors affecting the experiment that are not known, despite the best efforts to establish controls. This is especially true in environmental and biological research. For this reason, **data interpretation** is very important. In this step, you put all of your experimental data together and decide what each piece means. Incorrect and/or biased data interpretation will generate an incorrect conclusion. In these studies, data interpretation is very difficult and usually generates a lot of debate. Let's look at an environmental investigation to see how important data interpretation really is.

MARY'S BIRD FEEDER

Figure 4.4 Mary

Mary has noticed recently that there are fewer seed-eating birds coming to her bird feeder than there used to be. In January, Mary saw over 20 birds a day, representing four different species. There were 3 pairs of cardinals, 8 doves, 4 blue jays and 10 robins. Now, in late February, she sees fewer birds. She thinks the decrease in the number of birds was caused by the recent construction of a new apartment complex nearby. She reasons that the noise and dust or other construction-related causes might have scared the birds away.

Figure 4.5 Jerry

Figure 4.6 Tyrell

Her friend Tyrell does not agree. He thinks that some neighbors may have put up new bird feeders that contain tastier seeds. He reasoned that since the birds prefer the neighbor's seeds, they probably are all going across the street.

Jerry thinks both of these are hogwash. Clearly, he conjectures, the birds have changed their migratory patterns due to recent effects of global warming.

Mary, Tyrell and Jerry mentioned their debate to their science teacher, Mr. Blair. Mr. Blair suggested that they conduct some independent research, and see who was correct. The students agreed. Let's look at the students lab notebooks, and see what they found out.

Mary's Research

Hypothesis:

Nearby construction scared the birds away.

Research methods:

- To better understand the change in number and species, Mary made a line graph comparing the original number of each species to the current number. Each line represents one of the bird species

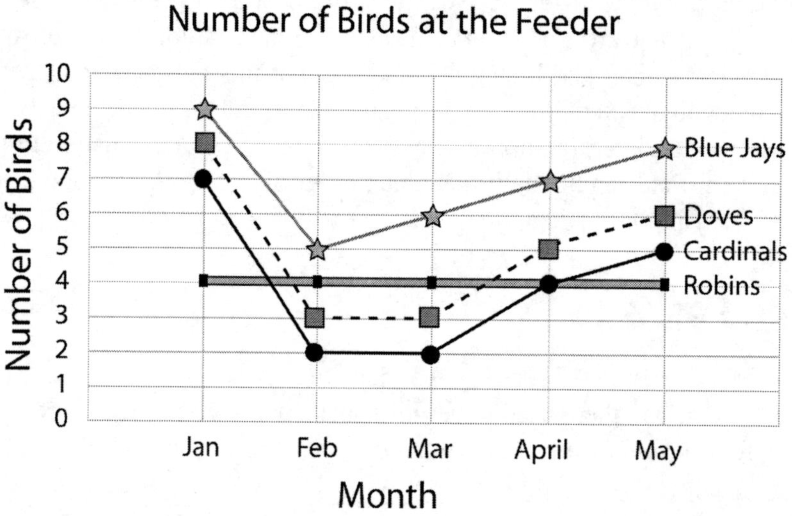

Number of Birds at the Feeder

Figure 4.7 Mary's Research Data

Additional Facts:

- Between January and February, a construction project began 0.5 miles from Mary's house.
- Bird counts were done on the 1st day of each month. Each count was done at 6:30 a.m.
- Construction noise was greatest between 1:00 and 4:00 pm.
- 112 trees were knocked down in January and February. In March, new trees were planted. In April, the whole project was complete.

Conclusion:

Loss of nearby trees changed the birds' habitat. Since there were less nesting sites, the birds moved.

Tyrell's Research

Hypothesis:

The birds preferred the food found at other bird feeders to the food in Mary's feeder.

Research methods:

- Performed Internet research on the feeding habits of the four species of bird at Mary's feeder. His data is shown below.

Bird Species	Preferred Food
Cardinal	Seeds, grains, berries
Dove	Seeds, grains, berries
Blue Jay	Seeds, grains, berries, other birds' eggs, nuts, acorns
Robin	Insects, earthworms

- Conducted interviews with local residents (1): February 20th: Asked 14 of Mary's neighbors this series of questions.

Question 1: Do you have a bird feeder? (5 said yes)

Question 2: Did you put the bird feeder in sometime in January? (0 said yes)

Question 3: What do you put in the feeder? (4 said mixed seed, 1 said sunflower seeds)

Question 4: Have you noticed that less birds are at your feeder now than in January? (3 said yes, 1 said no, 1 said don't know)

- Conducted interviews with local residents (2): March 20th: Asked each of the same neighbors Question 4 again. All said that they weren't sure, but it seemed as though there were less birds.

Conclusion:

Robins do not eat seeds, and would be unaffected by the addition of tastier seeds elsewhere. Also, no new feeders have been installed in Mary's neighborhood. So, the reason for the reduction in birds is not linked to their food supply.

Jerry's Research

Hypothesis:

Global warming has affected the migratory patterns of the birds, so that they decided to migrate south in later January.

Research Method:

- Performed Internet research on global and local climate trends.
- Checked the National Oceanic and Atmospheric Administration (NOAA) Climate Summary for the State of Georgia and found that there has been a zero overall temperature change in Georgia from 1895 to the present.
- The same website noted that the globally averaged annual mean surface temperature in 2005 was the warmest since measurements began in 1880.

Conclusion:

It was warmer in late 1880s in Georgia than it is today, so global warming has had no impact on the birds.

(Note: Clearly, Jerry is confused. His research and his conclusion are inconsistent.)

EXAMINING THE RESEARCH

Mary, Tyrell and Jerry took their research to Mr. Blair, and presented their findings. He looked their notebooks over carefully. Then he asked each student to read over the work of the other two, and fill out a form about their research. Since you are a peer of Mary, Tyrell and Jerry, you should fill in answers also.

Discuss your findings in class, and think about how YOU would research this problem.

Activity: Peer Review of Student Research

1. Was the experimental or research method sound? Why or why not?
2. What was missing?
3. Was the presentation of the data clear?
4. Was the data interpretation sound?
5. What other opinions could be drawn from the data?
6. Was there any bias in the research method or the conclusion?
7. Did your peers perform any research that agrees or disagrees with your research?

Discuss your findings in class, and think about how YOU would research this problem.

You are the future of science. In real life, there are no answers to be found "at the back of the book." Scientists like you must conduct investigations, review each other's finding and come up with conclusions based on research. This is how real people solve real-world problems. As a scientist, you will never run out of having a purpose! There will always be problems to be solved, research to be done and answers to find. Now, let's look at some other presentation of Mary's data, and see if we can interpret the data correctly.

Activity: Mary's Data

Mary's data could also be presented as a bar graph.

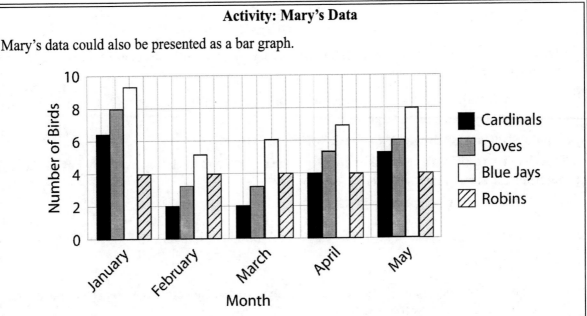

Figure 4.8 Mary's Data in Bar Graph

1. Are there any advantages to the bar graph format over the multiple line graph (Figure 4.7)?

2. Based only on this data, write one conclusion about the robins.

The construction company building the new apartment complex in Mary's neighborhood used her data to prove that the project had no impact on the avian community. The format that they chose is below.

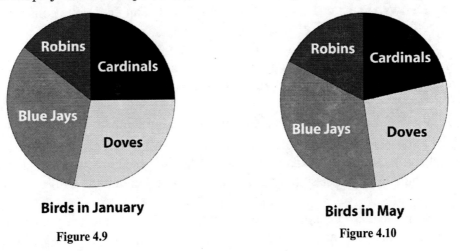

Birds in January

Figure 4.9

Birds in May

Figure 4.10

1. Discuss whether this presentation of Mary's data is accurate, inaccurate, biased or misleading.

2. What insight into the bird populations does this graph give you, that other representations (line graph, bar graph) do not?

3. Jerry's research uncovered the standard diets of the each species of bird at Mary's feeder. Can you use that data, along with these pie charts, to make any inferences?

Activity

Examine each situation below and determine a reasonable hypothesis, experimental setup and type of data that should be collected.

For example: Raja notices she has a red itchy rash on the ball of her foot. This rash makes her new shoes uncomfortable to wear.

Hypothesis: Raja is allergic to a material in her new shoes.

Experiment: Test Raja's reaction to different types of shoe material by exposing her to those materials for several minutes over several days.

Data: Observe any changes in Raja's skin.

1. A coral reef in Australia begins dying around the same time an exotic form of alga is discovered there.

2. A particular type of female bird is very particular when selecting a mate; she chooses only one out every ten possible suitors.

3. Markus notices that one plot in his garden repeatedly kills any plant he tries to grow there.

4. While on a camping trip, Sam hikes though several fields containing long grasses and shrubbery. Later he removes two ticks from his body.

5. Stellar sea lion populations are crashing throughout the arctic despite conservation efforts to protect its food sources.

6. No new diamond mines have been discovered in the past twenty years. However, there are more diamonds sold today than at any other time in the history of the world.

7. On 8 June 1783 Lakagígar, a volcanic fissure located in southern Iceland, erupted releasing 15 km^3 of lava and clouds of volcanic fluorine and sulfur-dioxide gases into the atmosphere. In North America, the winter of 1784 was the longest and coldest on record with freezing of the Mississippi river in New Orleans and into the Gulf of Mexico.

8. Nami was in a car accident on the freeway creating $15,600 in damage to her car. Her friend, Vanessa, was in an accident at a traffic light and received only $1,500 in damage to her car.

9. While standing in the checkout line, Oliver noticed the strong perfume odor in the air.

10. Fletcher noticed that in the afternoon his house was much warmer than it was in the morning.

CHAPTER 4 REVIEW

Melissa is reading the paper one Sunday and comes across a plant food ad.

Plant Food A claims in its advertising that it "Generates twice the growth rate of the leading national brand!" The advertisement features the graph below. Plant Food B is the leading national brand. Their ads claim that they generate higher growth rates than any other brand.

Use this data to complete exercises 1 and 2.

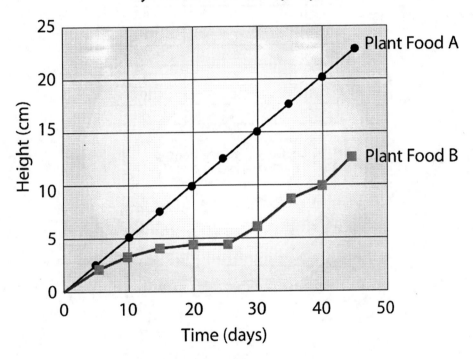

1. Use words to describe the trend in the growth of Plant Foods A and B.

2. Evaluate the claims of the advertisers, based on this evidence.

It struck Melissa as a little odd that Plant food A generated a growth of exactly 2.5 cm every five days. That seemed a little strange, given the usual growth fluctuation for all living things. Melissa decided to test these advertising claims for herself. She planted 10 seeds in 10 pots labeled Plant Food A. She planted 10 seeds in 10 pots labeled Plant Food B. The soil, light and water given each plant is identical. She recorded her data in a table and plotted it on a graph.

Use the table and graph to complete exercises 3-7.

Table with Melissa's Data

Height	Plant Food A	Plant Food B
0	0	0
5	1	1
10	3	2.8
15	5	5.2
20	7	6.3
25	7.6	7.2
30	8.4	8.4
35	9.7	9.6
40	10.3	10.3
45	11.2	11.3

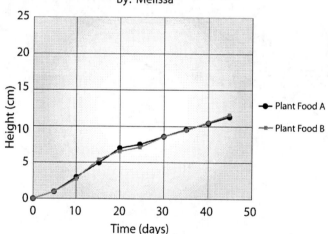

Plant Growth Experiment
By: Melissa

3. Again, use words to describe the trend in the growth of Plant Foods A and B.

4. Evaluate again the claims of the advertisers, based on this evidence. Is there any evidence of bias, or untruthfulness, in the advertising of Plant Food A and/or Plant Food B?

5. Think of other factors that could have affected Melissa's experiment, and caused this drastic deviation from advertised claims.

6. In this multiple line graph, each plant food is represented by only one line, even though there are 10 samples. What does that mean, and is that an acceptable way to present the data?

7. State a valid conclusion for Melissa's experiment.

Chapter 5
Cells and Cellular Transport

GEORGIA PERFORMANCE SCIENCE STANDARDS COVERED IN THIS CHAPTER INCLUDE:

SB1 a – d	Students will analyze the nature of the relationship between structures and functions in living cells.

CHARACTERISTICS OF LIFE

All living things, also called **organisms**, share the following characteristics:

1. Cells
2. Sensitivity (response to stimuli)
3. Growth
4. Homeostasis (stable internal environment)
5. Reproduction
6. Metabolism (transformation and use of energy)
7. Adaptation

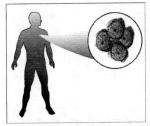

Figure 5.1 Cellular Makeup of Man

All living things share these seven characteristics, which are described below.

Cells: Cells make up all living things. Cells can sometimes organize into complex structures. Multicellular organisms have many cells and unicellular organisms have only one cell.

Sensitivity: Organisms respond to stimuli in the environment. A **stimulus** is a change in the environment. **Responses** are reactions to stimuli in the environment. Examples of responses to stimuli include a plant that grows toward a light source or an animal that flees from a predator.

Growth: Organisms change over their lifetime. This growth may be characterized by an increase in size, the development of new physical structures, or the refinement of reasoning or behavior.

Homeostasis: Organisms must maintain an internal environment that is suitable for life. Living things need the correct amount of fluids, salts, hormones and food sources in order to survive. **Homeostasis** is the ability of an organism to maintain a steady internal state, regardless of external influence.

Reproduction: All living things must be able to reproduce. Organisms can reproduce sexually or asexually. **Sexual reproduction** occurs when two organisms create offspring, and **asexual reproduction** occurs when one organism is capable of creating offspring by itself.

Metabolism: Organisms must get energy from the environment. The processes of extracting energy from the environment, using that energy and disposing of waste by-products are all chemical reactions. **Metabolism** is the sum of all chemical reactions within a cell or organism.

Adaptation: Over time, organisms can become specially suited to a particular environment. Sea turtles have long, flipper-like legs and cannot easily walk on land. They have become **adapted** to living in the ocean. **Adaptations** occur slowly, over the course of many, many generations.

Living things also carry out life processes. These are the specific events that allow cells to grow, respond to stimuli, maintain homeostasis, reproduce, metabolize and adapt. Non-living things cannot carry out these processes. A list of life processes is given in Table 5.1.

Table 5.1 Life Processes

Life Process	Description
Nutrition	the use of nutrients by an organism.
Digestion	the process that breaks large food molecules into forms that can be used by the cell.
Absorption	the ability of a cell to take in nutrients, water, gases and other substances from its surroundings.
Transport	the movement of nutrients, water, gases and other substances into and out of the cell.
Biosynthesis	the cellular process of building new chemical compounds for the purpose of growth, repair and reproduction.
Secretion	the release of substances from a cell.
Respiration	the release of energy from chemical breakdown of compounds within the cell.
Excretion	the ability of the cell to rid itself of waste products.
Response	the ability of a cell to react to stimuli from its environment.
Reproduction	the process of fission in which one cell divides to form two identical new cells.
Photosynthesis	the cellular process in which a plant makes food from water and carbon dioxide, using energy from the Sun.

Section Review 1:   Characteristics of Life

A. Define the following terms.

stimulus	life	sexual reproduction	asexual reproduction
response	homeostasis		
	metabolism		

B. Choose the best answer.

1. Which characteristic below is not a characteristic of life?

   A. growth   B. homeostasis   C. metabolism   D. excretion

2. How are life processes different from characteristics of life?

   A. Life processes are the characteristics shared by all organisms.

   B. Life processes are the specific events that allow organisms to live.

   C. Characteristics of life are the specific events that allow organisms to live.

   D. Life processes are the general characteristics shared by all organisms.

3. How are excretion and homeostasis similar?

   A. Cells are able to maintain homeostasis by excreting materials.

   B. Cells are able to maintain excretion through homeostasis.

   C. When cells excrete materials, they remove them from the cell.

   D. Excretion and homeostasis are not similar.

4. A plant cell traps and uses light energy. Which characteristic of life is this activity known as?

   A. adaptation   B. nutrition   C. metabolism   D. respiration

5. After several weeks as a tadpole, an amphibian in the vertebrate class of *Anura* develops legs and moves onto land. Which characteristic of life is this activity known as?

   A. adaptation   B. metabolism   C. digestion   D. growth

C. Complete the following exercises.

1. List the seven characteristics all living things must show.

2. Based on what you know, how would you explain the fact that fire is not considered life even though it grows and uses oxygen?

CELLULAR ORGANIZATION

PROKARYOTIC VS. EUKARYOTIC CELLS

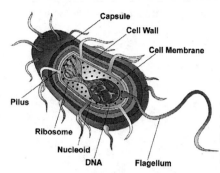

Figure 5.2 Prokaryotic Cell

There are two basic types of cells: prokaryotic and eukaryotic. A **prokaryotic** (*pro-* before; *karyotic-* nucleus) cell does not have a true nucleus. Although the genetic material is usually contained in a central location, a membrane does not surround it. Furthermore, prokaryotic cells have no membrane-bound organelles. Bacteria are prokaryotic. See Figure 5.2 for a schematic drawing of a prokaryotic cell.

A **eukaryotic** (*eu-* true; *karyotic-* nucleus) cell has a nucleus surrounded by a nuclear membrane. It also has several membrane-bound organelles. Eukaryotic cells tend to be larger than prokaryotic cells. Plant and animal cells are both eukaryotic and, although similar in structure, contain unique cell parts. For instance, plant cells have a cell wall and chloroplasts, while animal cells have centrioles and some even have cilia and flagella. See Figures 5.3 and 5.4 for schematic drawings of eukaryotic cells, including plant and animal cells. Table 5.2 lists functions of the parts in eukaryotic cells.

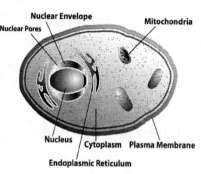

Figure 5.3 Eukaryotic Cell

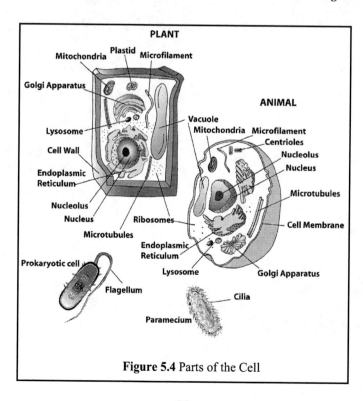

Figure 5.4 Parts of the Cell

Table 5.2 Parts of the Eukaryotic Cell

Name	Description
Cell Wall (plant cells only)	Rigid membrane around the plant cell; made of cellulose; provides shape and support
Modified Cell Wall (bacteria and fungi only)	Bacteria and fungi also have a cell wall, but it is made from different materials than that of a plant cell; see Chapter 8
Plastids (plant cells only)	Group of structures (chloroplasts, leukoplasts, chromoplasts) used in photosynthesis and product storage; have a double membrane and provide color and cellular energy
Vacuoles	Spherical storage sac for food and water
Cell Membrane	Membrane surrounding the cell that allows some molecules to pass through
Golgi Bodies	Flattened membrane sacs for synthesis, packaging, and distribution
Mitochondria	Rod-shaped double membranous structures where cellular respiration takes place
Microfilaments & Microtubules	Fibers and tubes of protein that help move internal cell parts
Endoplasmic Reticulum (ER)	Folded membranes having areas with and without ribosomes used for transport of RNA and proteins
Nucleolus	Dense body in the nucleus; site of ribosome production
Nucleus	Control center of the cell; location of hereditary information has a double membrane that has small holes
Ribosomes	Structures that manufacture proteins found on endoplasmic reticulum and floating in the cytoplasm
Centrioles (animal cell only)	Short tubes necessary for cell reproduction in some cells
Lysosomes	Spherical sac containing enzymes for digestive functions
Cilia (animal and bacteria cells only)	Short, hair-like extensions on the surface of some cells used for movement and food gathering
Flagella (animal and bacteria cells only)	Long, whip-like extension on the surface of some cells used for movement
Cytoplasm	Jelly-like substance in the cell around nucleus and organelles

Section Review 2: Cellular Organization

A. Define the following terms.

cell	Golgi bodies	centrioles
organelles	mitochondria	lysosomes
prokaryotic	microfilaments & microtubules	cilia
eukaryotic		flagella
cell wall	endoplasmic reticulum (ER)	cytoplasm
plastids	nucleolus	unicellular
vacuoles	nucleus	multicellular
cell membrane	ribosomes	

B. Choose the best answer.

1. The mitochondrion of a cell

    A. has only one membrane.

    B. has no membrane.

    C. is circular.

    D. is where cellular respiration occurs.

2. Which of the following statements is true of ribosomes?

    A. They are the site of protein synthesis.

    B. They are made by other ribosomes.

    C. They have their own DNA.

    D. none of the above

3. Structures that support and give shape to plant cells are

    A. microbodies.   B. Golgi bodies.   C. nucleus.   D. cell walls.

4. The storage of hereditary information in a eukaryotic cell is in the

    A. cytoplasm.   B. nucleus.   C. centrioles.   D. lysosomes.

C. Complete the following exercises.

1. Compare and contrast prokaryotic and eukaryotic cells.

2. Develop an analogy of comparing your school to the cell. Use all the cell parts and compare them to locations within your school.

THE CELL MEMBRANE AND CELLULAR TRANSPORT

Hormones are chemical messengers that regulate some body functions in multicellular organisms. One function of hormones is to help maintain homeostasis. Other functions of hormones include the control of movement of oxygen into cells and the removal of carbon dioxide from cells, the maintenance of the internal temperature of an organism and the regulation of fluids. Individual cells move fluids and nutrients in and out through the semi-permeable cell membrane. They can move these materials by either passive or active transport mechanisms to maintain homeostasis.

CELL MEMBRANE

The main purpose of the cell membrane is to regulate the movement of materials into and out of the cell. The cell membrane is **semi-permeable**, or selectively permeable, meaning that only certain substances can go through.

The cell membrane is composed of a phospholipid bilayer as shown in Figure 5.5. Each layer consists of phosphate groups (phosphorous bonded with oxygen) attached to two fatty acid tails. The layers arrange themselves so that the phosphate heads are on the outer edges of the membrane, and the fatty acid tails compose the interior of the membrane. Globular proteins used for various functions, such as transporting substances through the membrane, are embedded in the cell membrane. The phospholipids are free to move around, allowing the membrane to stretch and change shape.

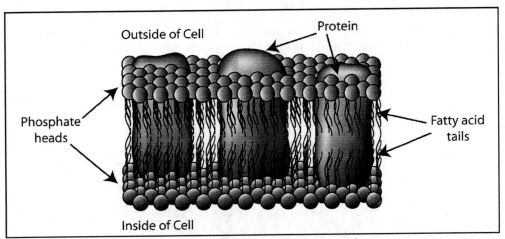

Figure 5.5 Phospholipid Bilayer

PASSIVE TRANSPORT

Passive transport is spontaneous and does not require energy. In passive transport, molecules move spontaneously through the cell membrane from areas of higher concentration to areas of lower concentration; they are said to move "with the **concentration gradient**." The three types of passive transport are diffusion, facilitated diffusion and osmosis.

Diffusion is the process by which substances move directly through the cell membrane as shown in Figure 5.6. **Facilitated diffusion** involves the help of a channel protein to move a substance from one side of the cell membrane to the other.

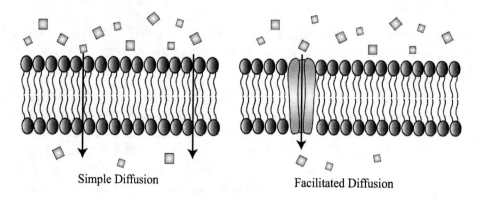

Simple Diffusion   Facilitated Diffusion

Figure 5.6 Diffusion

Osmosis is the movement of water from an area of high water concentration to an area of low water concentration through a semi-permeable membrane. Think of osmosis as the diffusion of water.

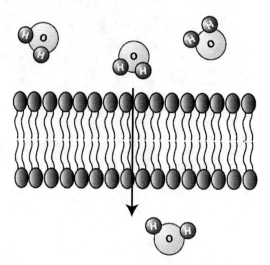

Figure 5.7 Osmosis

Osmosis can occur in either direction, depending on the concentration of dissolved material inside and outside the cell. Defining the solution concentrations relative to one another will predict the direction in which osmosis will occur. A **hypotonic** solution has the lower concentration of solute; this may be thought of as a higher concentration of water. A **hypertonic** solution has a higher concentration of dissolved solute, which may be thought of as a lower concentration of water. Diffusion of water (osmosis) across a cell membrane always occurs from hypotonic to hypertonic. Three situations are possible:

a) The solution surrounding the cell membrane has a lower concentration of dissolved substances than the solution inside the cell membrane. Here, the solution outside the membrane is hypotonic with respect to the solution inside the cell membrane. The cell will experience a net gain of water and swell.

b) The solution surrounding the cell membrane has a higher concentration of dissolved solute that the solution inside the cell membrane. In this case, the solution outside the membrane is hypertonic with respect to the solution inside the cell membrane. The cell will lose water to its surroundings, causing it to shrink.

c) In the third case, the concentration of dissolved solutes is the same inside the cell as it is outside the cell. These solutions are said to be isotonic with respect to each other. There will be no net movement of water across the cell membrane. This is a state of equilibrium, which the cell often reaches only after a prior exchange of water across the membrane.

These situations are illustrated in Figure 5.8.

Solution Type	Effect on Cell
Isotonic Particle concentration the same outside and inside cell.	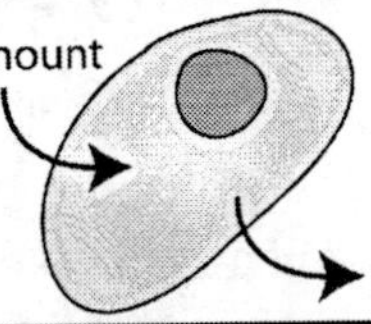 Same amount of water in → ← as water out
Hypotonic Particle concentration lower in solution than in cell.	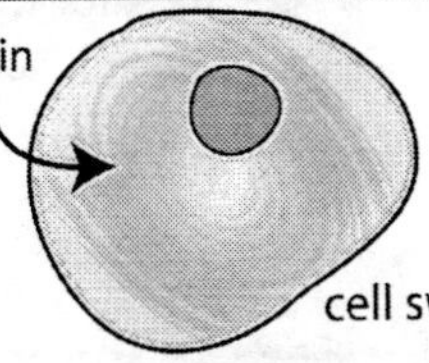 Water in → cell swells
Hypertonic Particle concentration higher in solution than in cell.	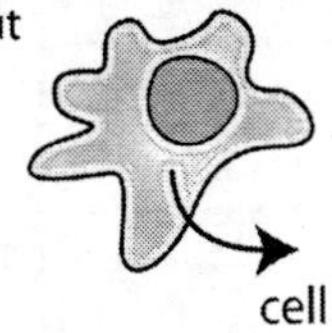 Water out → cell shrinks

Figure 5.8 Possible Results of Osmosis

Placing plant cells in a hypertonic solution causes the plant cell membranes to shrink away from the cell wall. This process is called **plasmolysis**. Plasmolysis can result in plant cell death due to water loss. A wilted plant is an example of plasmolysis. Placing a plant in a hypotonic solution has an opposite effect: the cell will swell until the cell wall allows no more expansion. The plant now becomes stiff and turgid.

Kidney dialysis is an example of a medical procedure that involves diffusion. Another example is food preserved by salting, sugar curing or pickling. All of these examples are methods of drawing water out of the cells through osmosis.

ACTIVE TRANSPORT

In some cases, the cell may need to move material across the cell membrane, against the concentration gradient. To do so, the cell must expend energy. The movement of substances from an area of low concentration to an area of high concentration is called **active transport**. The movement is characterized by its directionality.

One type of active transport involves the use of carrier proteins. Carrier proteins are special proteins embedded in the cell membrane. These proteins have a binding site specific to the type of molecule it transports and a binding site for ATP. When both ATP and the molecule are bound to the protein, it changes shape and allows the molecule into the cell. The transported molecule and the ADP molecule are then released by the protein.

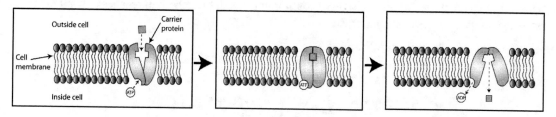

Figure 5.9 Active Transport Using Proteins

Exocytosis is a form of active transport that removes materials from the cell. A sac stores the material to be removed from the cell, and then moves near the cell membrane. The cell membrane opens, and the substance is expelled from the cell. Waste materials, proteins and fats are examples of materials removed from the cell in this way.

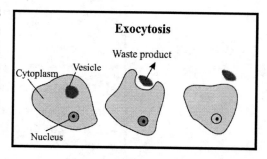

Figure 5.10 Exocytosis

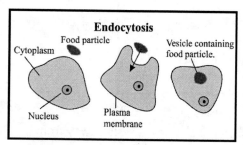

Figure 5.11 Endocytosis

Endocytosis
, another form of active transport, brings materials into the cell without passing through the cell membrane. The membrane folds itself around the substance, creates a **vesicle**, and brings the substance into the cell. Some unicellular organisms, such as an amoeba, obtain food this way.

Active transport is a mechanism that allows certain organisms to survive in their environments. For instance, sea gulls can drink salt water because their cells remove excess salt from their bodies through active transport. However, freshwater fish are not able to remove excess salt from their cells and, therefore, would become dehydrated in a salt-water environment. Another example of active transport involves blood cells. Blood cells use carrier proteins to transport molecules into the cell, but they have no mechanism to remove excess water. This combination is the source of some diseases. Medical science is aiming its study of treatment for diseases at the cell membrane and the carrier proteins that act to transport molecules into cells.

Section Review 3: The Cell Membrane and Cellular Transport

A. Define the following terms.

hormones	diffusion	hypertonic	exocytosis
semi-permeable	facilitated diffusion	isotonic	endocytosis
passive transport	osmosis	plasmolysis	vesicle
	hypotonic	active transport	

B. Choose the best answer.

1. The movement of substances into and out of a cell without the use of energy is called
   A. active transport.
   B. passive transport.
   C. exocytosis.
   D. endocytosis.

2. The movement of water across a semi-permeable membrane from an area of high water concentration to an area of low water concentration is called
   A. active transport.
   B. diffusion.
   C. osmosis.
   D. hypotonic.

3. A type of membrane which allows only certain molecules to pass through is called
   A. hypertonic.
   B. semi-permeable.
   C. active.
   D. porous.

4. A cell placed in a solution shrinks by the process of osmosis. What kind of solution is outside the cell?
   A. hypotonic   B. hypertonic   C. active   D. isotonic

5. If the solution surrounding a cell has a lower concentration of solutes than inside the cell, water will move into the cell through osmosis, causing it to expand. What kind of solution is surrounding the cell?
   A. active   B. passive   C. hypertonic   D. hypotonic

C. Answer the following questions.

1. What causes a plant's leaves to wilt?

2. How does active transport differ from diffusion?

3. Dried beans are soaked overnight in preparation for cooking. Explain the process affecting the beans. What will happen to the dried beans?

4. A celery stalk is placed in a solution. It begins to wilt. What is a likely component of that solution?

CATALYSTS AND ENZYMES

A **catalyst** is a substance that speeds up a chemical reaction without being chemically changed by the reaction. Catalysts decrease the amount of activation energy required for the reaction to occur. **Activation energy** is the amount of energy required in order for reactant molecules to begin a chemical reaction. When a molecule reaches its energy of activation, its chemical bonds are very weak and likely to break. Activation energy provides a barrier so that molecules will not spontaneously react with one another. One example of an inorganic catalyst is nickel, which is used in the hydrogenation of vegetable oil to make

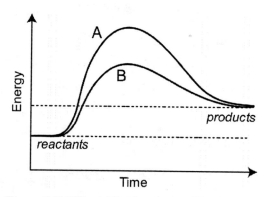

Figure 5.12 Effect of Catalysts on Activation Energy

margarine. The nickel is recovered; it is not used up, and it is not part of the final product.

Our bodies use catalysts called enzymes to break down food and convert it to energy. Every cellular activity is a result of many biochemical reactions that take place at a cellular level. Substances that speed these reactions are called enzymes. **Enzymes** are specific proteins that combine with other substances called **substrates**. There is one enzyme for one substrate, and they fit together like pieces of a puzzle. Metabolism cannot occur unless the energy of activation has been reached. These biological reactions would eventually take place on their own, but in the presence of enzymes, the reactions take place about a million times faster. Enzymes help to lower the energy of activation, making some chemical processes occur with greater frequency.

Some reactions use **cofactors** to help enzymes by transporting electrons, ions or atoms between substances. A **cofactor** is either a metal ion (a metal atom that has lost or gained electrons) or a coenzyme. A **coenzyme** is a non-protein molecule that activates the enzyme. Important cofactors in photosynthesis and cellular respiration are **NADP+** (nicotinamide adenine dinucleotide phosphate) and **NAD+** (nicotinamide adenine dinucleotide). These cofactors pick up free hydrogen ions and electrons and transport them so the next stage of the reaction can take place. We will not be addressing the specific movement of molecules and bonds in this text, but it is a good idea to have an idea of what these cofactors look like. Figure 5.13 shows the structure of the coenzyme NAD+.

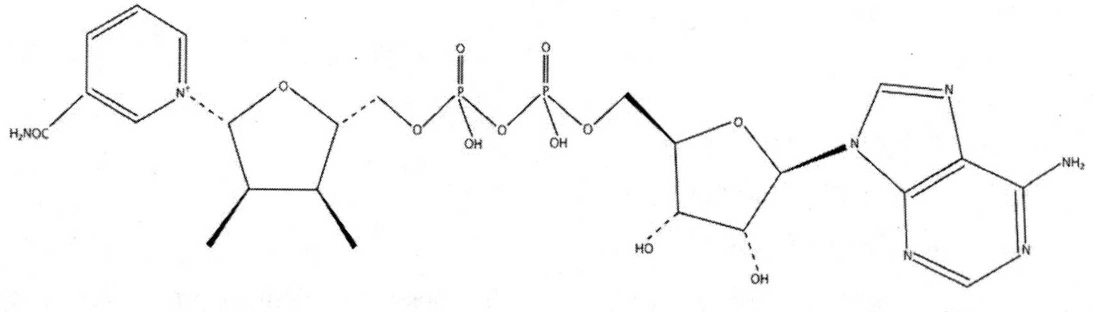

Figure 5.13 NAD+ Nicotinamide Adenine Dinucleotide

Metabolic processes can occur without enzymes, though at biological temperatures, metabolism would happen so slowly most organisms would be unable to survive. Some enzyme failures result in disease or death of the organism.

Factors that influence the rate at which enzymes act include such things such as temperature, pH and amount of substrate present. Most enzymes have an optimum temperature and pH. Their optimum temperature or pH is the range at which the enzyme functions best. Enzymes vary from one organism to another. Some bacteria have enzymes that have an optimum temperature of 70°C or higher; this temperature would destroy most human enzymes.

With a few exceptions, most enzymes have an optimum pH of between 6 and 8. Table 5.3 contains several enzymes and their optimal pH.

Table 5.3 pH for Optimum Enzyme Activity

Enzyme	pH Optimum
Lipase – hydrolyzes glycerides (pancreas)	8.0
Lipse – hydrolyzes glycerides (stomach)	4.0 – 5.0
Pepsin – decomposition of proteins	1.5 – 1.6
Urease – hydrolysis of urea	7.0
Invertase – hydrolysis of sucrose	4.5
Maltase – hydrolysis of maltose to glucose	6.1 – 6.8
Amylase (pancreas) – hydrolysis of starch	6.7 – 7.0
Catalase – decomposition of hydrogen peroxide into water and oxygen	7.0

Recall that a pH of 7 is considered **neutral**. Water has a pH of about 7. Substances with a pH less than 7 are **acids** and substances with a pH greater than 7 are **bases**. One example of an enzyme is pepsin, an acidic enzyme found in the human stomach. Pepsin has an optimum pH of 1–2.

CHEMISTRY OF THE CELL

KEY ELEMENTS

An **element** is a type of matter composed of only one kind of atom which cannot be broken down to a simpler structure.   There are six elements commonly found in living cells: **sulfur, phosphorous, oxygen, nitrogen, carbon** and **hydrogen** (easily remembered as **SPONCH**). These elements make up 99% of all living tissue and combine to form the molecules that are the basis of cellular function. Carbon is especially important because one carbon atom can make

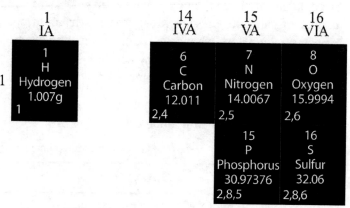

Figure 5.14 Key Elements in Living Cells

covalent bonds with four other atoms, resulting in the formation of very stable and complex structures. Carbon is in all living things as well as in the remains of living things. Molecules containing carbon are called **organic molecules**, while those without carbon are called **inorganic molecules**. Water is the most important inorganic molecule for living things, and serves as the medium in which cellular reactions take place.

Those cellular reactions occur in great part between biological molecules, often called **biomolecules**. The four primary classes of cellular biomolecules are carbohydrates, lipids, proteins and nucleic acids. Each of these is a **polymer** — that is, a long chain of small repeating units called **monomers**.

CARBOHYDRATES

Carbohydrates are often called sugars, and are an energy source. Structurally, they are chains of carbon units with hydroxyl groups (-OH) attached. The simplest carbohydrates are monosaccharides. The ends of these sugars bond and unbond continuously, so that the straight chain and cyclic (ring-like) forms are in equilibrium. Figure 5.15 (right) shows a Fischer diagram projection of glucose, a very common biomolecule. A Fischer projection depicts the straight chain form of a monosaccharide. Figure 5.16 (below) shows a Hayworth representation of ribose, another common carbohydrate. A Hayworth representation indicates the structure of a cyclic monosaccharide.

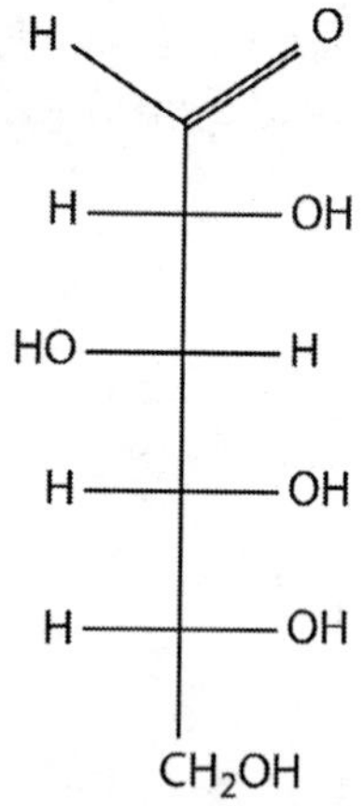

Figure 5.16 Ribose

Figure 5.15
Fischer Diagram
of Glucose

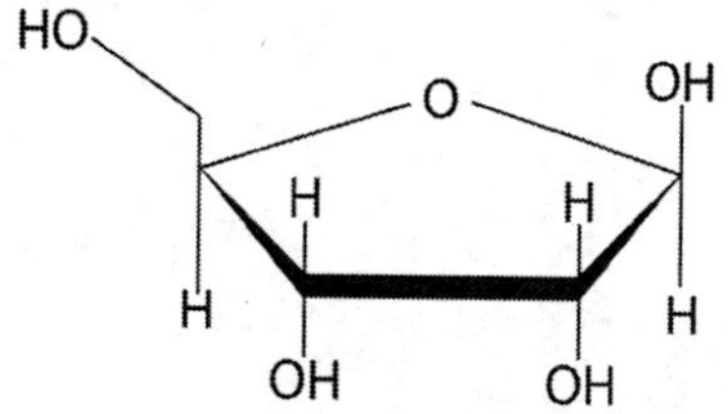

These monosaccharides may join together to form disaccharides (2), oligosaccharides (3 to 10) or polysaccharides (10+), depending on how many monosaccharides make up the polymeric carbohydrate. Disaccharides consist of two monosaccharide units. Common table sugar, or sucrose, is a disaccharide formed from the bound monosaccharides, fructose and glucose. Complex carbohydrates such as starch and cellulose are classified as polysaccharides.

Lab Activity 1: Testing for Starch

Iodine is useful in testing for the presence of starch. Use grapes, egg whites and butter. Place these bits of food on a paper towel. Put a drop of iodine on each bit of food. Observe any change in color.

- Reddish-brown means the food contains little or no starch.
- Yellow means the food contains some starch.
- Blue-black means the food contains a lot of starch.

LIPIDS

Lipids are fats, that are made up of chains of methyl (-CH) units. The chains may be long or short, they may be straight or fused into rings (cyclic). They have several functions but are most well known as fat molecules that store energy. They are also the structural components of the cell membrane. Several important lipids have names that you may recognize: waxes, steroids, fatty acids and triglycerides. The excess of triglycerides like the one pictured in Figure 5.17 is strongly linked to heart disease and stroke. It may not surprise you to know that butter is a triglyceride.

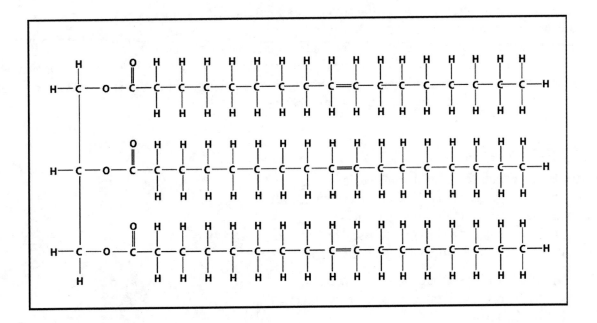

Figure 5.17 Lipid

Lab Activity 2: Testing for Fats in Food

Use a piece of brown paper bag to test for fat. Use the same kind of food bits as Lab Activity 2. Rub the brown paper with each bit of food. Wait for 10 minutes. Hold the paper up to the light.

- If no fat is present, the paper will appear opaque.

- If some fat is present, the paper will appear semi-translucent.

- If a lot of fat is present, the paper will appear translucent.

PROTEINS

Figure 5.18 Protein

Proteins consist of long, linear chains of **polypeptides**. The polypeptide is itself a chain of **amino acid** monomers. There are 20 standard amino acids which combine to form every single protein needed by the human body; protein synthesis, the process of making proteins, will be discussed later. Figure 5.19 shows a polypeptide; Figure 5.18 shows several polypeptides linked together to form a protein.

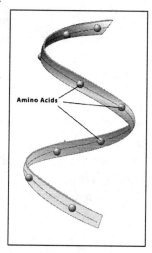

Figure 5.19 Polypeptide

There are many different types of proteins, all of which have different biological functions. They include: structural proteins, regulatory proteins, contractile proteins, transport proteins, storage proteins, protective proteins, membrane proteins, toxins and enzymes. Despite the wide variation in function, shape and size, all proteins are made from the same 20 amino acids. Since mammals cannot make all 20 amino acids, themselves, they must eat protein in order to maintain a healthy diet. Protein may be eaten in animal (meat) or vegetable (beans) form, but most organisms must have protein to survive.

NUCLEIC ACIDS

Nucleic acids are found in the nucleus of a cell. The nucleic acid polymer is made up of **nucleotide** monomers. The nucleotide monomer consists of a sugar, a phosphate group and a nitrogenous base. Nucleic acids are the backbone of the following genetic material:

a) **DNA** (deoxyribonucleic acid) directs the activities of the cell and contains the sugar deoxyribose.

b) **RNA** (ribonucleic acid) is involved in protein synthesis and contains the sugar ribose.

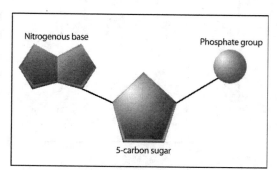

Figure 5.20 A Nucleotide

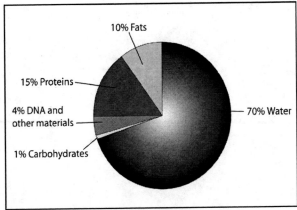

Figure 5.21 Composition of the Cell

Now that the biomolecules present in the cell have been introduced, can you guess which one makes up the bulk of a cell? Look at Figure 5.21. The bulk of a cell is not made up by a biomolecule — or even all the biomolecules put together! The bulk of the cell is made up of water.

CELLULAR ENERGY

The life processes of a cell are the end result of a series of chemical reactions. Each chemical reaction requires energy. In many cases, chemical reactions also require substances to speed reaction time. Energy comes in the form of a molecule called **ATP**, and the substances used to push reactions along are called **enzymes**.

THE ROLE OF BONDING IN ENERGY PRODUCTION

When chemical bonds are formed, energy is stored, and when chemical bonds are broken, energy is released. The stronger the bond, the more energy that will be released when the bond is broken. The role of bonding and energy production will be discussed later in Chapter 8.

In contrast, an **ionic bond** is the joining of two atoms based on their opposite electrical charges, which generate an electrostatic attraction. Covalent bonds generally occur between non-metallic elements, whereas metals tend to form ionic bonds.

A purely covalent bond is **nonpolar,** meaning that both atoms share electrons equally. Nonpolar bonding occurs between two atoms of the same element, like the carbon-carbon (C-C) bonds in an organic molecule, or the H-H bond in hydrogen gas (H_2). Most organic molecules form using covalent bonds. When atoms of different elements bond covalently, they bring to the bond their different electron configurations. This has the effect of one atom pulling electrons toward it more strongly than the other. These bonds are called **polar** covalent bonds. Water is a good example of polar covalent bonding: two hydrogen

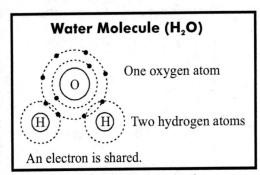

Figure 5.22 Water Molecule

atoms are bound to one oxygen atom to form the water molecule. The H-O bonds are polar because oxygen pulls electrons toward it and away from hydrogen. Polar covalent bonds are often said to have "ionic character."

Section Review 4: The Chemistry of the Cell

A. Define the following terms.

organic molecule	monomer	DNA	protein
inorganic molecule	biomolecule	RNA	amino acid
nucleotide	nucleic acid	carbohydrate	polymer
		lipid	polypeptide

B. Choose the best answer.

1. Carbon chains are principal features of both carbohydrates and lipids. What is the primary difference between these two types of biomolecules?

   A. Lipids always have longer carbon chains than carbohydrates.

   B. Carbohydrates carry hydroxyl groups on their carbon backbone.

   C. Carbohydrates cannot form rings as lipids can.

   D. Lipids provide energy, but carbohydrates do not.

2. What molecules make up the bulk of a cell?

   A. carbohydrates   B. lipids   C. proteins   D. water

3. Why is carbon important to living things?

   A. Because it metabolizes easily, creating a quick energy source.

   B. Because it is abundant on the earth's surface.

   C. Because it can form four covalent bonds with other atoms.

   D. Because it has twelve protons and neutrons.

4. Nucleotides are to nucleic acids as amino acids are to

   A. DNA.   C. proteins.

   B. polypeptides.   D. carbohydrates.

C. Complete the following exercises.

1. All living things have a common tie with the earth on which we live. Explain why this is true.

2. What are the six elements commonly found in living things?

3. Why is carbon important to living things?

100

CHAPTER 5 REVIEW

1. In order to be classified as living, an organism must have:

    A. a heart and lungs.

    B. the ability to nourish itself, grow and reproduce.

    C. the ability to photosynthesize and to eliminate waste products.

    D. a true nucleus and nuclear membrane.

2. What are the main products produced in a cell?

    A. lipids

    B. amino acids

    C. proteins

    D. carbohydrates

3. A _____ is a type of cell that has a true nucleus.

    A. prokaryote   B. eukaryote   C. bacterium   D. virus

4. How does a plastid function within a cell?

    A. It digests food and breaks down wastes.

    B. It produces proteins.

    C. It carries on cellular respiration.

    D. It carries out photosynthesis and provides color.

5. If a cell has a flagellum on its surface, it is MOST likely which type of cell?

    A. an animal cell

    B. a plant cell

    C. a homologous cell

    D. a diseased cell

6. If an animal cell is placed in distilled water, it will

    A. remain the same size.

    B. shrink.

    C. swell and eventually explode.

    D. swell, but stop when the cell wall prevents further expansion.

7. When you perspire on a hot, humid day, drinking water will restore _____ in your body.

    A. substances   B. oxygen   C. homeostasis   D. proteins

8. If a plant cell is placed in distilled water, it will

    A. remain the same size.

    B. shrink.

    C. swell and eventually explode.

    D. swell, but stop when the cell wall prevents further expansion.

9. The process by which food is taken into the cell is called

    A. nourishment.   B. resuscitation.   C. absorption.   D. nutrition.

10. The ability of the cell to rid itself of waste products is called

    A. excretion.   B. elimination.   C. voiding.   D. absorption.

11. What are two structures found in plant cells that are NOT found in animal cells?

    A. mitochondria and ribosomes   C. cell membrane and centrioles

    B. cell wall and plastids   D. nucleolus and endoplasmic reticulum

12. Prokaryotic cells lack which cellular component?

    A. nucleus   C. cell membrane

    B. energy exchange   D. metabolism

13. When more water goes in through a cell membrane than out of it, the solution around the membrane is

    A. isotonic.   B. hypotonic.   C. permeable.   D. hypertonic.

14. Which organelle is the site of protein synthesis?

    A. plastid   B. ribosome   C. nucleolus   D. mitochondrion

15. What is the movement of substances into and out of a cell without the use of energy called?

    A. diffusion   B. locomotion   C. active transport   D. glycolysis

16. The type of membrane that allows only certain molecules to pass through is

    A. openly permeable.   C. non-permeable.

    B. semi-permeable.   D. rigidly permeable.

17. Amoebas obtain food by wrapping the cell membrane around the food particle, creating a vesicle. The food is then brought into the cell. This process is called

    A. exocytosis.   B. endocytosis.   C. osmosis.   D. photosynthesis.

Chapter 6
Nucleic Acids and Cell Division

GEORGIA PERFORMANCE SCIENCE STANDARDS COVERED IN THIS CHAPTER
INCLUDE:

SB2 a, b and e	Students will analyze how biological traits are passed on to successive generations.

THE ROLE OF DNA

The genetic basis of life is a molecule called **DNA** or **deoxyribonucleic acid**. DNA is carried in the nucleus of all cells and performs two primary functions. First, it carries the code for all the genes of an organism, which in turn create the proteins that perform all the work of living. Second, the code of the DNA itself is the template for future generations. First, we will look at the role of DNA in protein synthesis and then its role in heredity.

DNA, RNA AND PROTEIN SYNTHESIS

DNA

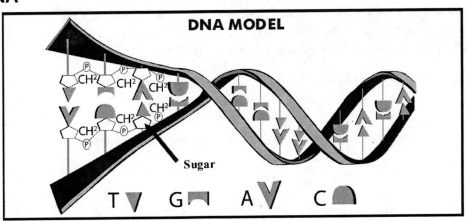

Figure 6.1 Model of DNA

DNA is a complex molecule with a double helix shape, like a twisted ladder. Each side of the helix is composed of a strand of **nucleotides** that are the building blocks of nucleic acids. Each nucleotide contains a phosphate group, the sugar **deoxyribose** and a **nitrogenous base**. There are four bases in DNA, and they pair together in a very specific way. The bases are **adenine** (A), **thymine** (T), **guanine** (G) and **cytosine** (C). A and T always pair, and G and C always pair. The A-T and G-C pairings are called **complementary pairs**. Each pair forms one of the rungs of the ladder as shown in Figure 6.1.

The DNA molecule carries the code for all the genes of the organism. **Genes** are pieces of the DNA molecule that code for specific proteins. The process of making genes into proteins is called **protein synthesis**.

DNA is located in the nucleus of the cell. The assembly of proteins occurs outside of the nucleus, on the ribosome. So the manufacture of proteins involves three basic steps:

1. The DNA code of the gene segment must be copied in the nucleus of the cell.

2. The code must then be carried from the nucleus into the cytoplasm and finally to a ribosome.

3. The protein is then assembled in the cytoplasm on the surface of the ribosome and released.

These steps are carried out by RNA, or ribonucleic acid.

RNA

RNA (ribonucleic acid) is a molecule used to translate the code from the DNA molecule into protein. It is similar to DNA, except it is single stranded. Its sugar is **ribose**. RNA, like DNA, has four nitrogenous bases. It shares adenine, guanine and cytosine but replaces thymine with **uracil** (U), so the bases A and U pair up instead of A and T. There are several types of RNA. Messenger, ribosomal and transfer RNA are <u>all</u> involved in protein synthesis. Now let's examine how RNA functions during protein synthesis.

Activity

Use the Venn Diagram below to compare and contrast DNA and RNA. A Venn Diagram is a graphic tool students use to compare and contrast two topics. To use this type of tool, students begin by writing one topic over each circle. In this activity, we will write DNA over the left hand circle and RNA over the right hand side. To complete the diagram, you, the student, must write factors that both DNA and RNA share in the space where the two circles overlap and factors exclusive to each topic inside their respective circles.

PROTEIN SYNTHESIS

TRANSCRIPTION

The first step of protein synthesis is the manufacture of a specific kind of RNA called **messenger RNA (mRNA)**. This copying process is called **transcription**. Transcription begins when a region of the DNA double helix unwinds and separates, as shown in Figure 6.2. The separated segment is a gene, and it serves as a template for the soon-to-be-formed mRNA strand.

The mRNA strand is assembled from individual RNA nucleotides that are present in the nucleus. An enzyme called **RNA polymerase** picks up these unattached nucleotide bases and matches them to their complementary bases on the DNA template strand. This continues until the entire gene segment has been paired, and a complete mRNA strand has been formed. This mRNA strand has a sequence that is complementary to the original gene segment. At that point, the mRNA separates and leaves the nucleus, moving out into the cytoplasm to settle on the **ribosome**, an organelle composed of another kind of RNA, called **ribosomal RNA (rRNA)**. Here on the surface of the ribosome, the process of translation begins.

TRANSCRIPTION

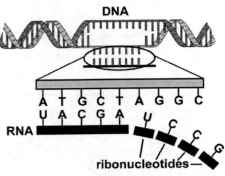

Figure 6.2 Transcription

TRANSLATION

Translation is the step in protein synthesis where mRNA is decoded (translated) and a corresponding polypeptide is formed. (Remember that a polypeptide is made up of **amino acids**.) Let's look at the "language" of mRNA.

One way to think of a strand of mRNA is as a chain of nucleotides, as in:

AUGACAGAUUAG

While this is correct, a more accurate way of thinking of the chain is that it is divided into segments consisting of three nucleotides each, as in:

AUG ACA GAU UAG

The mRNA strand is not *actually* divided, but writing its code in this way emphasizes an important concept: the **codon**. The three-nucleotide codon has the specific function of corresponding to a particular amino acid. Here is how it works: The molecule of mRNA is bound to the surface of the ribosome at the first three-nucleotide segment, called the **start codon**. The cytoplasm in which they float contains, among other things, amino acids and a third kind of RNA — **transfer RNA (tRNA)**. Transfer RNA is a molecule of RNA that contains a three-part nucleotide segment called an **anticodon**, which is the exact complement of one mRNA codon. The anticodon corresponds exactly to one of the 20 kinds of amino acids. Once the tRNA binds the amino acid, it travels to the ribosome surface. There the three tRNA nucleotide bases (the anticodon) pair with their three complementary mRNA bases (the codon). The amino acid that is bound to the tRNA is then added to the growing polypeptide chain at the surface of the ribosome, as shown in Figure 6.3. The ribosome facilitates this process by moving along the mRNA chain until it reaches a **stop codon**, a three-nucleotide segment that tells the ribosome that the translation process is complete. The ribosome then releases the newly-formed polypeptide chain, which moves out into the cell as a fully functioning protein.[1]

---

1. To see a free downloadable animation of protein synthesis, go to www.americanbookcompany.com/science

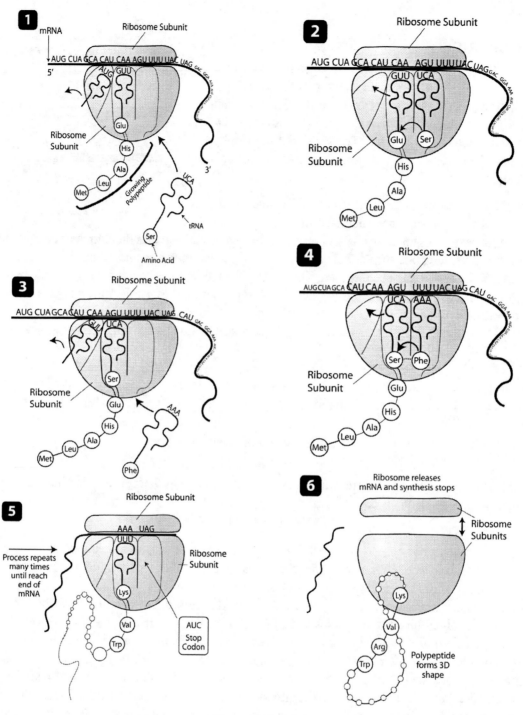

Figure 6.3 Translation

There are many proteins within every cell. Proteins make up **enzymes** that help to carry out reactions within the cell. Proteins also compose **hormones**, which are chemical messengers that regulate some body functions. Proteins provide structure and act as energy sources. They transport other molecules and are part of our bodies' defenses against disease. In short, proteins are essential for survival because almost everything that happens in the cell involves proteins.

Section Review 1: DNA, RNA and Protein Synthesis

A. Define the following terms.

DNA	nucleotide	ribose	amino acid
gene	deoxyribose	transcription	translation
RNA	base	messenger RNA (mRNA)	transfer RNA (tRNA)
anticodon	ribosome	ribosomal RNA (rRNA)	enzyme
protein synthesis	adenine	codon	hormone
polymerase	cytosine	complementary pairs	thymine
guanine	uracil	stop codon	start codon

B. Choose the best answer.

1. Protein synthesis begins with the manufacture of which molecule?
   A. mRNA   B. rRNA   C. tRNA   D. nucleotide

2. What are ribosomes made of?
   A. mRNA   B. rRNA   C. tRNA   D. protein

3. Proteins are made up of polypeptide chains. Polypeptide chains are composed of
   A. mRNA.   B. rRNA.   C. tRNA.   D. amino acids.

4. What does transfer RNA (tRNA) carry?
   A. the mRNA to the ribosome
   B. the nucleotide bases to the mRNA
   C. an amino acid to the ribosome
   D. an amino acid to the cytoplasm

5. Which of the following is the first step in protein synthesis?
   A. tRNA bonds to an amino acid in the cytoplasm.
   B. DNA unravels to expose an mRNA segment.
   C. DNA unravels to expose a gene segment.
   D. mRNA bonds to tRNA.

C. Complete the following exercises.

1. Describe the process of translation.
2. Which sugars are found in DNA and RNA?
3. What are proteins made of?
4. List the DNA bases that pair and the RNA bases that pair.
5. What role does DNA play in protein synthesis?

DNA REPLICATION

In the previous section, we examined the role that DNA plays in protein synthesis. In this section, we will examine the pivotal role that DNA plays in **cell division**.

Cells must be able to divide in order for the organism to grow, reproduce and repair itself. Multicellular organisms are made up of two kinds of cells: reproductive (or sex) cells and somatic (or body) cells. Both kinds of cells contain DNA, which is stored in the nucleus in the form of chromatin. **Chromatin** consists of long strands of DNA, jumbled up with proteins, that together form a kind of disorganized mass of genetic material in the nucleus. When the cell is ready to divide, the chromatin coils and condenses to form chromosomes. A **chromosome** is a single macromolecule of DNA, organized into a long chain. **Reproductive cells** have a single set, or **haploid** number (n), of chromosomes. **Somatic cells** have two sets, or a **diploid** number (2n), of chromosomes.

Figure 6.4 DNA

When the cell divides, the chromosomes must be distributed between the newly produced cells. This means that the DNA must be able to copy itself, which it does through the process of **replication**.

The number of chromosomes varies by species. Human reproductive cells have a haploid number of chromosomes, n=23. Our somatic cells contain 2n chromosomes: 23 pairs = 46 total chromosomes. Other species have different numbers of chromosomes. For instance, the common fruit fly (*Drosophila melanogaster*) has 8 chromosomes (4 pair); the laboratory rat (*Rattus norvegicus*) has 42 chromosomes (21 pairs).

During replication, the double strands of the DNA helix break apart, unzipping like a zipper, to become two individual strands. In a process very similar to that of mRNA formation, new DNA strands are assembled from the free-floating nucleotides in the cell's nucleus. An enzyme called **DNA polymerase** collects the nucleotide bases and matches them to their complementary pair along the single-strand DNA. When the entire process is complete, two new DNA double helices, identical to the original helix, have been formed. The replication process is just one part of the cell cycle.

THE CELL CYCLE

The **cell cycle** is the sequence of stages through which a cell passes between one cell division and the next. The length of time it takes a cell to complete the cell cycle varies from one cell to another. Some cells complete the entire cycle in a few minutes, and other cells spend their entire life frozen in a particular phase.

Most of the cell cycle is spent in **interphase** as shown in Figure 6.5. Interphase consists of three major parts: G_1, S and G_2. During the G_1 phase of interphase, the cell grows in size. In the S phase, replication of the DNA containing the genetic material occurs, which gives the cell a double amount of DNA. In the G_2 phase, the cell prepares for mitosis by replicating organelles and increasing the amount of cytoplasm.

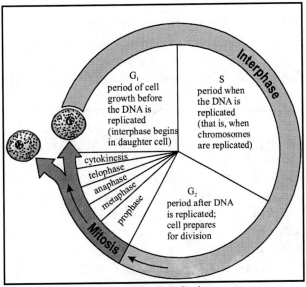

Figure 6.5 The Cell Cycle

MITOSIS

All of the cells in the body, with the exception of reproductive cells, are called somatic cells. Some examples are heart cells, liver cells and skin cells. Somatic cells undergo a process called mitosis. **Mitosis** is a type of cell division that generates two daughter cells with the identical components of the mother cell.

The daughter cells that result from mitotic cell division are identical to each other as well as to the parent cell. The daughter cells have the same (diploid) number of chromosomes as the parent cell. Mitosis is the mechanism for **asexual reproduction**, which only requires one parent. Mitosis also allows multicellular organisms to grow and replace cells.

The stages of mitosis are:

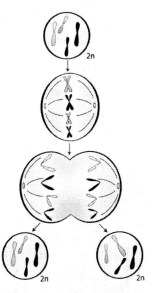

Figure 6.6 One Cell Divides Into Two Cells During Mitosis

Prophase:	The nucleus of the cell organizes the chromatin material into thread-like structures called chromosomes. The centriole, in animal cells only, divides and moves to each end of the cell. Spindles form between the centrioles.
Metaphase:	The chromosomes attached at the center, or centromeres, line up on the spindle at the center of the cell.
Anaphase:	Chromosomes separate at the center, and the spindles pull them toward either end of the cell. A nuclear membrane forms around the chromosomes as they disorganize.
Telophase:	Chromatin again forms from the chromosomes, and a cell membrane begins to grow across the center between the two new nuclei.

CYTOKINESIS

Cytokinesis, the division of the cell cytoplasm, usually follows mitosis. Cytokinesis generally begins during telophase of mitosis. It finalizes the production of two new daughter cells, each with approximately half of the cytoplasm and organelles as well as one of the two nuclei formed during mitosis. The processes of mitosis and cytokinesis are together called **cell division**.

MEIOSIS

Meiosis is a type of cell division necessary for **sexual reproduction**. It is limited to the reproductive cells in the testes, namely the **sperm cells**, and the reproductive cells in the ovaries, namely the **eggs**. Meiosis produces four reproductive cells, or **gametes**. These four cells contain half the number (haploid) of chromosomes of the mother cell, and the chromosomes are not identical. There are two phases of this type of cell division, **meiosis I** and **meiosis II**. Before meiosis begins, each pair of chromosomes replicates while the cell is in its resting phase (interphase).

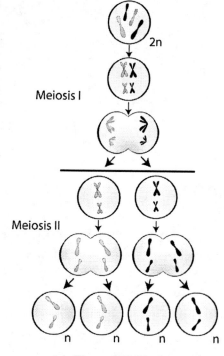

Figure 6.7 Meiosis

Figure 6.8 Crossing Over of Chromosomes

During meiosis I, each set of replicated chromosomes lines up with its homologous pair. **Homologous chromosomes** are matched pairs of chromosomes. Homologous chromosomes are similar in size and shape and carry the same kinds of genes. However, they are not identical because each set usually comes from a different parent. The homologous pairs of chromosomes can break and exchange segments during the **crossing over** process, a source of genetic variation. The homologous pairs of chromosomes separate. The cell then splits into two daughter cells, each containing one pair of the homologous chromosomes. **Interkinesis** is the resting period before meiosis II begins.

During meiosis II, the two daughter cells divide again without replication of the chromosomes. The result is four gametes, each having half the number of chromosomes of the mother cell.

Section Review 2: Reproduction of Cells

A. Define the following terms.

reproductive cells	cell cycle	metaphase	sexual reproduction
haploid	interphase	anaphase	gamete
somatic cells	asexual reproduction	telophase	crossing over
diploid	prophase	cytokinesis	interkinesis
homologous chromosomes	mitosis	cell division	
chromatin	replication	meiosis	

B. Choose the best answer.

1. All body cells, except the sperm and the ova are what type of cells?
    A. germ   B. reproductive   C. somatic   D. spindle

2. Which type of nuclear division produces gametes?
    A. meiosis   B. cytokinesis   C. interphase   D. mitosis

3. When DNA is in long strands prior to coiling, it is in the form of
    A. chromosomes.   B. centromeres.   C. chromatin.   D. chromatids.

4. Which type of nuclear division takes place in somatic cells?
    A. meiosis   B. cytokinesis   C. interphase   D. mitosis

5. The length of time it takes for a cell to complete the cell cycle is
    A. around two hours.   C. the same for each kind of cell.
    B. different for each cell.   D. around two minutes.

C. Complete the following exercises.

1. Why is sexual reproduction dependent on meiosis?

2. The normal number of chromosomes in a yellow pine tree is 24. With pictures taken from a high-powered microscope, you determine that the pollen from the yellow pine only has 12 chromosomes. How can this be explained?

3. Which type of cell division results in a diploid number of chromosomes in the new cells? Which type of cell division results in a haploid number of chromosomes in the new cells?

4. Anaphase in both mitosis and meiosis is the phase in which chromosomes get separated and pulled to opposite ends of the poles. Explain how anaphase in mitosis is different from anaphase I in meiosis. Draw a diagram of these two phases to help explain the difference.

Asexual vs. Sexual Reproduction

Asexual reproduction by mitosis is a careful copying mechanism. Some unicellular organisms, like amoeba produce asexually. Many plants also produce asexually. There are several mechanisms by which this occurs. However, the offspring produced are always genetically identical to the parent.

In contrast, sexual reproduction by meiosis brings with it the enormous potential for genetic variability. The number of possible chromosome combinations in the gametes is 2^n, where n is the haploid chromosome number and 2 is the number of chromosomes in a homologous pair. Look at Figure 6.10, which shows the possible distribution of chromosomes resulting from meiosis in organisms with small numbers of chromosomes, in this case 2 and 3.

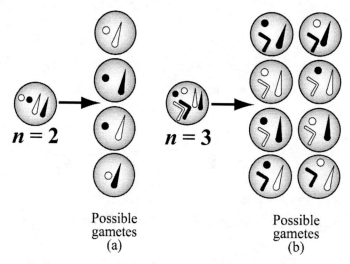

Possible
gametes
(a)

Possible
gametes
(b)

Figure 6.9 Genetic Variability

When n=2, four distinct distributions are possible. When n=3, eight distinct distributions are possible. If humans have a haploid number of n=23, then 2^{23}, or 8,388,608 distinct distributions are possible. Remember, this is only the genetic variation that occurs *before* fertilization.

Activity
Great potential for genetic variability results from the number of potential combinations of chromosomes resulting from meiosis. Use the information given, along with a calculator, to determine the statistical number for the following organisms. Discuss your findings in class.

Organism	Diploid Number of Chromosomes (body cells)	Haploid Number of Chromosomes (gametes)	Number of Possible Chromosomes Combinations
wheat	14		
earthworm	36		
domestic sheep	54		
algae	148		

FERTILIZATION AND CELL DIFFERENTIATION

The haploid gametes produced during meiosis are spermatozoa in males and ova in females. During **fertilization**, these gametes fuse to form a new diploid parent cell, called the **zygote**. The zygote is one cell, with a set of 2n chromosomes. Each parent contributes one homolog to each homologous pair of chromosomes. It then begins the process of mitosis to grow in size, becoming an **embryo**.

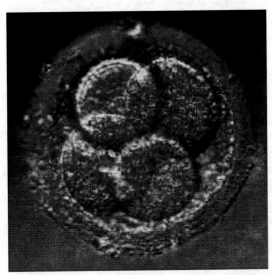

Figure 6.10 Zygote

The group of cells produced in the very early stages of the embryo's growth are similar to the original zygote. They are called embryonic **stem cells**. Eventually, when the embryo reaches 20 – 150 cells in size, this group begins to produce cells that are different from themselves. This process is called **cell differentiation**. The cells become specialized and later become tissues. As each cell differentiates, it produces proteins characteristic to its specific function.

Stem cells have the capability to become any type of cell. This is possible because genes within the cell can be "turned on" or "turned off" at specific times. Every cell of the organism has the same genetic information that was present in the initial zygote. Thus, cell differentiation occurs by the selective activation or inactivation of only some of these genes. For example, some cells could become liver cells while other cells become skin cells, but both of these cell types contain genes for every other cell type within the organism.

In the next chapter, we will discuss genes and the role they play in heredity.

Section Review 3: Asexual vs. Sexual Reproduction/Fertilization & Cell Differentiation

A. Define the following terms.

fertilization   embryo   cell differentiation

zygote   stem cells

B. Choose the best answer.

1. In fertilization, gametes fuse to form a(n)
   A. embryo.
   B. somatic cell.
   C. zygote.
   D. reproductive cell.

2. Stem cells are
   A. cells that can produce any type of offspring cell.
   B. cells that contain stem structures used in reproduction.
   C. haploid cells that can produce any type of offspring cell.
   D. found only in plant cells.

3. A dove has a diploid number of 16 chromosomes. How many possible distributions of chromosomes can occur in the homologous pairs of a dove's gametes?
   A. 16   B. 32   C. 256   D. 65,536

4. A zygote becomes an embryo through the process of
   A. mitosis.
   B. meiosis.
   C. cell differentiation.
   D. fertilization.

5. What process of reproduction brings with it, the greatest potential for genetic variability?
   A. mitosis
   B. meiosis
   C. cell differentiation
   D. interkinesis

CHAPTER 6 REVIEW

A. Choose the best answer.

1. During which phase of mitosis do chromosomes line up on spindles in the center of a cell?

    A. anaphase   B. telophase   C. metaphase   D. prophase

2. In the DNA molecule, guanine pairs with another base called

    A. quinine.   B. riboflavin.   C. cytosine.   D. thymine.

3. What are the long strands of DNA made of?

    A. elastic rubber bases

    B. sugar nucleotides and potassium

    C. sugar, phosphates and nitrogenous bases

    D. oxygen and nucleotides

4. What are the sections of DNA that resemble rungs on a ladder called?

    A. genetic codes

    B. reprocessors

    C. base pairs

    D. lipid pairs

5. What does mitosis generate?

    A. daughter cells identical to the mother cell

    B. many reproductive cells

    C. diseased cells

    D. gametes

6. Meiosis is a type of cell division that

    A. leads to genetic mutation.

    B. causes deformity.

    C. is necessary for sexual reproduction.

    D. causes alleles to deform.

7. DNA can make exact copies of itself. What is this process known as?

    A. translation   B. duplication   C. replication   D. transcription

8. A type of cellular reproduction when the nuclear division of somatic cells takes place is

    A. meiosis.   B. cytokinesis.   C. interphase.   D. mitosis.

9. When preparing for cell division, the chromatin condenses and becomes which of the following?

    A. gene   B. chromosome   C. protein   D. codon

10. Which molecule transports the code of information from DNA to the ribosome?

    A. tRNA   B. rRNA   C. mRNA   D. an amino acid

11. What is the process in which paired twin chromosomes exchange pieces of DNA during meiosis called?

    A. crossing over   B. fertilization   C. self pollina-   D. replication
                                                  tion

12. Somatic cells have two sets of chromosomes, one from the mother and one from the father. What are matched pairs of chromosomes called?

    A. clones   C. homologous chromosomes

    B. gametes   D. mutations

13. During translation, adenine on mRNA will pair with which base on tRNA?

    A. uracil   B. guanine   C. thymine   D. cytosine

14. Amino acids that are not yet part of a polypeptide are found in which part of the cell?

    A. mitochondria   B. cytoplasm   C. Golgi appara-   D. nucleus
                                            tus

15. What is the correct way to refer to the number of chromosomes in gametes?

    A. chromatin   B. haploid   C. heterozygous   D. controlled

16. Prior to cell differentiation, all the cells in an embryo are

    A. the same.   B. stem cells.   C. gametes.   D. A and B.

17. A fruit fly has a haploid number of 4 chromosomes. How many possible distributions of chromosomes can occur in its homologous pairs?

    A. 4   B. 8   C. 16   D. 256

18. What is the function of a stop codon?

    A. to instruct tRNA to stop delivering amino acids to mRNA

    B. to bind to the ribosome and cause amino acids to stop arriving at the mRNA

    C. to bind to the ribosome and stop the translation process releasing the protein

    D. to instruct the ribosome to stop the transcription process and release the protein

Chapter 7
Genetics, Heredity and Biotechnology

GEORGIA PERFORMANCE SCIENCE STANDARDS COVERED IN THIS CHAPTER INCLUDE:

SB2 c, d and f	Students will analyze how biological traits are passed on to successive generations.

GENETIC EXPRESSION

Genes, which are specific portions of DNA, determine hereditary characteristics. Genes carry traits that can pass from one generation to the next. **Alleles** are different molecular forms of a gene. Each parent passes on one allele for each trait to the offspring. In animals, each offspring has two alleles for each trait. The expression of physical characteristics depends on the genes that both parents contribute for that particular characteristic. **Genotype** is the term for the combination of alleles inherited from the parents.

Genes are either dominant or recessive. The **dominant gene** is the trait that will most likely express itself. If both alleles are dominant, or one is dominant and one is recessive, the trait expressed will be the dominant one. In order for expression of the **recessive gene** to occur, both alleles must be recessive. For example, a mother might pass on a gene for having dimples, and the father might pass on a gene for not having dimples. Having dimples is dominant over not having dimples, so the offspring will have dimples even though it inherits one allele of each trait. For the offspring not to have dimples, both the mother and father must pass along the allele for not having dimples. The **phenotype** is the physical expression of the traits. The phenotype does not necessarily reveal the combination of alleles.

When studying the expression of the traits, geneticists use letters as symbols for the different traits. We use capital letters for dominant alleles and lowercase letters for recessive alleles. For dimples, the symbol could be D. For no dimples, the symbol could be d. The genotype of the offspring having one allele for dimples and one allele for no dimples is Dd. The phenotype for this example is having dimples.

If an individual inherits two of the same alleles, either dominant or recessive, for a particular characteristic, the individual is **homozygous**. If the offspring inherits one dominant allele and one recessive allele, such as in the example in the above paragraph, the individual is **heterozygous**.

Geneticists use the **Punnett square** to express the possible combinations for a certain trait an offspring may inherit from the parents. The Punnett square shows possible genotypes and phenotypes of one offspring. Figure 7.1 below shows an example of a **monohybrid cross**, which involves one trait, done on a Punnett square.

The Punnett Square

The Punnett square is a tool geneticists use to determine the possible genotype of one offspring. The possible alleles donated by one parent are written across the top and the possible alleles donated by the other parent are written along the left side. In the example, the cross between two heterozygous parents is examined.

D = allele for dimples

d = allele for no dimples

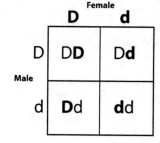

Each time this male and female produce an offspring, there is a 3/4 (or 75%) chance the offspring will have dimples and a 1/4 (or 25%) chance the offspring will have no dimples.

Figure 7.1

The phenotype depends not only on which genes are present, but also on the environment. Environmental differences have an effect on the expression of traits in an organism. For example, a plant seed may have the genetic ability to have green tissues, to flower and to bear fruit, but it must be in the correct environmental conditions. If the required amount of light, water and nutrients are not present, those genes may not be expressed.

Temperature also affects the expression of genes. Primrose plants will bloom red flowers at room temperature and white at higher temperatures. Himalayan rabbits and Siamese cats have dark extremities like ears, nose and feet, at low temperatures. Warmer areas of the animals' bodies are lighter colored.

MENDEL'S CONTRIBUTION TO GENETICS

Around 1850, **Gregor Mendel** (1822 – 1884) began his work at an Austrian monastery. Many biologists call Mendel "the father of genetics" for his studies on plant inheritance. Mendel and his assistants grew, bred, counted and observed over 28,000 pea plants.

Pea plants are very useful when conducting genetic studies because the pea plant has a very simple genetic make up. It has only seven chromosomes, its traits can be easily observed and it can cross-pollinate (have two different parents) or self-pollinate (have only one parent). Table 7.1 lists some of the pea plant traits, along with their attributes. To begin his experiments, Mendel used plants that were true breeders for one trait. A **true breeder** will have a known genetic history and will self-pollinate to produce offspring identical to itself.

Table 7.1 Possible Traits of Pea Plants

Seed Shape	Round* Wrinkled		Pod Color	Green* Yellow	
Seed Color	Yellow* Green		Flower Position	Axial* Terminal	
Seed Coat Color	Gray* White		Plant Height	Tall* Short	
Pod Shape	Smooth* Constricted				

*Dominant

PRINCIPLE OF DOMINANCE

Through his experiments, Mendel discovered a basic principle of genetics, the principle of dominance. Mendel's **principle of dominance** states that some forms of a gene or trait are dominant over other traits, which are called recessive. A dominant trait will mask or hide the presence of a recessive trait. When Mendel crossed a true-breeding tall pea plant with a true-breeding short pea plant, he saw that all the offspring plants were tall. The tallness trait *masks* the recessive shortness trait. The crossing of the true breeders is the **parental generation**, or the **P** generation. The offspring produced are the **first filial (F_1) generation**. The offspring of the F_1 generation are called the **second filial (F_2) generation**.

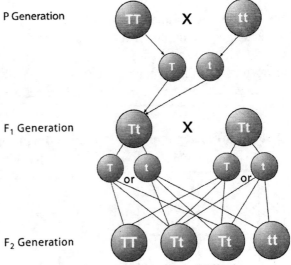

Figure 7.2 Possible Genotypes of Offspring

PRINCIPLE OF SEGREGATION

Crossing plants from the F_1 generation creates the F_2 generation. Mendel soon discovered that a predictable ratio of phenotypes appeared. For every one recessive plant, there were three dominant plants present. Mendel realized that this ratio could only occur if the alleles separate sometime during gamete formation.

As a result, Mendel developed his **principle of segregation**. This principle states that when forming sex cells, the paired alleles separate so that each egg or sperm only carries one form of the allele. The two forms of the allele come together again during fertilization.

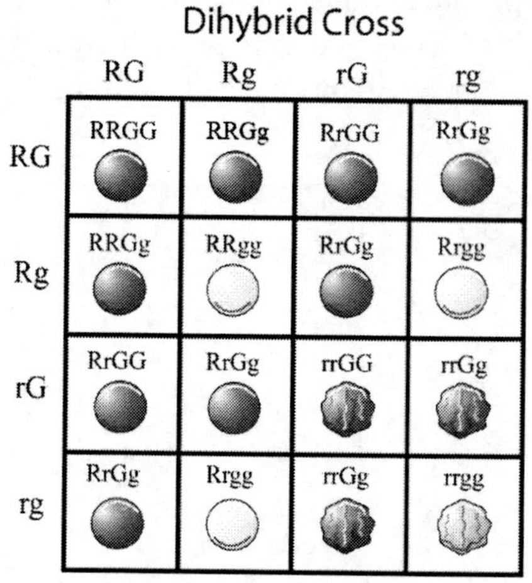
Dihybrid Cross
RG
Rg
rG
rg
RG
Rg
rG
rg
RRGG
RRGg
RrGG
RrGg
RRGg
RRgg
RrGg
Rrgg
RrGG
RrGg
rrGG
rrGg
RrGg
Rrgg
rrGg
rrgg

Figure 7.3 Dihybrid Cross of F_1 Heterozygous Offspring

PRINCIPLE OF INDEPENDENT ASSORTMENT

When Mendel began to study **dihybrid crosses,** which involve two traits, he noticed another interesting irregularity. Mendel crossed plants that were homozygous for two traits, seed color and seed texture. Round seed texture and green color are both dominant traits. Mendel assigned the dominant homozygous P generation the genotype of (RRGG). Wrinkled seed texture and yellow color are both recessive traits. The recessive homozygous P generation seeds were assigned the genotype (rrgg). When (RRGG) was crossed with (rrgg) the resulting F_1 generation was entirely heterozygous (RrGg). The F_1 generation was then allowed to self-pollinate, resulting in an F_1 dihybrid cross of (RrGg) with (RrGg). The result of and F_2 generation with a distinct distribution of traits, as depicted in Figure 7.3. Counting up the genotypes of the F_2 generation should give you the result that 9/16 of them will have the round, green phenotype, 3/16 will have the round, yellow phenotype, 3/16 will have the wrinkled, green phenotype and 1/16 will have the wrinkled, yellow phenotype.

The consistent observation of this trend led to the development of the **principle of independent assortment**. This principle states that each pair of alleles segregates independently during the formation of the egg or sperm. For example, the allele for green seed color may be accompanied by the allele for round texture in some gametes and by wrinkled texture in others. The alleles for seed color segregate independently of those for seed texture.

Activity

Use the given genotypes to determine the probable genotypes of offspring from each mating.

1. GG (male), Gg (female)

2. Jj (male), jj (female)

3. pp (male), PP (female)

Section Review 1: Genetics

A. Define the following terms.

gene	phenotype	Gregory Mendel
allele	homozygous	true breeder
genotype	heterozygous	principle of dominance
dominant gene	Punnett square	principle of segregation
recessive gene	monohybrid cross	dihybrid cross
		principle of independent assortment

B. Choose the best answer.

1. What is the combination of inherited alleles called?

   A. heterozygote   B. phenotype   C. genotype   D. dihybrid

2. What is the expression of traits called?

   A. phenotype   B. genotype   C. mutation   D. allele

3. If an individual inherits one dominant allele and one recessive allele, what is the genotype?

   A. homozygous   B. recessive   C. heterozygous   D. phenotype

4. If an individual inherits two of the same allele, either both dominant or both recessive for a particular characteristic, what is the individual's genotype?

   A. heterozygous   B. phenotypic   C. homozygous   D. mutated

5. Use a Punnett square to predict the cross of a homozygous green parent with a homozygous yellow parent if yellow is dominant over green. What will the phenotype of the offspring be?

   A. all yellow   C. neither yellow nor green

   B. all green   D. some yellow and some green

C. Complete the following exercises.

1. The gene for cystic fibrosis is a recessive trait. This disorder causes the body cells to secrete large amounts of mucus that can damage the lungs, liver and pancreas. If one out of 20 people is a carrier of this disorder, why is only one out of 1,600 babies born with cystic fibrosis?

2. What is the relationship between phenotype and genotype?

3. Compare homozygous alleles to heterozygous alleles.

4. What specifically determines hereditary characteristics in an individual?

MODES OF INHERITANCE

SEX-LINKED TRAITS

Recall humans have 46 chromosomes (23 pairs). In fact, these chromosomes are of two different kinds. 44 chromosomes (22 pairs) are autosomes. An **autosome** is a non-sex chromosome that is the same in both genders of a species (male or female). The other 2 chromosomes (1 pair) are **sex chromosomes**. These are different in each gender of the species. In human males, the 23rd pair of chromosomes is XY. In human females, the 23rd pair of chromosomes is XX. In females, one X comes from their mother and one X comes from their father. In males, the X chromosome comes from their mother and the Y chromosome comes from their father.

	X^B	X^b
X^B	$X^B X^B$	$X^B X^b$
Y	$X^B Y$	$X^b Y$

B = Normal
b = Color Blind

Figure 7.4 Punnett Square for Color Blindness

If a recessive trait, like color blindness, is located on the X chromosome, it is not very likely that females will have the phenotype for this condition. It is more likely that males will have the condition since they only have one X chromosome. Males do not have another X chromosome or a duplicate copy of the gene. A female that has a recessive gene on one X chromosome is a **carrier** for that trait.

Examine the Punnett square in Figure 7.4, which shows the cross of a female who is heterozygous for color blindness with a normal male. This Punnett square shows how a mother contributes to the color blindness of her sons.

INCOMPLETE DOMINANCE

Incomplete dominance is the situation when one trait is not completely dominant over the other. Think of it as blending the two traits. All of the offspring in the F_1 generation will show a phenotype that is a blending of both the parents. If the F_1 generation is self-pollinated, the ratio of phenotypes in the offspring (F_2 generation) will appear in a predictable pattern. One offspring will look like one parent, two offspring will look like both parents and one offspring will look like the other parent.

A cross between a red and a white four o'clock flower demonstrates incomplete dominance. One flower in the parental generation is red with genotype $R^1 R^1$. The other flower is white with genotype $R^2 R^2$. The offspring of this cross appear pink and have a genotype of $R^1 R^2$. See Figure 7.5 for the genotypes and the phenotypes of the P, F_1 and F_2 generations.

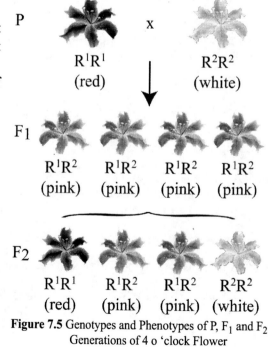

Figure 7.5 Genotypes and Phenotypes of P, F_1 and F_2 Generations of 4 o'clock Flower

CO-DOMINANCE

When both traits appear in the F_1 generation and contribute to the phenotype of the offspring, the trait is **co-dominant**. One example occurs in horses in which the trait for red hair is co-dominant with the trait for white hair. A roan is a foal that has both traits. The horse appears to look pinkish-brown from far away. However, if you look closely at the coat of this animal, you will notice that both solid red and solid white hairs found on the coat give the animal its unique color.

Though they sound similar, there is an important difference between the situations of co-dominance and incomplete dominance. When one allele is incompletely dominant over another, the blended result occurs because *neither allele is fully expressed*. That is why the F_1 generation four o'clock flower is a *totally different color* (pink). In contrast, when two alleles are co-dominant, *both alleles are completely expressed*. The result is a combination of the two, rather than a blending. The roan horse's hair may look pink from afar, but it is actually a combination of distinct red hair and white hair.

MULTIPLE ALLELES AND POLYGENIC TRAITS

Traits like blood type, hair color and eye color are determined by two genes for every trait, one from each parent. Different molecular forms of the same gene are called alleles. Although each individual only has two alleles, there can be many different combinations of alleles in that same population. For instance, hamster hair color is controlled by one gene with alleles for black, brown, agouti (multi-colored), gray, albino and others. The specific combination of each of these **multiple alleles** produces different colorations.

Polygenic traits are the result of the interaction of multiple genes. It is commonly known, for instance, that high blood pressure has a strong hereditary linkage. The phenotype for hypertension is not, however, controlled by a single gene that elevates or lowers blood pressure. Rather, it is the result of the interaction between one's weight (partially controlled by one or more genes), their ability to process fats in general and cholesterol in particular (several metabolic genes), their ability to process and move various salts through the bloodstream (transport genes) and their lifestyle habits, such as smoking and drinking (which may or may not be the result of the expression of several genes that express themselves as addictive behavior). Of course, each of the genes involved may also have multiple alleles, which vastly expands the complexity of the interaction.

Section Review 2: Modes of Inheritance

A. Define the following terms.

sex chromosomes   carrier   autosome

co–dominance   multiple alleles   incomplete dominance

polygenic traits

B. Choose the best answer.

1. A male has the genotype XY. Which parent is responsible for giving the son the Y chromosome?

     A. mother   C. both the father and the mother

     B. father   D. neither the father nor the mother

2. What is the difference between co–dominance and incomplete dominance?

     A. Co–dominant traits are blended and incompletely dominant traits appear together.

     B. Co–dominant traits are recessive and incompletely dominant traits appear together.

     C. Co-dominant traits appear together and incompletely dominant traits are blended.

     D. Co-dominant traits are recessive and incompletely dominant traits are blended

3. Roan horse and cattle fur is a common example of

     A. incomplete dominance.   C. multiple alleles.

     B. co–dominance.   D. polygenic traits.

C. Complete the following exercises.

1. The phenotype for blood type is an example of a multiple allele trait. The three alleles are A, B and O. A and B are co–dominant to O. Determine the phenotypes of the offspring in each of the situations below.

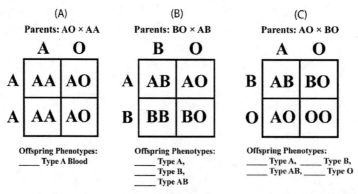

(A)
Parents: AO × AA

	A	O
A	AA	AO
A	AA	AO

Offspring Phenotypes:
____ Type A Blood

(B)
Parents: BO × AB

	B	O
A	AB	AO
B	BB	BO

Offspring Phenotypes:
____ Type A,
____ Type B,
____ Type AB

(C)
Parents: AO × BO

	A	O
B	AB	BO
O	AO	OO

Offspring Phenotypes:
____ Type A, ____ Type B,
____ Type AB, ____ Type O

2. Given the information that the offspring phenotypes for blood type are 2/4 AB and 2/4 AO, draw a corresponding Punnett square.

MUTATIONS

Mutations are mistakes or misconnections in the duplication of the chromatin material. Mutations usually occur in the nucleus of the cell during the replication process of cell division. Some mutations are harmful to an organism, some are beneficial and some have no effect. Mutations play a significant role in creating the diversity of life on Earth today. Geneticists classify mutations into two groups: **gene mutations** and **chromosomal mutations**.

Gene mutations are mistakes that affect individual genes on a chromosome. For instance, one base on the DNA strand substitutes for another base. A substitution of bases will change the codon and, therefore, the amino acid. Consequently, the protein being synthesized may be different from what the DNA originally coded for, thus possibly affecting one or more functions within the organism. Gene mutations also occur by the insertion or deletion of nucleotides from a gene.

Chromosomal mutations are mistakes that affect the whole chromosome. Recall that during meiosis homologous chromosomes pair and may exchange segments through a process called crossing over. If errors occur during crossing over, chromosomal mutations result. There are four major categories of chromosomal mutations.

- **Duplication mutations** occur when a chromosome segment attaches to a homologous chromosome that has not lost the complementary segment. One chromosome will then carry two copies of one gene, or a set of genes.

- **Deletion mutations** occur when a chromosome segment breaks off and does not reattach itself. When cell division is complete, the new cell will lack the genes carried by the segment that broke off.

- **Inversion mutations** occur when a segment of chromosome breaks off and then reattaches itself to the original chromosome, but backwards.

- **Translocation mutations** occur when a chromosome segment attaches itself to a non-homologous chromosome.

Mutations in the somatic cells affect only the tissues of the organism. Mutations occurring in the reproductive cells may be transmitted to the gametes formed in meiosis and thus pass on to future descendants. These mutations sometimes cause abnormal development and a variety of genetic diseases. In other cases, the mutation benefits the organism. Many times, the mutation has little or no noticeable impact on the organism.

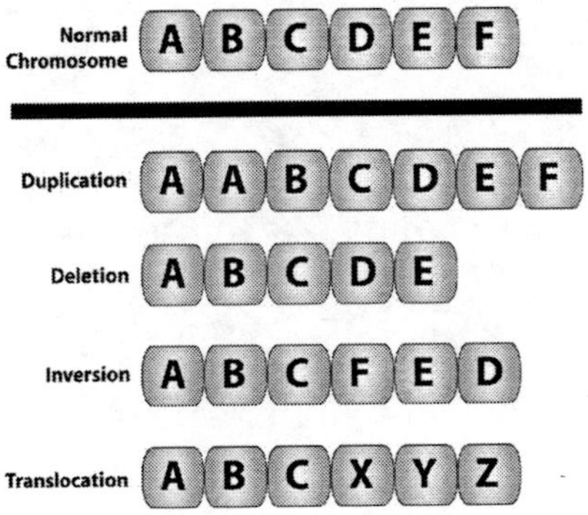

Figure 7.6 Mutations

Although mutations do occur spontaneously, environmental factors can increase the likelihood of developing mutations. These types of environmental factors are called **mutagens**. Radiation exposure through X-rays or UV light can alter DNA in humans. Exposure to large amounts of radiation, like the kind following a nuclear bomb, can adversely affect all cells within the human body, including sex cells. This increases the statistical probability of developing mutations in organisms. Japanese survivors of the atom bomb have a higher than normal cancer and birth defect rate. Natural mutation-causing chemicals in food, cookware, man-made chemicals and pollutants can also cause mutations. Extremely high temperatures and some kinds of viruses can also cause mutations.

Activity

Your teacher will provide you with a plastic sandwich bag that contains 3 or 4 homologous pairs of "chromosomes" made with yarn. The "chromosomes" come in two colors, blue and pink. The color represents the chromosome's original donor (father or mother). On your "chromosomes" you might notice some knots. These knots represent different alleles for traits. You will notice that one knot from each pair is colored, this is the dominant allele.

Use the bag provided by your teacher to examine how traits are passed from parents to offspring by sexual and asexual reproduction. Begin by drawing a large circle on ½ of a blank sheet of paper. Next match the homologous chromosome pairs together.

NOTE: You will not use all of your yarn pieces in this step. Remember you will only have 3 or 4 pairs.

Continue by placing your "chromosomes" inside the circle. This is your parent cell. Next you will move your cell through the process of mitosis. You will do this by moving your "chromosomes" into daughter cells near the bottom of the page. Be sure you have the correct number of daughter cells for mitosis. Examine how the alleles were passed from the parent to the offspring.

Next, repeat the process, only this time you will move your cell through the process of meiosis.

As an extension, you can pretend to have mutations occur to your chromosomes by cutting (deletion) or adding (inserting) yarn to your chromosomes. Inversion mutations are simulated by twisting a loop into the yarn segment.

Examine the drawing below to help you.

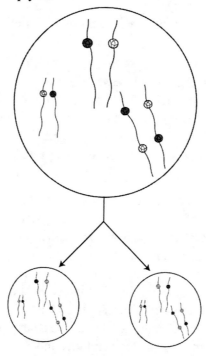

Section Review 3: Mutations

A. Define the following terms.

mutation   mutagens   chromosomal mutation   inversion mutation

gene mutation   duplication mutation   deletion mutation   translocation mutation

B. Choose the best answer.

1. A change in the chromosome structure caused by radiation, chemicals, pollutants or during replication is a/an

   A. mutation.   B. allele.   C. gene.   D. replicator.

2. Which of the four types of mutations cause a change in the arrangement, rather than the number, of genes on a chromosome?

   A. deletion   C. translocation

   B. deletion and translocation   D. translocation and inversion

3. What type of mutation affects individual genes?

   A. chromosomal mutations   C. crossing over

   B. gene mutations   D. meiosis

4. When someone spends a lot of time sunbathing and rarely puts on sunscreen, they have an increased risk of developing skin cancer. Why is this true?

   A. because radiation exposure caused by too many medical X-rays alters their DNA in a harmful way

   B. because UV light from the Sun alters their DNA in a harmful way

   C. because the extremely high temperatures experienced while sunbathing alters their DNA in a harmful way

   D. because their skin becomes too dry

C. Complete the following exercises.

1. Describe how mutations are passed on to future generations.

2. Make a table describing the different types of mutations. Then draw each type of mutation.

3. Identify mutagens found in your area. Research how to limit your exposure to each type of mutagen and present your findings in a table.

BIOTECHNOLOGY

Biotechnology is the commercial application of biological products and has been in existence for thousands of years. It includes the production of wine, beer, cheese and antibiotics, but today it more commonly refers to processes that manipulate DNA. DNA technologies, or biotechnology, manipulate DNA to benefit humans. DNA technologies have impacted the following three areas of modern life: forensics, medicine and agriculture.

FORENSICS

Forensics uses scientific techniques to collect evidence for the legal system. DNA is used in forensics to collect and analyze different samples found at crime scenes. Sometimes a sample of DNA is found at a crime scene. This unknown DNA sample is analyzed and compared with a database containing known DNA samples. This process is known as DNA fingerprinting.

DNA FINGERPRINTING

With the exception of identical twins, every person's DNA is different. **DNA fingerprinting** is the identification of a person using their DNA. Laboratory tests are performed by forensic scientists to determine if the suspect of a crime, for example, was present at the scene of the crime. It is also used to determine paternity, or the father of a child. This process has a high degree of accuracy, greater than 99%. A DNA fingerprint is not the same as an actual fingerprint taken by inking your finger. Neither is it a blueprint of your entire DNA sequence. Rather, it is the analysis of a small number of sequences of DNA that are known to vary a great deal among individuals. These sequences are analyzed to get a probability of a match. That means that DNA fingerprinting can be used to compare sample DNA from, say, a crime scene to sample DNA taken from a suspect. It cannot be used to tell who you are, independent of a comparative sample.

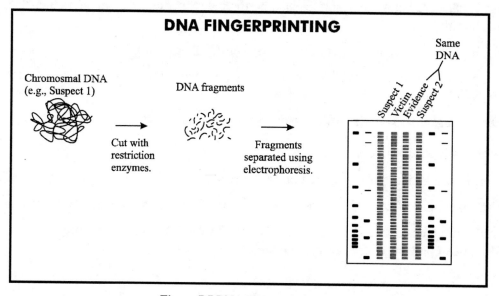

Figure 7.7 DNA Fingerprinting

DNA fingerprinting is performed by cutting DNA with enzymes and separating the fragments using electrophoresis. **Electrophoresis** uses electrical charges to separate pieces of molecules based on both size and charge. The nucleic acids of DNA have a consistent negative charge imparted by their phosphate backbone, and thus migrate toward the positive terminal of the electrophoresis apparatus! The speed at which they migrate depends on both the size and molecular structure of the fragments. The result is a column of bands, each representing a specific fragment of DNA. Since two identical samples of DNA will both fragment and migrate in the same fashion, matching bands indicate that the DNA of those samples is the same, and thus the person from which those samples came is one and the same person.

In years past, there have been errors in the results of DNA fingerprinting. Today, however, there is only a tiny possibility of error, a fraction of a percent, since such advances have been made in the precision and accuracy of electrophoretic techniques that DNA sequences differing by a single base pair can now be easily resolved.

BIOTECHNOLOGY IN MEDICINE

The medical establishment is a strong proponent of biotechnology. Biotechnological research is encouraged in government, academic and private laboratories. This has generated a need for many analysts and researchers with a biochemistry background. Every year, greater advances are made in biotech medicines and therapies.

Recombinant DNA technology uses the natural process of transcription and translation to alter organisms. The DNA containing the desired gene is cut into segments by humans. The fragment that contains the desired gene is inserted into the genome of a microscopic biological agent like a bacteria or virus. The newly inserted DNA segment will now produce the desired protein. The biological agent now contains the recombinant (re-combined) DNA. Once inserted into a human, it reproduces, inserting the desired DNA segment into

Figure 7.8 Biotech Analyst

other cells. The vaccine for Hepatitis B is a recombinant product. Human insulin and growth hormone as well as a clot-dissolving medication have been created using recombinant DNA technology. Interferon is a recombinant product used to fight cancer and a broad array of other diseases.

Monoclonal antibodies are exact copies of an antibody that bind to a specific antigen, such as a cancer cell. Once the binding takes place, the immune system detects and responds to the target cancer cell. These antibodies have been created and are used as therapy for breast cancer and non-Hodgkin's lymphoma. Research is ongoing to produce antibodies to target cells responsible for causing other diseases. As with all medications, side effects are evaluated, and each drug must prove to be more beneficial than harmful before it is approved for use.

In addition to medications, **gene therapy** is used to help cure diseases. The idea is that if a defective protein is replaced with a good one, then the disease caused by the defective protein can be eliminated. Gene therapy has the greatest potential for success in treating diseases with only one defective gene.

Gene therapy is currently used in people who have SCID, severe combined immunodeficiency. People with this disease are also called "bubble babies" because they must be kept in sterile, bubble-like environments to prevent even minor infections, which can kill them. To treat the disease, cells with the gene to make a certain protein are introduced into the body via the white blood cells. The new cells can then multiply and produce the protein necessary to have a functional immune system.

STEM CELL RESEARCH

Stem cells are cells found in the human body that have yet to become a specialized type of cell. They are a "pre cell." Stem cells have the amazing ability to become any type of cell or tissue. For example, a stem cell could develop into a nerve cell, skin cell or a liver cell. The potential for using stem cells to help cure many chronic human diseases is great. There are three main sources of stem cells available. Stem cells can be harvested from adult bone marrow, umbilical cord blood after delivery or from human embryos. The harvesting of stem cells from human embryos results in the death of that embryo. For this reason, many people oppose using embryonic stem cells in medicine. There are other avenues of harvesting stem cells, however: sources such as bone marrow and umbilical cord blood are being researched as possible alternatives to the use of embryonic stem cells. More research is needed to determine the full range of therapeutic possibilities of stem cells.

CLONING

Cloning is the creation of genetically identical organisms. The cloning of Dolly the sheep from a somatic cell of an adult sheep created great debate about the possibility of cloning humans. The possible benefits of human cloning include allowing a childless couple to have a child, creating tissues for transplantation that would not be rejected by their host and using genetically altered cells to treat people with Alzheimer's or Parkinson's, both diseases caused by the death of specific cells within the brain. Another application is to create therapeutic proteins, like antibodies, through the modification of the cells and then cloning the cells to have several copies.

Figure 7.9 Dolly and Her Offspring Bonnie

Although creating a human clone is theoretically possible, it would be very difficult. Dolly was the 277th attempt in cloning a mammal and her death sparked a huge array of new research questions. Both scientific and moral questions must be debated, researched and solved if cloning technology is ever to become mainstream science. In the United States, federal research funds are not given to scientists who research human cloning, but the research is not banned.

GENETIC ENGINEERING OF AGRICULTURAL CROPS

Figure 7.10 Crops

Many scientists and researchers believe that recombinant technology holds great potential for improvements in agricultural products. There have already been many successes with the technology. These modified crops and animals allow farms to produce higher quality and more bountiful products, which in turn give the farmers a greater earning potential. For centuries, traditional methods of plant hybridization have been widely used to improve the genetic characteristics of various agricultural products. Recombinant technology takes this to an improved level by allowing scientists to transfer specific genetic material in a very precise and controlled manner and in a shorter period of time than traditional methods. For example, in plant crops the characteristics of pest resistance and improved product quality are highly desirable.

Recombinant technology has already resulted in improved strains of corn, soybeans and cotton. The desirable genes inserted into the plants' DNA enable crops to resist certain insects or tolerate herbicides used to kill weeds. These improvements also enable farmers to reduce the use of chemicals, which reduces costs for the farmers, as well as helping to reduce environmental damage and run-off pollution. Rot-resistant tomatoes have been made possible by agricultural biotechnology. This improved variety allows grocery stores to offer naturally vine-ripened tomatoes instead of tomatoes that were picked green and artificially ripened on their way to the store.

Some improved products show promise for a global impact on the problem of malnutrition. Researchers working in cooperation with the International Rice Research Institute have used genetic engineering to develop an improved variety of rice. This hybrid "golden rice" has been designed to overcome Vitamin A deficiency and to combat iron-deficiency anemia. A diet containing this improved rice could prevent blindness in millions of children in Third World countries. Another product in development is a variety of rice that will grow in the 33 million acres of land in China that have salty soil.

Figure 7.11 Rice Farm

There are many questions about the possible long term effects of these genetic technologies. One concern is that genetically modified foods may be detrimental to human health. Genetically engineered foods may cause unexpected allergic reactions in people, since proteins not naturally found in the product have been inserted. Without labeling, a person with allergies may find it difficult to avoid a known food allergen if part of the food causing the allergy is genetically added into another food product. In many European and Asian countries, modified foods must be labeled as such, but, in the United States, the FDA has not yet required consumer information labeling.

Genetically modified crops could pose some threat to the environment. Since herbicide-tolerant crop plants do not die when exposed to the weed-killing chemicals, some crops might be sprayed more heavily to ensure greater weed control. Some studies have indicated that the destruction of plant life naturally surrounding the crops reduces the habitats and food supplies of birds and beneficial insects.

Genetic pollution can occur through the cross-pollination of genetically modified and non-genetically modified plants by wind, birds and insects. Also, farmers who want to grow non-genetically modified crops may have a hard time avoiding genetic pollution if their farms are located near fields with genetically modified plants.

Section Review 4: Biotechnology

A. Define the following terms.

biotechnology   monoclonal antibody   cloning

recombinant DNA   gene therapy   DNA fingerprinting

genetic pollution   stem cell   electrophoresis

B. Choose the best answer.

1. What is the commercial application of biological products?

    A. illegal   C. unethical

    B. biotechnology   D. agricultural

2. What is a DNA fingerprint?

    A. a blue print of the entire DNA   C. an analysis of a small segment of DNA

    B. A print made by inking your finger.   D. transformed loop

3. Strawberries have been created to resist the harmful effects of frost. This is an application of what?

    A. genetic engineering   C. DNA fingerprinting

    B. gene therapy   D. cloning

4. A person with a defect in a gene that codes for a specific protein could be a candidate for which of the following?

    A. cloning   C. gene therapy

    B. DNA fingerprinting   D. protein injections

5. Which of the following is a potential carrier of DNA to create recombinant products?

    A. clone   C. enzyme

    B. virus   D. electrophoresis

C. Complete the following exercises.

1. What are the positive and negative aspects of cloning humans?

2. How is genetically modified food beneficial to farmers? How can it be harmful?

3. Give an example of an advance in biotechnology that you have heard about in the news or read about in this chapter. Explain the benefits of the application of biotechnology as well as possible negative effects.

CHAPTER 7 REVIEW

A. Choose the best answer.

1. Use a Punnett square to predict the cross of a homozygous tall parent with a homozygous short parent if tall is dominant over short. What will be the phenotype of the offspring described in this example?

   A. all tall

   B. all short

   C. neither short nor tall

   D. some tall and some short

2. How is the medical industry helped by technology?

   A. through the development of better treatments and drugs

   B. through the more effective disposal of wastes

   C. by better helping people deal with loss of a loved one

   D. through better care for the ill members of society

3. Which of the following statements about stem cells is true?

   A. They only come from human embryos.

   B. They can definitely help many people with diseases.

   C. They are found on the ends of neurons.

   D. They are undifferentiated cells capable of becoming any tissue.

4. A police officer is at a crime scene and is collecting samples of blood, hair and skin. What is the officer probably going to do with the samples?

   A. The officer is cleaning the crime scene based on protocol.

   B. The officer is keeping samples to be filed with the police report.

   C. The officer is going to have the samples analyzed for a DNA fingerprint.

   D. The officer will show them to the victim's family, the judge and the prosecutor.

5. Genetically altered DNA is referred to as which of the following?

   A. restricted   B. fingerprinted   C. transformed   D. monoclonal

6. How has genetic engineering improved the quality of agricultural crops?

   A. It allows farmers to harvest foods sooner, allowing them to stay on the shelf longer.

   B. It allows corn to be grown in nutrient poor soil.

   C. It adds nutrients not naturally found in crops.

   D. It adds nitrogen to the food chain.

B. Answer the following questions.

7. Name at least two products created through recombinant DNA technology.

8. How can genetically modified plants be harmful to the environment? Give at least two reasons.

9. In the diagram below, circle the biomolecule that will move the fastest toward the positive terminal.

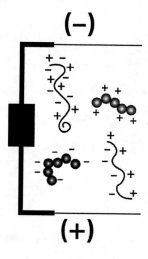

Use this information and the information given in the Punnett square to answer questions 10 – 12.

A variety of pea plant may be either purple (A) or white (a); two purple pea plants are crossed, and it is known that the genotypes of the parent plants are both heterozygous dominant.

	A	a
A	AA	Aa
a	Aa	aa

10. Which trait is dominant? Which trait is recessive?

11. What percentage of the flowers will be purple? How many will be white?

12. What are the genotypes and phenotypes of the parents?

Chapter 8
Cellular Energy & Organism Complexity

GEORGIA PERFORMANCE SCIENCE STANDARDS COVERED IN THIS CHAPTER INCLUDE:

SB3 a, b and d	Students will derive the relationship between single-celled and multi-celled organisms and the increasing complexity of systems.

CELLULAR ENERGY

The life processes of a cell, like metabolism, are the end result of a series of chemical reactions. Each chemical reaction requires energy. In many cases, chemical reactions also require substances to speed reaction time. Energy comes in the form of a molecule called **ATP**, and the substances used to push reactions along are called **enzymes**. (Recall the function of enzymes.) But how does ATP store energy? The energy is stored in the chemical bonds of the molecule. **Chemical bonds** describe the connection between atoms based on shared or transferred electrons.

A glucose sugar molecule, which has the chemical formula of $C_6H_{12}O_6$, forms a molecule with 6 atoms of carbon, 12 atoms of hydrogen and 6 atoms of oxygen. The atoms of the molecule are held together by covalent bonds, and electrons are shared within the molecule.

Bond strength is a measure of the amount of energy required to break a bond. It depends on several factors, including the number of electrons shared (a single, double or triple bond), the identity of the atoms involved in the bond and the polarity of the bond. In general, the greater the polarity of a bond, the easier it is to break and the lower the bond strength. Bond strength is important because it can be a source of energy. Bond strength is measured in joules; the joule is the SI unit of work or energy.

ATP

ATP (adenosine triphosphate) is a molecule that serves as the chemical energy supply for all cells. Adenine, the sugar ribose and three phosphates compose ATP. The covalent bonds between the phosphate groups contain a great deal of energy. Energy is released when the last phosphate in ATP breaks off, – that is, the P-O bond at position 1 in Figure 8.1 is broken. The products of this chemical reaction are **ADP (adenosine diphosphate)** and P_i (an inorganic phosphate molecule).The bonding of ATP is shown in Figure 8.1.

After the ATP molecule breaks down, ADP picks up free phosphate to form a new ATP molecule. Each ATP molecule is recycled in

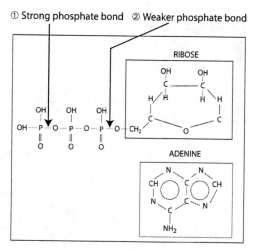

Figure 8.1 Bond Strength in ATP Molecule

this way 2000 – 3000 times a day in the human body. The energy released during each cycle drives cellular processes. Examples of cellular processes that require energy include heat production, muscle contractions, photosynthesis, cellular respiration, locomotion protein production and DNA replication.

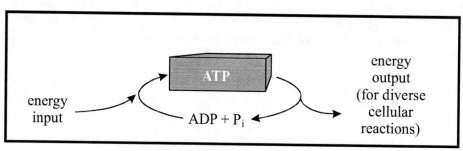

Figure 8.2 ATP/ADP Cycle

FOOD ENERGY

If ATP stores all the energy in our body, why do we need to eat? Well, it turns out that it actually takes energy to break the chemical bonds of ATP. However, the energy gained from the small steps of a variety of enzymatically catalyzed reactions that occur after this breakage more than make up for the initial energy investment. Said another way, the actual reaction ATP ➤ ADP is actually one step in a long chain of biological reactions that, as a whole, produce energy. But where does the energy come from for that first step? In plants, it comes from the Sun. In animals, it comes from the food we eat. One of the easiest molecules for our body to break down for quick energy is glucose.

When the chemical bonds of glucose are broken, energy is released. When a muscle contracts, it converts the free energy from glucose into energy that can be used to shorten muscle cells. The movement of the muscle is work. The energy conversion is not completely efficient and much of the energy is lost as heat. However, the energy conversions in living cells are significantly more efficient than most other types of energy conversion. One reason is that the cell has a variety of ways to store energy and break down processes into small energy saving steps. For instance, mitochondria are useful in the conversion of glucose because they break the chemical reaction into smaller steps, allowing organisms to harness the greatest amount of energy possible. The whole process of breaking down glucose is known as **cellular respiration** and is better than 40% efficient at transferring the chemical energy of glucose into the more useful form, ATP. By contrast, only 25% of the energy released from a gasoline engine is converted to work.

In the next section, we will look more closely at how organisms use ATP, sugar and other factors to make food, grow and carry out life's functions.

Activity

Use gumdrops and toothpicks provided by your teacher to make a model of ATP using Figure 8.1. For example, you can use red gumdrops for carbon, green for oxygen and yellow for nitrogen.

Section Review 1: Cellular Energy

A. Define the following terms.

ATP	enzyme	coenzyme	free energy
ADP	p_i	pepsin	base
			neutral

B. Choose the best answer.

1. What does ATP stands for?

   A. adenosine triphosphate

   B. adenine triphosphate

   C. a triphosphate

   D. adenosine triple phosphate

2. What are enzymes?

   A. catalysts used by living things

   B. catalysts used in all reactions

   C. chemicals used to increase activation energy

   D. fats used by living things to help speed up chemical reactions

3. What does NOT determine bond strength within molecules?

   A. number of shared electrons

   B. identity of atoms involved in bonding

   C. polarity of a bond

   D. length of proteins

C. Complete the following exercises.

1. In your own words, describe the relationship between ATP and ADP.

2. What is the purpose of ATP?

3. Briefly describe the function of enzymes.

OBTAINING CELLULAR ENERGY

In the last section, we gave a brief description of how ATP serves as energy currency. Both plants and animals use ATP, but they fuel the first step in different ways. Animals consume food to obtain energy. Plants use energy from the Sun, in a process called photosynthesis.

PHOTOSYNTHESIS

Photosynthesis is the process of converting carbon dioxide, water and light energy into oxygen and high energy sugar molecules. The chemical equation representing this process is shown in Equation 8.1. Plants, algae and some bacteria can use the sugar molecules produced during photosynthesis to make **complex carbohydrates** such as starch or cellulose for food. The process of photosynthesis consists of two basic stages: **light-dependent reactions** and **light-independent reactions**. The light-independent reactions are also called the **Calvin cycle**.

$$6CO_2 + 6H_2O + light \rightarrow C_6H_{12}O_6(glucose) + 6O_2 \qquad \text{Equation 8.1}$$

Photosynthesis takes place inside an organelle called a **chloroplast**. A chloroplast belongs to a group of organelles called plastids. **Plastids** engage in photosynthesis and store the resulting food. The chloroplast is a specific organelle with a double membrane that contains stacks of sac-like membranes called **thylakoids**. The thylakoid membrane contains within itself a green pigment called **chlorophyll**. **Pigments** are substances that absorb light. Light-dependent reactions take place inside the thylakoid membrane. Light-independent reactions take place in the **stroma**, which is the region just outside the thylakoid membrane. In the **light-dependent phase**, sunlight hits the leaf of the plant where it is absorbed by the pigments in the leaf. There are several pigments in plant leaves, but the main one used in photosynthesis is chlorophyll, the green pigment. Chlorophyll is stored in the chloroplasts of the plant cell.

When light hits the chlorophyll, electrons absorb the energy, become excited, and leave the chlorophyll molecule. Carrier molecules transport the electrons, which follow an electron transport chain. Electron acceptor molecules pick up the electrons in a series and pass them from one molecule to another. As this occurs, energy is released, and ATP is formed. The final electron acceptor is NADP+.

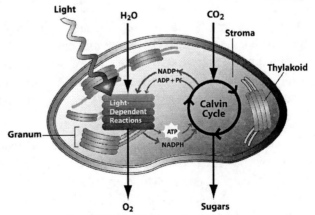

Figure 8.3 The Photosynthesis Process

Splitting a molecule of water replaces the electrons released from the chlorophyll. These electrons, now available, combine with the NADP+ to form **NADPH**. The next stage of photosynthesis uses the NADPH, while oxygen leaves as an end product of the reaction.

The end products of the light-dependent reactions are ATP, oxygen and NADPH. The ATP and NADPH will be used in the light-independent reactions, and the oxygen will be released into the atmosphere.

The next phase, the **light-independent** or **carbon fixation reactions**, uses the ATP formed during the light-dependent reaction as an energy source. In this phase, carbon, from carbon dioxide, and NADPH are used to form **glucose**. To accomplish this, a five-carbon sugar (a monosaccharide called a **pentose**) uses a carbon atom from carbon dioxide to create a six-carbon sugar (a **hexose**). Glucose is the end result, after several conversions have taken place. The glucose can then be used as food to enter cellular respiration, or it can be converted to other carbohydrate products such as sucrose or starch.

CELLULAR RESPIRATION

Cellular respiration is the process of breaking down food molecules to release energy. Plants, algae, animals and some bacteria use cellular respiration to break down food molecules. There are two basic types of cellular respiration: aerobic and anaerobic.

AEROBIC RESPIRATION

Aerobic respiration occurs in the presence of oxygen, and is represented by the chemical equation in Equation 8.2. The energy released through cellular respiration is used to create ATP. Cellular respiration occurs in three phases: **glycolysis**, **Krebs cycle** and **electron transport**. The process starts with a molecule of glucose. Remember, the reactions of cellular respiration occur with the use of enzymes. Respiration is the primary means by which cells obtain usable energy.

$$C_6H_{12}O_6 + 6O_2 \rightarrow 6CO_2 + 6H_2O + energy \qquad \text{Equation 8.2}$$

Glycolysis is the first phase in cellular respiration. This step occurs in the cytoplasm of the cell, and it can occur whether or not oxygen is present. In this phase, the glucose molecule (a 6-carbon sugar) is broken in half through a series of reactions. The energy released by breaking down the glucose is used to produce ATP. Additionally, some high-energy electrons are removed from the sugar during glycolysis. These electrons pass on to an electron carrier called NAD^+, converting it to **NADH**. These electrons will later be used to create more energy.

In aerobic respiration, the 3-carbon sugars produced from glycolysis enter the **mitochondria** along with the oxygen. As the sugars enter the mitochondria, they convert to citric acid in phase two of cellular respiration. The **citric acid cycle**, or **Krebs Cycle**, is the cyclical process that breaks down the citric acid through a series of reactions. The citric acid cycle produces more ATP, as well as some **GTP** (a high-energy molecule similar to ATP). More high-energy electrons are released, forming NADH from NAD^+.

The last phase of cellular respiration is the **electron transport chain**, which occurs on the inner mitochondrial membrane. In this phase, the NADH releases the hydrogen ions and high-energy electrons it picked up during glycolysis and the citric acid cycle. The energy from these electrons is used to convert large quantities of ADP into ATP. The electrons transfer through a series of carrier proteins. At the end of the electron transport chain, the free electrons and H^+ ions bond with oxygen. The oxygen and H^+ ions form water, which is released from the cell as a waste product. Each electron transfer releases energy.

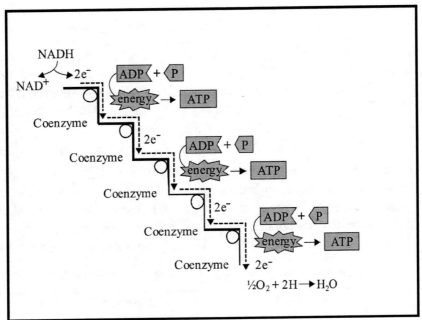

Figure 8.4 Electron Transport Chain

The multi-step processes carried out during aerobic cellular respiration are very efficient. From the input of one glucose molecule, 36 ATP molecules can be produced.

ANAEROBIC RESPIRATION

Anaerobic respiration, or **fermentation**, is the process by which sugars break down in the absence of oxygen. Our muscle cells, fungi and some bacteria are capable of carrying out anaerobic respiration. These cells convert the products of glycolysis into either **alcohol** or **lactic acid**. Glycolysis releases energy, while the production of alcohol or lactic acid provides NAD^+, the electron carrier needed for glycolysis.

Yeast and some bacteria can carry out alcoholic fermentation. Yeast produces **ethanol** (C_2H_5OH) through a process called **alcoholic fermentation**. The chemical equation representing this process is shown in Equation 8.3 below. Carbon dioxide gas is released during alcohol formation. This carbon dioxide gas is responsible for the holes in bread. Yeast is commonly put in bread to make it rise. The fermentation of the yeast produces carbon dioxide, which becomes trapped in the dough, forming small bubbles and causing the bread to rise. Carbon dioxide produced by yeast in beer gives the beer its bubbles. Alcoholic fermentation is also used in the making of wine and liquors.

$$C_6H_{12}O_6 \rightarrow 2C_2H_5OH + 2CO_2 + \text{energy}$$ **Equation 8.3**

Animal cells can also use anaerobic cellular respiration, but not through alcoholic fermentation. Instead, animal cells can use **lactic acid fermentation**. This generally occurs when the organism is engaging in strenuous exercise. During this period, the organism is not able to take in enough oxygen to meet the demand of all the cells in the body. So, in order to keep working, the cells begin to break down glucose in the absence of oxygen. The products of the reaction are energy and lactic acid.

Lactic acid fermentation proceeds at a very fast rate, but the amount of energy produced is far less than with aerobic respiration. Remember that 36 ATP molecules could theoretically be produced during aerobic respiration? By comparison, lactic acid fermentation produces only 2 ATP molecules.

So, can you tell if your cells are respiring aerobically or anaerobically? Well, you can assume that if you are doing anything that causes muscle fatigue — like weight lifting — those muscles have needed extra energy and obtained it through lactic acid fermentation. Your suspicions will be confirmed the next day if you are sore. Muscle soreness occurs because of lactic acid build-up in the muscle.

COMPARING PHOTOSYNTHESIS AND CELLULAR RESPIRATION

All organisms must be able to obtain and convert energy to carry out life functions, such as growth and reproduction. **Photosynthesis** is one way that organisms can trap energy from the environment and convert it into a biologically useful energy source. **Cellular respiration** is a way that organisms can break down energy sources to carry out life's processes. Photosynthesis takes place in plants, algae and some bacteria. Cellular respiration takes place in all eukaryotic cells and some prokaryotic cells.

Table 8.1 Comparison of Photosynthesis and Cellular Respiration

	Photosynthesis	**Cellular Respiration**
Function	energy storage	energy release
Location	chloroplasts	mitochondria
Reactants	CO_2 and H_2O	$C_6H_{12}O_6$ and O_2
Products	$C_6H_{12}O_6$ and O_2	CO_2 and H_2O
Chemical Equation	$6CO_2 + 6H_2O + \text{light} \Rightarrow$ $C_6H_{12}O_6 + 6O_2$	$6O_2 + C_6H_{12}O_6 \Rightarrow$ $6CO_2 + 6H_2O + \text{energy}$

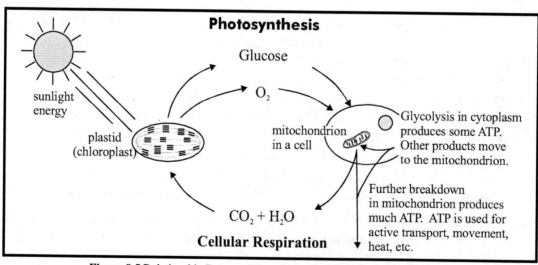

Figure 8.5 Relationship Between Photosynthesis and Cellular Respiration

Activity

For each of the following statements, decide which process it relates to: photosynthesis (P), respiration (R) or both (B). Mark each statement accordingly.

1. ___ Carbon dioxide is a reactant in the reaction.

2. ___ End product is ATP.

3. ___ converts energy from one form to another

4. ___ takes place in mitochondria

5. ___ produces carbon dioxide

6. ___ takes place in chloroplasts

7. ___ glucose changed into energy for cells

8. ___ produces oxygen

9. ___ uses cofactors

10. ___ Oxygen is a reactant in the reaction.

11. ___ produces glucose

12. ___ uses chlorophyll

13. ___ has an electron transport chain

14. ___ Light, water and chlorophyll create glucose.

Section Review 2:   Obtaining Cellular Energy

A. Define the following terms.

photosynthesis	light-dependent phase	glycolysis
Calvin cycle	light-independent phase	Krebs cycle
chloroplast	carbon fixation	electron transport chain
thylakoid	cellular respiration	alcoholic fermentation
chlorophyll	aerobic respiration	lactic acid fermentation
pigment	anaerobic respiration	chemosynthesis
		plastid

B. Choose the best answer.

1. What form of energy is used by cells?

   A. enzymes   B. cofactors   C. ATP   D. DNA

2. What is the process of releasing energy from the chemical breakdown of compounds in a cell?

   A. hesitation   B. expiration   C. elimination   D. respiration

3. In photosynthesis, plants use carbon dioxide, water and light to produce which molecule(s) below?

   A. carbon monoxide   C. glucose and oxygen

   B. energy   D. chlorophyll

4. What is released when ATP is broken down into ADP and one phosphate?

   A. oxygen   B. water   C. energy   D. hydrogen

5. The Krebs Cycle and the electron transport chain phases of cellular respiration take place in which organelle?

   A. nucleus   B. cytoplasm   C. ribosome   D. mitochondrion

6. What is the function of a plastid within a cell?

   A. digest food and breakdown wastes

   B. produce proteins

   C. carry on cellular respiration

   D. carry out photosynthesis and provide color

C. Complete the following exercises.

1. Compare and contrast aerobic and anaerobic respiration.

2. Compare and contrast alcoholic and lactic acid fermentation.

3. What is the chemical equation for photosynthesis and cellular respiration?

BIOLOGICAL CLASSIFICATION

Biologists classify living things according to the traits they share. **Taxonomy** is the classification of an organism based on several features, such as structure, behavior, development, genetic makeup (DNA), nutritional needs and methods of obtaining food. Evolutionary theory is the basis for this classification system. Taxonomy divides organisms into several categories that start out broadly and become more specific. These categories are **kingdom, phylum, class, order, family, genus** and **species**.

Occasionally, subphylum, subclasses and suborders are used to further delineate characteristics among the primary classifications.

Table 8.2 lists the six **kingdoms** based on general characteristics. Each kingdom further divides into **phylum**, to name organisms in the kingdoms of Eubacteria. Phylum further break down into **classes,** and classes break down into **orders.** The categories become progressively more detailed and include fewer organisms as they are further broken down into **family, genus** and **species.** The species is the most specific category. Organisms of the same species are grouped together based on their ability to breed and produce fertile offspring.

Figure 8.6 Classification System for Organisms

To remember the order of the subdivisions, memorize the silly sentence, "King Phillip Came Over From Greece Sneezing." The first letter of each of the words in this sentence is also the first letter of each of the classification categories for organisms.

Table 8.2 The Six Kingdoms

Super Kingdom	Kingdom	Basic Characteristic	Example
Prokaryotes	Eubacteria	found everywhere	cyanobacteria
	Archaebacteria	live without oxygen, get their energy from inorganic matter or light, found in many habitats	halophiles
Eukaryotes	Protista	one-celled or multicellular, true nucleus	amoeba
	Fungi	multicellular, food from dead organisms, cannot move	mushroom
	Plantae	multicellular, cannot move, make their own food, cell walls	tree
	Animalia	multicellular, moves about, depends on others for food	horse

Aristotle (384 – 322 BC) made the first recorded attempt at classification of plants and animals. He grouped all living things into two main categories: plants and animals. According to Aristotle, animals were further divided into two groups: blooded and bloodless. Blooded animals included viviparous quadrupeds (live-bearing four legged), birds, oviparous quadrupeds (egg laying four legged), fish and cetaceans (whales). Bloodless animals included land arthropods (insects), aquatic arthropods (crustaceans), shelled animals (mollusks), soft animals (octopus) and plant-animals (jelly fish).

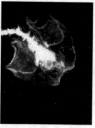

Figure 8.7 Two of Aristotles' Bloodless Animals

Aristotle's classification system had many flaws because the relatedness and reproductive strategies of organisms was not completely understood in his time. However, Aristotle's contribution to taxonomy was important because early on it promoted the scientific way of organizing information.

Carl Linnaeus (1707 – 1778), a Swedish botanist, devised the current system for classifying organisms. Linnaeus used **binomial nomenclature**, a system of naming organisms using a two-part name, to label the species. The binomial name is written in Latin and is considered the scientific name. It consists of the generic name (genus) and the specific epithet (species). The entire scientific name is italicized or underlined, and the genus name is capitalized, as in *Homo sapiens* for humans. Table 8.3 is a complete classification of three members of the kingdom Animalia, which we will examine later in the chapter.

A classification system is necessary to distinguish among the great number of organisms and to avoid confusion created by the use of common names. Common names are used for many organisms, but not all organisms have common names and some have multiple common names.

Figure 8.8 Carl Linnaeus

Table 8.3 Examples of Classifications

Example:	Human	Grasshopper	Dog
Kingdom	Animalia	Animalia	Animalia
Phylum	Chordata	Arthropoda	Chordata
Class	Mammalia	Insecta	Mammalia
Order	Primate	Orthoptera	Carnivora
Family	Homindae	Locuslidea	Canidae
Genus	*Homo*	*Schistocerca*	*Canis*
Species	*sapiens*	*americana*	*familiaris*

The hierarchical classification devised by Linnaeus has been, and still is, quite useful in organizing organisms. However, limitations do exist. For instance, even though classification is based on evolutionary theory, it does not reflect the idea that evolutionary processes are continual, and species are not fixed. Changes will occur over time and, therefore, classification will also have to change. Also, classification does not take into account the variation that exists among individuals within a species. All domestic dogs have the scientific name *Canis Lupus familiaris*, but a great deal of variation exists among different breeds of dogs and even among individual dogs of the same breed.

Finally, the most definitive test to determine if organisms are of the same species is to confirm their ability to breed successfully, producing fertile offspring. However, controlled breeding of wild organisms for the purpose of observation and study can sometimes be impractical, if not impossible. Also, sometimes closely related species can interbreed, such as in the mating of a horse and donkey to produce a mule. Classification has been instrumental in bringing about an understanding of similarities and possible evolutionary relationships of organisms. However, it is not static and may need to change with the discovery of new organisms and as more evidence of evolutionary patterns surface.

THE SIX KINGDOMS

As you might expect from examination of Table 8.2, organisms vary greatly in form between the six kingdoms. Think of all the different types of organisms found in the world. From a single celled-bacterium, to a multicellular human, organisms can have a great diversity of structures. In this text, we will only discuss major highlights of structure and function found in each kingdom.

One major characteristic of each kingdom is how its members obtain food.

However, all living things are composed of ordered systems of structures that work together to sustain life by carrying out life processes (Chapter 5).

ARCHAEBACTERIA

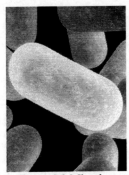

Figure 8.9 Microbes

The Kingdom **Archaebacteria** contains prokaryotic bacteria that thrive in many habitats, including harsh environments previously thought uninhabitable. The prefix *archae-* means ancient. The organisms in this kingdom are believed to be similar to the first types of living things found on planet Earth. These bacteria can be single-celled or cluster together to form filaments. In some environments archaebacteria are producers and in other environments archaebacteria are considered consumers or decomposers. Archaebacteria have a uniquely structured cell wall, cell membrane and ribosomal RNA. The cell walls of archaebacteria lack peptidoglycan, a protein-carbohydrate molecule found in all other bacterial cell walls. Archaebacteria are **anaerobic**, meaning they cannot tolerate oxygen, and live in many habitats.

Archaebacteria are classified according to the environment in which they live. **Methanogens** produce methane gas and live in places such as the soil and the intestines of herbivores. **Halophiles** live in extremely salty environments like the Dead Sea. **Thermoacidophiles** live in areas like the acidic sulfur springs of Yellowstone National Park and undersea vents. These bacteria live in areas where temperatures are near 80°Celsius (176°F) and the pH is as low as 2. Archaebacteria can reproduce using asexual reproduction through budding or binary fission.

EUBACTERIA

The Kingdom **Eubacteria** are the "true bacteria". The prefix *eu-* means true. These bacteria can be single celled or cluster together to form colonies. Because they are bacteria, Eubacteria are prokaryotic. Eubacteria have a cell wall, cell membrane and circular DNA called a **plasmid**. The cell wall of Eubacteria is made up different materials and is more complex than the cell walls of plants or fungi. Eubacteria are classified according to how they obtain food. **Heterotrophs,** found nearly everywhere, need organic molecules as an energy source and feed on living organisms, dead organisms or organic wastes. Heterotrophic bacteria are considered consumers or

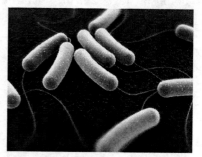

Figure 8.10 *E. Coli* Bacteria

decomposers depending on their environment and food sources. **Autotrophs** are photosynthetic and are found in ponds, lakes, streams and most areas of land. Autotrophic bacteria are considered producers. Cyanobacteria are a type of autotrophic Eubacteria. Despite their common name (blue-green algae), cyanobacteria are not an algae but a bacteria. **Chemotrophs** obtain energy from the breakdown of inorganic, or non-living, substances such as nitrogen and sulfur compounds. Chemotrophs can be considered a producer, consumer or decomposer depending on their environment and food source. Eubacteria are found everywhere, and most are harmless. Eubacteria are used to make cheese, vinegar, soy sauce and yogurt. Some Eubacteria are decomposers and are important to the proper functioning of many ecosystems. Eubacteria can also reproduce using asexual reproduction through budding or binary fission.

PROTISTA

Figure 8.11 Slime Mold

Kingdom **Protista** contains a diverse group of unicellular and multicellular organisms. All protist cells are eukaryotic with a membrane-bound nucleus. Protists can be *plant-like, animal-like or fungus-like*. **Plant-like protists** are known as algae and may be unicellular or multicellular. Although algae come in different colors, all algae have chlorophyll-containing chloroplasts and are **autotrophs**, meaning they can make their own food. Plant-like protists are producers. **Animal-like protists** are one-celled organisms known as protozoa. They cannot make their own food, so they are **heterotrophs**. Many protozoa are parasites living in water, on soil and on living and dead organisms. Protozoa can move using a flagella or cilia. Animal-like protists are considered consumers. **Fungus-like protists** include several phyla that have features of both protists and fungi. They obtain energy from decomposing organic material, so they are also heterotrophic.

FUNGI

Fungi are heterotrophic organisms that secrete enzymes, allowing them to digest their food. They are also **decomposers**, which are organisms that live in or on matter that they decompose as they use it for food. Fungi can be unicellular or multicellular organisms and are made of eukaryotic cells surrounded by a cell wall. Some fungi are edible, while other species are poisonous. Fungi live in aquatic or moist environments like soil, mud and decaying plants. They include black bread mold, yeast, mushrooms and truffles. The slime mold phylum is a group of fungus-like protists commonly found in damp soil and on rotting wood. The fungus *Penicillium* is responsible for the flavors of Roquefort and Camembert cheeses. The widely-used antibiotic penicillin is also derived from a species of this group.

Fungi reproduce sexually and asexually with reproductive cells called spores. Spores are produced sexually by the fruiting body, usually the visible portion of a mushroom. The fruiting body forms gametes that reproduce sexually. Fungi reproduce asexually through mitosis or budding. Budding occurs when a piece of the organism becomes detached and continues to live and grow on its own as a complete structure. Fungi, along with bacteria, are the great recyclers. Together, they keep the Earth from becoming buried under mountains of waste.

PLANTAE

Figure 8.12 Moss

The Kingdom **Plantae** consists of multicellular organisms that have eukaryotic cells. Plant cells all have a cell wall. Almost all use photosynthesis to obtain food and are producers in most ecosystems. There are many different types of plants with a variety of structure types. Plants can be nonvascular, vascular seedless or vascular seed-bearing. **Nonvascular plants** lack tissues used to transport substances like water and sugars. Instead they absorb nutrients through their cells. As a result, nonvascular plants tend to remain small in size. Bryophytes are a type of nonvascular, seedless plant. Bryophytes live in fresh water or moist habitats. They include the mosses, liverworts and hornworts.

Vascular plants contain specialized structures for conducting substances, and as a result can live in drier environments than the nonvascular plants. Vascular plants are divided into two main groups: seedless and seed-bearing. The seedless vascular plants produce spores and include the ferns, whiskbrooms, lycophytes and horseferns. They must live in moist environments because their gametes require water for fertilization to take place. The seed-bearing plants grow from seeds and include **gymnosperms** and **angiosperms**. Gymnosperms include most conifers and *Ginkgo biloba*. Gymnosperms can live in dry, wet, hot or cold environments.

Figure 8.13 Vascular Plants

Angiosperms include flowering plants and can also live in dry, wet, hot or cold environments. Plant reproduction is a complicated cycle called alteration of generations that will not be addressed here. What is important, is for you to understand that plants can reproduce using sexual reproduction with flowers or asexual reproduction with budding or vegetative propagation.

ANIMALIA

All **animals** are multicellular organisms made of eukaryotic cells. Animal cells group together to form tissues which then group together to form organs which further group into organ systems. Some animals have complex organ systems capable of carrying out highly complicated tasks. Animals are heterotrophic. They are diploid organisms and most reproduce sexually, although some reproduce asexually. Animals produce haploid gametes through meiosis. A diploid zygote is formed upon fertilization. The zygote undergoes mitosis and cell differentiation to grow into a multi-celled body. Some animals provide parental care, but most do not. All animals are capable of movement at some stage in their lives. They are either invertebrates (without a backbone) or vertebrates (with a backbone).

Figure 8.14 Starfish

Invertebrates are animals without a backbone; they are the most abundant group of animals. They are all multicellular, and most form tissues, organs and organ systems. Invertebrates can reproduce asexually and sexually. They are comprised of the following phyla: porifera (sponges), cnidarians (jellyfish, anemones and corals), platyhelminthes (flatworms), nematoda (roundworms), annelida (segmented worms), mollusca (mollusks), echinodermata (starfish and sea urchins) and arthropods (crustaceans, insects and spiders).

Vertebrates are animals that share several distinct characteristics sometime during their life cycle and belong to the phylum Chordata. These characteristics are: a notochord, gill slits and an endoskeleton. A **notochord** is a firm, flexible rod that provides support and stability. It often changes into a vertebral column later in life. **Gill slits** (aka pharyngeal pouches) are openings used in respiration that lead to the outside of an animal's body. The gill slits take oxygen into the body and release carbon dioxide. An **endoskeleton** is an internal skeleton composed of bones, cartilage or both. It grows with the animal. Fish, amphibians, reptiles, birds and mammals are all vertebrates and are all members of phylum Chordata.

Figure 8.15 Tibetan Fox

VIRUSES ARE DIFFERENT FROM LIVING THINGS

A **virus** is a small particle that contains proteins and hereditary material (DNA or RNA), but it is not alive. The virus is surrounded by a protein coat, or **capsid**. A virus particle cannot eat, and it can only reproduce inside a cell. Outside the cell, a virus particle does nothing and remains inactive. Viruses are cell specific, meaning they can only infect a cell if the capsid of the virus can fit into a receptor site in the host cell membrane.

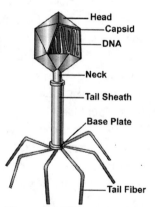

Figure 8.16 Virus Schematic

Section Review 3: Six Kingdoms

A. Define the following terms.

Archaebacteria	anaerobic	gill slits
Methanogens	plasmid	endoskeleton
Halophiles	capsid	vascular plants
Thermoacidophiles	Protista	Animalia
Eubacteria	Fungi	invertebrates
gymnosperms	Plantae	vertebrates
angiosperms	nonvascular plants	heterotroph
chemotroph	notochord	autotroph
decomposers		

B. Choose the best answer.

1. Why are archaebacteria placed in a kingdom separate from Eubacteria

    A. they are structurally and functionally different from all other types of life on planet Earth

    B. they are used in the food making process and must be separated from wild types of bacteria

    C. because their DNA forms a special ring called a plasmid

    D. they are not placed in a kingdom separate from other types of bacteria

2. Which kingdom below contains organisms that are *not* made up of eukaryotic cells?

    A. eubacteria   B. animalia   C. fungi   D. plantae

3. Which group of animals can reproduce asexually?

    A. vertebrates   B. invertebrates   C. fish   D. amphibians

4. Which kingdom listed below contains eukaryotic cells surrounded by a cell wall?

    A. fungi   B. plantae   C. animalia   D. both A and B

5. Which organism listed below is an invertebrate animal?

    A. kangaroo   B. gymnosperm   C. cyanobacteria   D. sponge

C. Complete the following exercises.

1. Make a VENN diagram comparing different structures found in the six kingdoms.

2. Compare and contrast cells and viruses.

CHAPTER 8 REVIEW

1. Cellular respiration takes place inside
   A. an animal cell only.
   B. a plant cell only.
   C. both plant and animal cells.
   D. neither plant or animal cells.

2. The chemical energy supply for all living cells is contained in a molecule that, when broken down, releases the energy so that it may be used for activities such as muscle contractions, photosynthesis, and locomotion. This molecule that is a storehouse of energy is
   A. ATP.   B. DNA.   C. RNA.   D. ADP.

3. To obtain and use cellular energy, plant cells use
   A. photosynthesis only.
   B. photosynthesis and cellular respiration.
   C. cellular respiration only.
   D. chemosynthesis.

4. How do cells store and release chemical energy?
   A. with hypotonic solutions
   B. through chemical bonds
   C. vacuoles
   D. optimum temperature and pH

5. Why do scientists find it useful to use a classification system to group organisms?
   A. easier to learn about them
   B. helps avoid duplication of names
   C. organizes all information
   D. all of the above

6. What characteristics do all vertebrates share in common at some time in their lives?
   A. gill slits and exoskeleton
   B. spinal cord and endoskeleton
   C. notochord and exoskeleton
   D. gill slits and endoskeleton

7. The two major divisions of the kingdom Plantae are
   A. gymnosperms and angiosperms.
   B. vascular and nonvascular.
   C. mosses and ferns.
   D. monocots and dicots.

8. Why are chemical bonds important to living things?
   A. They rearrange the amino acids into living tissue.
   B. They store energy that can be released to do work.
   C. They share electrons resulting in a non-charged molecule.
   D. They help enzymes function.

9. Which factor listed below *usually* results in a weak chemical bond?

    A. sharing of three electrons

    B. covalent bonds formed with carbon

    C. bonds formed using a highly polar molecule

    D. bonds formed with electrons in the first subshell

10. Which taxonomic classification below contains the *fewest* organisms?

    A. kingdom   B. family   C. order   D. class

11. What was Aristotle's contribution to taxonomy?

    A. He developed the current system of classification still in use today.

    B. He established the idea of grouping similar living things together.

    C. He taught others how to identify living things based on their type of reproduction.

    D. He made no noticeable contribution to the field of taxonomy.

12. Your dog has a runny nose and a cough. You take him to the vet and discover that he has a viral lung infection. What are the chances that you could contract this disease from your dog?

    A. 0.0000001%   B. 1%   C. 10%   D. 100%

13. Which kingdom listed below contains prokaryotic organisms?

    A. Archaebacteria   B. Plantae   C. Animalia   D. Fungi

14. Recall that animal cells can use anaerobic respiration to obtain energy. However, one of the by products of this reaction can be harmful to cells and anaerobic respiration produces far less ATP than aerobic respiration. The question remains, why do animal cells use this type of energy production?

    A. because anaerobic respiration happens much faster than aerobic respiration

    B. because evolution has forced animal cells to obtain energy in this way

    C. because the toxic by products produced become food for important bacteria living in muscle cells

    D. because oxygen cannot enter the electron transport chain

15. What are the two major divisions of the animal kingdom?

    A. vascular and non-vascular   C. plant-like and fungus-like

    B. invertebrate and vertebrate   D. warm blooded and cold blooded

16. Non-vascular plants are limited mainly by which abiotic factor?

    A. soil type   B. temperature   C. moisture   D. predators

17. What do pigments do?

    A. store energy   C. form stroma

    B. produce chlorophyll   D. absorb light

18. During aerobic respiration, how many ATPs are produced from one glucose molecule?

    A. 2   B. 6   C. 36   D. 54

19. Which processes listed below do NOT require cellular energy?

    A. growth   B. photosynthesis   C. metabolism   D. reproduction

20. How is light converted to cellular energy?

    A. When light waves strike the pigments contained in the plastid, electrons become excited and move out of the chlorophyll molecule.

    B. When light waves strike the pigments contained in the plastid, one phosphate is released from the ATP molecule.

    C. When light energy strikes the sugar molecule glucose, it degrades into three simple carbon sugars.

    D. Light energy cannot be converted to cellular energy by living things. Only humans can do this with solar cells.

21. Which statement below is true about viruses?

    A. Viruses can eat and metabolize food.

    B. Viruses can reproduce only when inside a host cell.

    C. Viruses can reproduce on their own at any time.

    D. Viruses contain DNA, so they are alive.

Chapter 9
Evolution

GEORGIA PERFORMANCE SCIENCE STANDARDS COVERED IN THIS CHAPTER INCLUDE:

SB3 c	Students will derive the relationship between single-celled and multi-celled organisms and the increasing complexity of systems.
SB4 e and f	Students will assess the dependence of all organisms on one another and the flow of energy and matter within their ecosystems.
SB5 a – d	Students will evaluate the role of natural selection in the development of the theory of evolution
SCSh7 c	Students analyze how scientific knowledge is developed.

BIOLOGICAL CLASSIFICATION

Scientists estimate that there may be up to 14 million different species inhabiting the planet. Approximately 1.75 million species have been scientifically named and described, including 250,000 plant species and 792,000 animal species. The variation among organisms is called **biodiversity**. Biodiversity includes ecosystem diversity, species diversity and genetic diversity.

Ecosystem diversity is the variety of ecosystems available. An ecosystem is a community of organisms and their environment. Forests, prairies, coral reefs and lakes are examples of ecosystems.

Species diversity is the number of different species of organisms. Within an ecosystem, the activities of all organisms are interwoven and interrelated. Each ecosystem is bound by a dependence between organisms within the ecosystem. The organisms that cannot adapt or no longer have a function in an ecosystem are soon gone. On the other hand, if an organism vital to an ecosystem is removed, its absence will eventually affect the entire ecosystem in some way.

Genetic diversity distinguishes among individuals within a species. Mixing of the gene pools promotes diversity and creates physical and genetic changes in the offspring. According to the theory of **evolution**, new species evolve from preexisting species over long periods of time. This evolution of new species promotes diversity. However, evolution does not always affect the entire species. Organisms within the same species may evolve differently over time, or remain unchanged, depending on their needs and environment. **Adaptation** is a change in structure or function that allows an organism to be more successful. Adaptation is another way species can diversify. **Extinction** is the condition where there are no living representatives of an organism. Extinction impacts biodiversity by reducing the number of species.

CLASSIFICATION

In the last chapter, we discussed structures and functions that are characteristic of different kingdoms. How were these organisms classified, though? Scientists use similarities in reproductive strategies and nutritional strategies to classify organisms. Evolutionary relationships are also a major factor when classifying living things. Biologists assume that organisms with common traits come from a common ancestor. Physical structures, embryo development and genetic make-up are all studied for clues.

REPRODUCTIVE STRATEGIES

Some organisms, such as fungi and animals, are grouped partially based on their method of reproduction. Examples of distinguishing characteristics in animals include whether or not reproduction is sexual or asexual and whether or not fertilization occurs internally or externally.

NUTRITIONAL STRATEGIES

Organisms are also grouped based on their nutritional strategies, or the way they acquire their food. The exception to this general rule is the kingdom Plantae, as almost all plants produce their food through photosynthesis. Most organisms in the other kingdoms are heterotrophs, meaning they feed off other forms of life. The prokaryotes and fungi both feed on dead organic matter. Animals get their food by ingestion. Nutritional strategies may also subdivide a kingdom. For example, the protists are grouped in different division based on how they store their reserve food supply.

ANATOMICAL SIMILARITIES

Anatomical similarities are evident in the study of homologous structures and vestigial organs. **Homologous structures** develop from a common ancestor and are similar in shape, but have different functions. The human arm, the wing of a bird and the flipper of a whale are all homologous structures. They contain the same bones. In fact, we see a

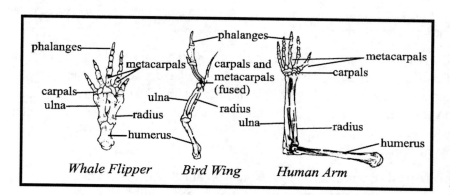

Figure 9.1 Examples of Homologous Structures

similar pattern of limb arrangement in all land dwelling (or previously land dwelling) organisms. The limb pattern is one bone, two bones and then many bones. Biologists believe these structures come from a common ancestor. Their different functions correspond to their use in different environments. A whale uses a flipper for swimming, and a bird uses a wing for flying. A whale, a bird and a human all belong in the same phylum, Chordata.

Vestigial organs, structures that are no longer used or have greatly decreased in importance, are another anatomical similarity. A whale and some snakes have a pelvis and femur, structures necessary for walking, but whales and snakes no longer have any use for these structures. These structures may have become smaller since they are unused. Their presence also suggests a common ancestor.

EMBRYONIC DEVELOPMENT

Scientists agree that studying the embryonic development of an organism often leads to a greater understanding of the evolutionary history of that organism. The early development of an embryo is the most important time during its life cycle. Like laying a foundation for a house, the structures and tissues formed at the beginning of development lay the basis for many other tissues later in life. Vertebrates (organisms with a backbone or spine) pass through some stages that are similar to each other. The more closely related an organism is, the more similar its stages of development will be.

GENETIC MAKEUP

Biochemical similarities demonstrate relationships among various organisms. DNA sequences are studied and compared. The closer the sequences, the more closely related the organisms. Humans and chimpanzees show a great deal of overlap in their DNA sequences. Humans and reptiles show some similarities, but there is less overlap than between the human and chimpanzee sequences. When the DNA from humans and yeast are compared, there is very little overlap. This suggests that humans and chimpanzees are much more closely related than humans and yeast. Another example is the horseshoe crab. The horseshoe crab was once grouped with other crabs, but is now grouped with the spiders based on genetic data. Figure 9.2 shows a comparison of chromosome #7 from different organisms.

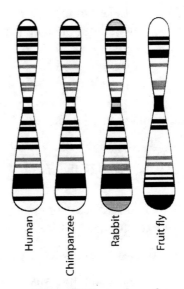

Figure 9.2 Comparison of Chromosome in Animal Kingdom

Section Review 1: Biological Classification

A. Define the following terms.

biodiversity	adaptation	genetic diversity	homologous structure
ecosystem diversity	extinction	evolution	vestigial organ
species diversity			

B. Choose the best answer.

1. The dodo bird was a flightless bird that became extinct in the last century. Although its disappearance had no significant recorded impact on other members of the ecosystem, it did affect what aspect of the ecosystem?

   A. The ability for other species to adapt.

   B. The genetic diversity of other species.

   C. The biodiversity of the ecosystem as a whole.

   D. The process of evolution within the ecosystem.

Use the following scenario to answer questions 2 – 3:

> Lake Lanier is a man-made like in Georgia. The floor of the lake is filled with dead trees and construction debris remaining from the time of its construction. Over time, these items have become the natural habitat of the organisms living in the lake.

2. If a new species of fish were transferred from a natural lake to Lake Lanier, which of the following would be altered?

   A. the fish's ability to adapt   C. the ecosystem of the lake

   B. the genes of the fish   D. the ability of other fish to adapt

3. The fish turns out to hungrily consume two other species of fish in the lake, eventually causing their extinction. What is a correct description of this circumstance?

   A. The species diversity of the ecosystem initially increased, then decreased.

   B. The genetic diversity of the fish initially increased, then decreased.

   C. The genetic diversity of the ecosystem immediately decreased.

   D. The species diversity of the ecosystem immediately decreased.

4. Wisdom teeth are the common name for the third molar in humans. They generally appear much later than all other adult teeth, and usually not until the age of 18. The teeth have no noticeable purpose to the modern human and are often pulled to make room for the other teeth in the mouth. The continued presence of wisdom teeth is a good example of

   A. homologous structures in humans.   C. genetic diversity in humans.

   B. vestigial structures in humans.   D. adaptation to better dental care.

DEVELOPMENT OF EVOLUTIONARY THOUGHT

Scientists observe the natural world and come up with many questions. How can a rhea in South America, an ostrich in Africa and an emu in Australia look so much alike but be different birds? How can the finches on the Galapagos Islands all have different beaks? How can sharks and dolphins have similar-looking structures when one is a fish and one is a mammal? The theory of evolution attempts to answer such questions and more.

Figure 9.3 Ostrich

Figure 9.4 Emu

The theory of evolution states that organisms go through a process of change over time and develop new species from preexisting ones. **Phylogeny** is the evolutionary history of one organism or a group of related organisms. The following sections will describe the mechanisms and patterns of modern evolutionary theory.

DARWIN

Charles Darwin (1809 – 1882), who was born in England, attended Cambridge to train for the ministry after a short period of study at a medical school. While at Cambridge, he developed a passion for studying biology and geology. Through the efforts of his professors, he was able to get aboard a British science ship, the *Beagle*, bound on a five-year trip around the world.

Figure 9.5 Darwin

During this trip, Darwin observed fossils on many different continents. Darwin observed and collected many different organisms from places all around the globe. He took notes about every place he visited. One place that was of particular interest to Darwin was the Galapagos Islands off the coast of South America.

Figure 9.6 Galapagos on the Globe

Darwin noticed that all the organisms on this island looked very similar to the organisms on the South American continent, especially the finches. On the South American continent, finches only eat seeds and have very few species. Every bird Darwin saw on the Galapagos Islands was a type of modified finch. The finches were about the same size and all very similar in color. The only differences in the finches Darwin saw were their beaks and what they ate. There were finches that ate insects, seeds, plant matter, egg yolks and blood. The finches on the

Figure 9.7 Evolution of Finches on the Galapagos Islands

Galapagos Islands looked very similar to one type of finch on the South American continent, but none of the Galapagos Island types of finches were found on the South American mainland.

The types of finches seen were indeed very diverse. Darwin began to ask many questions; one of which began to plague him above all others: "How did one species change into a different species?" It is important to note that scientists in the 19th century did not know how a trait passes from one animal to its offspring; they did not know of the existence of DNA. After the trip on the *Beagle*, Darwin studied his collection of organisms as well as many different books and readings. He also talked with several domestic animal breeders.

After 20 years of study, Darwin published his book, *The Origin of Species*, in 1859. In this book, Darwin describes his theory of how one species changes into another species. According to Darwin, in all living populations of organisms there is some natural variation among individual organisms.

Darwin had repeatedly observed that environmental pressures can change how an organism interacts with its environment. He developed a theory based on these observations and called it the theory of **natural selection**.

Recall that the entire diet of the Galapagos finches changed in response to their isolated environment. That was a modification of behavior (eating habits) in response to environmental pressure (limited food resources). The existence of certain physical traits may also be modified over time. As the finches began to eat more varied food items, the actual function of their beaks began to change. Finches that began to eat insects needed longer beaks for digging beetles out of their burrows. Finches that ate seeds or nuts required stronger jaw muscles to crack the shells.

How did the finches change their beaks in response to these needs? Modern science now views the process of natural selection in this way. The finches' beaks did not change overnight, but rather over many, many generations. Among the population of beetle-eating finches, those that were born with longer, sharper beaks naturally had access to more beetles than those finches with blunter beaks. The sharp-beaked finches thrived, and had many offspring, while the blunt-beaked finches gradually died out. The

Figure 9.9 Finch

Figure 9.8 Finch

sharp beak was a trait that was, in effect, *selected* by nature to thrive. The same thing happened in each finch population, until finches from a given population began to look similar to each other and different than other finches.

To be clear: the individual physical traits of a finch are not modified by the finch (his beak does not grow and change to suit his changing needs). Rather, the animals who already possess a trait that is favored by the current environmental pressures survive and pass that trait on to their offspring. This insures that, over time, the expression of the favored trait becomes more pronounced, and other traits disappear. This is why Darwin's theory of natural selection is also called the **survival of the fittest**.

Figure 9.10 Giraffes with Their Offspring

MODERN IDEAS

Darwin's ideas, along with Mendel's work and the work of others, have lead to modern ideas about evolution. Modern synthesis is the merging of Darwinian ideas along with modern knowledge about genetics. Modern synthesis forms the foundation of ever changing ideas about evolution. There are four important facets to know about modern evolutionary thought.

It recognizes:

1. There are several mechanisms responsible for the evolution of organisms. One of the most important is **genetic drift** (random change in genes), which occurs through natural selection, and which we will discuss later in this chapter.

2. Characteristics that are inherited are carried by genes, and natural variation within a population is the result of several alleles working together.

3. **Microevolution** is the process that is responsible for the variations that exist within a species, or a change in the allele frequency. The many breeds of dogs known today are good examples of microevolution. All dogs are of the genus and species *Canis lupus familiaris* and can therefore produce fertile offspring, but many variations are present among breeds. Consider Great Danes and Chihuahuas. **Macroevolution** is evolution that occurs between species. The separation of a species to form two distinct species or the development of a new species from many small changes within an existing species are examples of macroevolution.

Figure 9.11 Great Dane vs. Chihuahua

4. **Speciation** (formation of new species) is due to gradual genetic changes, and large scale evolution is the result of a lot of small scale evolution.

Most importantly, modern synthesis recognizes that evolution can be seen as the changes in gene frequencies of a population. Darwinian evolution saw evolution as changes in individual organisms of that population.

Section Review 2: Development of Evolutionary Thought

A. Define the following terms.

phylogeny   genetic drift   microevolution

survival of the fittest   speciation   macroevolution

B. Choose the best answer.

1. Ideas about evolution

     A. have already been thought.

     B. are perfect and need no refinement.

     C. may change based on new data.

     D. only involve animals.

2. What is genetic drift?

     A. The random change in genes within a population.

     B. The formation of new species.

     C. The isolation of individual organisms of a population.

     D. The ability of an organism to survive in its environment.

       Oncillas, margays and ocelots are all small cats, common in South American. All three are spotted cats with long tails. The oncilla and margay are nearly the same size, 2-3 kg; the ocelot is a little larger, 10-15 kg. All three cats are equipped for an arboreal lifestyle, but the margay is the only one that dwells almost exclusively in the trees. The margay is one of only two cats that can climb headfirst down a tree, owing to its extremely flexible ankles. (The other cat that can do this is the leopard.)

Use the following table to answer questions 3 – 4.

	Oncilla	Margay	Ocelot
Leopardus	*tigrinus*	*wiedii*	*pardalis*

3. What taxonomic category do all three cats share?

     A. Genus   B. Species   C. Order   D. Family

4. Choose the sentence that could correctly describe the evolution of the margay.

     A. Microevolution is responsible for the differences between the margay and the oncilla.

     B. The margay is a tree-dwelling oncilla.

     C. The margay likely evolved to become a strictly arboreal species because of its small size and flexible ankles.

     D. The margay's small size and flexible ankles evolved in response to habitat changes that oncillas and ocelots were unable to respond to.

THE FOSSIL RECORD: MORE EVIDENCE OF EVOLUTION

The evolutionary relationships used to classify organisms provide evidence for evolution, such as the existence of homologous structures, vestigial organs and biochemical similarities. Fossils also provide evidence for the change in organisms over time. Darwin himself observed fossils found on many different continents while aboard the HMS Beagle. Fossil evidence was instrumental in the development of Darwin's ideas on evolution. A **fossil** is the recognizable remains or body impressions of an organism that lived in the past. The existence of animal life on land is relatively recent. Fossils indicate that insects first came onto land around 440 million years ago, and vertebrate animals moved onto land about 417 million years ago (mya).

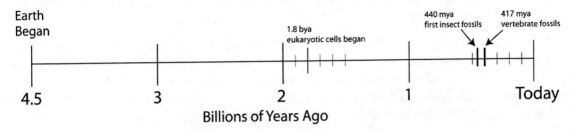

Figure 9.12 Timeline of Earth's Existence

In general, fossils come from organisms that are now extinct. One exception is the **living fossil**. This is an organism, like a horseshoe crab or a ginkgo tree, that has remained essentially unchanged from earlier geologic times. Fossils found of these organisms look very similar to the living organism today. These organisms have many successful characteristics that do not need extensive modification and so remain virtually unchanged for long periods of time. This is not to say they have ceased to evolve, think of it like more like changing very little. Crocodilians are one example; they have changed very little over their 84 million year history. They have had some variation in size over the years. After all, crocodiles that preyed upon dinosaurs would have to be much larger than today's crocodiles!

Why is it important to know that organisms change over time? The answer is that if there is change, then there must be a cause of the change. Discovering both the cause of, and the mechanism through which the change occurs, is central to the survival of organisms and the ecosystems they populate. Of course, the study of fossils also gives us a fascinating historical perspective — snapshots from an Earth of long ago. Taken together, these snapshots are referred to as the **fossil record**.

Scientists use the body of evidence accumulated from the fossil record to make hypotheses about organism development and migration over the course of history of the planet.

RELATIVES AND ABSOLUTE DATING

Fossils have another use: they allow scientists to date rock and rock formations. The process is called **relative dating**, and it depends on the identification of an **index fossil**. An index fossil is the remains of animal that existed on the planet during a very defined period of time. **Trilobites** have been used extensively for this purpose. How?

Well, let's say that a geologist discovers a geological feature, like a black shale beds at Burgess Pass in the Canadian Rockies. Taking several rock samples at the Burgess Shale beds, he discovers trilobite fossils! Knowing that trilobites flourished in the Cambrian period, and that they were extinct by the end of the Devonian period, the geologist can infer the time period when the shale sediment was deposited. He can also infer the age of any other fossils found in the beds. This is particularly useful if the fossils are of a new species.

Finally, knowing that trilobites were exclusively marine animals, the geologist can infer that the Burgess Shale area was once under water, and infer the tectonic plate movement required to produce the current geography.

So, relative dating is a powerful tool. But not all fossils are index fossils, so there must be another way to date them. In fact, there is.

Carbon dating is a type of **absolute dating**, which uses the rate of **radioactive decay** of isotopes to determine the age of rocks and fossils. Isotopes are elements that have the same number of protons in the nucleus but differ in number of neutrons. In some isotopes, the nuclei are unstable because the forces binding protons and neutrons together are not very strong. These nuclei break apart or decay in a process known as **radioactivity**. Unstable isotopes, called **radioactive parents**, decay and form other more stable elements, called **daughter products**. This decay happens at a measurable rate. The calculation of the ratio of parent to daughter products is known as **radiometric dating**. **Half-life** is the time required for one-half of the parent isotope in a rock to decay into a daughter product. **Carbon-14** has a half-life of 5,730 years. Carbon-14 decays into its daughter product, nitrogen-14. By comparing the number of parent and daughter isotopes, a scientist can determine the age of a fossil using the known half-life of carbon-14. For example, if a fossil contains one-quarter carbon-14 isotopes and three-quarters nitrogen-14 isotopes, then the fossil has existed for two half lives, or 11,460 years. Other radioactive isotopes such as uranium-235 and potassium-40 are frequently used in radiometric dating.

Based on radiometric dating of rock layers, scientists agree that Earth is around 4.55 billion years old. The oldest rocks found on Earth are 3.8 billion years old. During much of that time, only bacteria inhabited the Earth. Eukaryotic cells have only developed in the past 1.8 billion years. The early atmosphere of Earth was a **reducing atmosphere** and contained no free oxygen. It consisted of gases released from volcanic activity occurring underneath the surface of Earth. As plant life developed, the process of photosynthesis resulted in the creation of atmospheric oxygen. Most of the oxygen build-up in the atmosphere was a result of photosynthetic plants in the ocean, such as algae. Today's **oxidizing atmosphere** contains nitrogen, oxygen, carbon dioxide and water vapor. The idea of an ancient reducing atmosphere is supported by rock samples drilled from different layers of Earth's crust. These rocks were deposited during ancient volcanic eruptions. These rock samples contain iron that would oxidize in the presence of oxygen to form rust. The samples show no sign of rust or oxidation. As a result, scientists speculate that there was no free oxygen in Earth's early atmosphere.

Even though radiometric dating is called "absolute dating," it does not always produce undisputed ages of fossils. Using radiometric dating requires scientists to make several assumptions that may or may not be correct. First, radiometric dating assumes that the decay of radioactive elements is not affected by external environment. Second, it assumes the sample was isolated so that no parent or daughter isotopes were lost or added over time. Third, it assumes that the starting conditions are known. Scientists generally agree that the first assumption is valid, although some argue that certain types of decay do depend on the external environment. The second and third assumptions depend on unknown factors.

Since there is no guarantee that the sample was isolated and there is no proof of the starting conditions of an ancient sample, the effect of these assumptions is not certain and may cause discrepancies in the dating process.

GAPS IN THE FOSSIL RECORD

The fossil record is an important tool scientists use when attempting to better understand the history of the Earth. However, it is important to note the record itself is not complete.

All scientists agree that there are gaps in the fossil record. There are periods of time that organisms seem to either disappear — there are no fossils found — or to evolve rapidly and without apparent explanation. Estimates indicate that the fossil record only represents 0.1% of the organisms that have lived on the planet. Scientists differ as to what these gaps mean. In general, however, gaps can be rationalized in three ways.

Figure 9.13 Trilobite Fossil

Not enough animals were fossilized to fully represent the diversity of the Earth's biotic history.

It is important to note that every living organism does not become a fossil. In the normal course of events, organisms that die either rot or are eaten. Either way, they become food for some other organism. Bones become scattered and unrecognizable as their original organisms. Fossil bones are different; they have been preserved. This only occurs under certain circumstances, usually when the animal is buried very quickly. Catastrophic events, like floods, mudslides and volcanic eruptions often preserve a wide variety of organisms at one time. Smaller scale catastrophes like sinkholes and quicksand, may entomb smaller numbers of animals.

What kinds of animals are fossilized? Bony animals are the most common, for obvious reasons. Bones are much more easily preserved than flesh. Jellyfish fossils, for instance, are rare. They do, however, exist, as faint body impressions of the deflated animal.

Those organisms that were fossilized have not all been found.

In the big picture, not much of Earth's surface has been sifted for fossils. To put this point in perspective, let's look at the impact of expanding development on the fossil record. In this century, a huge number of fossils have been found as a result of excavation for the purpose of societal progress (mining, drilling, excavating, road-building, etc.). In undeveloped areas (much of Africa, Siberia, great swathes of Asia and South America) less societal progress of this ilk has been made. We can expect more fossils to be found as these areas develop.

The theory of evolution is *simply not evolved enough* to explain the full mystery of Earth's biotic history.

Remember that the theory of evolution is still a theory. It is scientifically sound, and sounds very reasonable to some people. Others, however, have doubts. One thing is certain though: all theories change and evolve as more information becomes available. In the next section, we will look at how Darwin's theory of evolution has evolved over time.

Section Review 3: Fossils and the Fossil Record

A. Define the following terms.

fossil	absolute dating	radioactive parent	half-life
fossil record	radioactive decay	daughter product	reducing atmosphere
index fossils	radioactivity	radiometric dating	oxidizing atmosphere

B. Choose the best answer.

1. A fossil recognized as unique to a certain time period is known as what?

    A. an index fossil   C. a marker fossil

    B. a distinct fossil   D. a time marker fossil

2. What led to the development of the Earth's oxidizing atmosphere?

    A. a change in the gases emitted from volcanoes

    B. the weathering of ancient rock formations

    C. the development of oxygen-producing life forms

    D. A and C only

3. Which event listed below does NOT lead to fossil formation?

    A. floods   B. forest fires   C. earthquakes   D. mudslides

4. When is it hypothesized that the first living organisms appeared on Earth?

    A. 3.8 billion years ago   C. 440 million years ago

    B. 1.8 billion years ago   D. 3.8 million years ago

5. Why is it difficult to find fossils of cells?

    A. because none exist

    B. because humans cannot dig deep enough into the Earth

    C. because no catastrophic events occurred in the ecosystems of the early Earth

    D. they are rare because cells have no hard parts that will fossilize

C. Complete the following exercises.

1. Explain the difference between relative dating and absolute dating.

2. A new rock cooling in a magma chamber contains a parent isotope with a half-life of 10 million years. If we begin with 10,000 atoms of a parent isotope, how many atoms of the parent isotope will be present after the third half-life? How much time will have passed since the magma cooled?

3. What conclusions can you draw about the completeness of the fossil record?

MECHANISMS OF EVOLUTION

Mechanisms of evolution deal with how evolution occurs. Most scientists consider natural selection one of the most important mechanisms of evolution, but other mechanisms like mutations, gene flow and genetic drift are also significant.

NATURAL SELECTION

Naturalist Charles Darwin proposed the idea of natural selection in 1859. Natural selection states that organisms best suited to the environment are the ones most likely to survive and reproduce. A few important points Darwin made in his book, *The Origin of Species*, are:

- **Resources are limited in all environments**. The availability of food, water and shelter in an environment is limited. This leads to competition among organisms. **Competition** is the fight among living things to get what they need for survival. For example, moths must find food before other moths take all the food.

- **Most organisms have more offspring than the environment can support**. For example, a moth lays thousands of eggs or one tree produces millions of seeds.

Figure 9.14 Tree Seeds

- **There is natural variation within a population**. A **variation** is a difference in a trait between organisms within a population. Not all organisms are exactly alike. For example, not all moths are the exact same color. Another example of variation is that not all humans are the same height.

- **Natural selection is always taking place**. Organisms with traits that are the most desirable are selected to survive. Organisms in any environment have a specific fitness for that environment. **Fitness** is the ability of an organism to live, survive and reproduce in that environment. Not all of the individual animals within a population have the same fitness.

Figure 9.15 Natural Variation in Human Height

Figure 9.16 The Cheetah

Variations in physical characteristics make some organisms better suited, or more fit, to live in their environments. Much of this variation is inherited. For example, the fastest cheetah is better equipped to hunt than a slower cheetah. As a result, the faster cheetah will get more food. The most successful cheetah lives the longest and is, therefore, able to produce the most offspring. Scientists would say that the fastest cheetahs are the most fit for their environment. This is where the idea of survival of the fittest comes from.

Inherited traits that are more versatile than others improve the chances of the organisms' survival and reproduction. For example, having long legs and a skinny body helps a cheetah stay cool. These adaptations also help the cheetah to run fast. These traits are favorable for more than one reason, making them highly likely to pass on to offspring.

An improved chance of survival allows organisms to produce offspring that will make up more of the next generation, while passing along their favorable traits. Unfavorable traits will eventually be lost since there is less reproduction among the individuals with such traits.

The slowest cheetahs will get the least amount of food, and will, therefore, have a greater chance of dying. These slow cheetahs are said to be less fit, or unfit, for their environments. In many cases, the most successful traits are maintained and change very little over a long period of time. Sharks, turtles, crocodiles and ferns are examples of organisms that have successful traits that have remained virtually unchanged over millions of years. Remember the living fossil?

ENVIRONMENT AND VARIATIONS

Environmental conditions also contribute to variations in traits among individuals of the same species. The size of house sparrows in North America varies depending on location. House sparrows living in colder climates are larger than those living in the warmer climates. As a general rule, the larger the body size of an animal, the more body heat it can trap or conserve.

The size of extremities, such as ears or legs in some animals, also demonstrates environmental differences. Since extremities give off heat to help cool the animals' bodies, mammals living in hot climates tend to have larger ears and longer legs than their cousins in cooler climates. A desert jackrabbit has much larger ears than a rabbit found in a temperate (cooler winter) climate.

Figure 9.17 Desert and Temperate Rabbits

Natural variation within a population allows for some individuals to survive over other individuals in a changing environment. This natural variation can eventually lead to the formation of new species, which is also called **speciation**.

MUTATIONS

Mutations are random changes in DNA that act as another mechanism for evolution. These changes result in a variation in traits, which then pass from one generation to the next. Mutations can be beneficial, neutral or harmful to an organism. Mutations beneficial to the organism in a particular environment lead to furthering of the species. For example, a mutation can result in the production of an enzyme that breaks down a particular food product predominant in an area. Individuals with the expression of that gene have more food choices, giving them greater survival chances, and allowing them to be more successful. Another example could be a mutation in color pigments that leads to an individual that is a different color than the normal population.

GENE FLOW

Gene flow is the change in the occurrence of genes in a population. Population refers to the group of organisms of the same species in a given geographic area. Gene flow occurs when an individual leaves a population or a new individual joins a population. **Immigration** occurs when organisms enter into a new population, and **emigration** occurs when organisms leave a population. Gene flow tends to increase the similarity of individuals from different populations, since these individuals share their genes with each other through reproduction. Emigration often leads to the formation of new species.

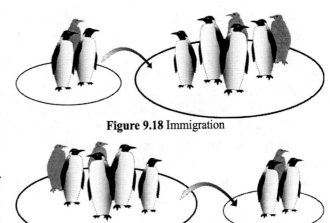

Figure 9.18 Immigration

Figure 9.19 Emigration

Gene flow happens easily in plants that have seeds carried by wind. The wind carries the seeds of a plant from one population to another population. When these new seeds grow into plants, the plants can cross-pollinate with the existing plants, and genes from different populations are shared.

GENETIC DRIFT

Genetic drift provides random changes in the occurrence of genes through chance events. It can occur if a large number of the population is killed because of disease, starvation, change in natural environment or a natural disaster. When this happens to a population, it is called **bottlenecking**. A large population is reduced to a few individuals, and the genes of subsequent generations become very similar.

Inbreeding between these few individuals leads to populations that have very few genetic differences. It is believed that African cheetahs went through two bottlenecks, one about 10,000 years ago and one about 100 years ago. All African cheetahs alive today are descendents of a few cheetahs, and possibly only three females. Because cheetahs are genetically similar, they have become very susceptible to diseases.

Figure 9.20 Bottleneck

PATTERNS OF EVOLUTION

The theory of evolution suggests that there is more than one way to evolve or change. These different patterns provide different paths to explain the degree of variation among organisms. Some ways that organisms evolve include convergent evolution, divergent evolution and co-evolution.

CONVERGENT EVOLUTION

Convergent evolution explains how unrelated species can develop similar characteristics. Convergent evolution is demonstrated through the porpoise and the shark. The porpoise is a mammal, and the shark is a fish. These two unrelated animals share similar characteristics that suit their environment: long, streamlined bodies and fins that closely match in both appearance and function. These structures are said to be analogous. **Analogous** structures are similar in function but have different ancestors. Another example of analogous structures included the wing of a butterfly and the wing of a bird.

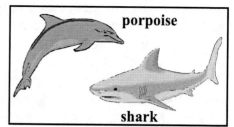

Figure 9.21 Convergent Evolution of Porpoise and Shark

Convergent evolution also occurs in the plant kingdom. Cacti and Euphorbs are both plants that look very similar and live in desert climates. They both have spines, small leaves and water storage tissues in large, fleshy stems. Cacti are found in North America and Euphorbs are found in Asia and Africa. Despite the similarity in characteristics, these plants have very different flowers and are not closely related. These organisms evolved similar characteristics to suit their specific environments. Their spines are analogous structures, not homologous structures.

DIVERGENT EVOLUTION

Divergent evolution suggests that many species develop from a common ancestor. The different species adapt to their particular environments. A good example of divergent evolution is Darwin's finches. A few birds from one species of finch were carried to the Galapagos islands. Since their food supply changed in the new locations, they adapted their diets accordingly. Geographic isolation from other finches and environmental differences caused them to diverge from their ancestors and even from one another. There are now many recognized species of finches, all diverging from a common ancestor. Divergent evolution is demonstrated by homologous structures. Recall the flipper of a whale and the arm of a human from the beginning of this chapter?

CO-EVOLUTION

Co-evolution occurs when two or more organisms in an ecosystem evolve in response to each other. Co-evolution is believed to occur frequently with flowers and their pollinators. Hummingbirds have long, narrow beaks, an attraction to the color red and a poor sense of smell. The fuchsia plant, whose flowers bloom in various shades of red, emit little fragrance and have long, narrow flowers. Fuchsias rely on hummingbirds as their pollinators. Over time, the red- flowered fuchsias and the long-beaked hummingbirds have had great success as partners in survival.

Section Review 4: Mechanisms and Patterns of Evolution

A. Define the following terms.

speciation	gene flow	bottlenecking
competition	immigration	convergent evolution
variation	emigration	divergent evolution
fitness	genetic drift	co-evolution
	analogous structures	

B. Choose the best answer.

1. What are the effects of genetic drift and gene flow?

    A. change in gene occurrences   C. change in DNA replication patterns

    B. change in vision acuity   D. change in organism size

2. Which of the following are patterns of evolution?

    A. structural replication, reproductive homology and special creation

    B. metabolic pathways, hormonal indicators and genetic studies

    C. modern creationism, fossil theory and punctuational model

    D. convergent evolution, co-evolution and divergent evolution

3. If two organisms evolve in response to each other, which evolutionary pattern is demonstrated?

    A. divergent evolution   C. co-evolution

    B. emigration   D. convergent evolution

4. Darwin identified at least 13 different species of finch during his time on the Galapagos Islands. The main difference between the finches was the size and shape of their beaks. Which of the following statements best describes these differences?

    A. The beaks are vestigial structures.

    B. The beaks are analogous structures.

    C. The beaks co-evolved to suit their environment.

    D. The beaks are homologous structures.

C. Complete the following exercises.

1. What is the difference between convergent and divergent evolution? Give an example of each.
2. Explain the theory of natural selection.
3. How is variation beneficial to an organism? How is it harmful?

ADAPTATIONS AND BEHAVIOR

ADAPTATION

Adaptations are physical and behavioral changes that make organisms better suited to their environments. Plants and animals adapt in a variety of ways in an effort to protect themselves from predators and survive in their environment. There are many, many different plant and animal adaptations. In fact, we could probably fill the rest of this book with examples of plant and animal adaptations! (Don't worry, we won't.)

PLANT ADAPTATIONS

Figure 9.22 Animal Seed Dispersal

Plants cannot flee from predators, but they do have spines, thorns and leathery leaves to discourage herbivores from consuming them. Some plants manufacture chemicals that are poisonous or have a foul odor to keep animals away. Milkweed, tobacco and peyote cactus are three

Figure 9.23 Wind Seed Dispersal

such plants. The Venus flytrap plant has adapted a unique way to gather food by catching insects within its modified leaves. Some plants have developed unique methods of spreading seeds. Some plants have seeds with spines that attach to animal fur. Some have seeds with "wings" or parachutes used to harness the wind and some seeds have watertight buoyant outer shells used to travel in the water.

Mechanical stress — such as wind, rain and animal — has an effect on the growth of plants. Indoor plants will grow taller than outdoor plants of the same species because they are protected from the weather. Adaptations to mechanical stress include shorter, thicker stems, which helps outdoor plants withstand the stress and increases their survival chances, even if the plants' overall growth is inhibited.

BEHAVIORAL PLANT ADAPTATIONS

Response to internal and external stimuli by an organism is called **behavior**. Plants respond to stimuli in a variety of ways to increase their chances for survival.

Tropisms are the growth of a plant in response to a stimulus. **Positive tropisms** are toward the stimulus and **negative tropisms** are away from the stimulus.

Phototropism is the response to light. Light is important to plants, since they use it to trap energy and make glucose. Plants are **photosynthetic**. Photosynthetic structures, like leaves and stems, are positively phototropic. These plant tissues will grow in a variety of directions to get the best possible light. Roots are negatively phototropic; they grow away from the light source.

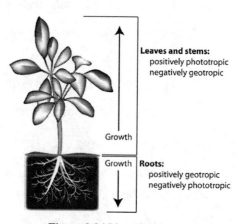

Leaves and stems:
positively phototropic
negatively geotropic

Growth

Growth **Roots:**
positively geotropic
negatively phototropic

Figure 9.24 Plant Tropisms

Geotropism is a plant's response to gravity. Roots are positively geotropic. They grow toward the Earth in response to gravity. Stems and leaves are negatively geotropic. Plants also respond to touch. This is called **thigmotropism.** Climbing plants, like kudzu, honeysuckle or beans, generally have weak stems and will wrap around another plant, wall, fence or other structure for support. The tentacles of climbing plants respond to the touch of something else and coil around the object, sometimes in a matter of hours.

OTHER PLANT BEHAVIORS

Figure 9.25 Venus Fly Trap

Nastic movements are the responses of plants to stimulus regardless of direction. Examples include flowers opening and closing in response to light, or mimosa leaves curling up when touched by an object or blown by wind. Carnivorous plants, like the Venus flytrap, will close in response to something touching the little hair-like structures inside their leaves, which helps them obtain food.

Plants also follow circadian rhythms. **Circadian rhythms** are behavior cycles that follow roughly 24 hour patterns of activity. Some plants fold their leaves and flowers during the night and open them during the day, to preserve water. For many plants, light stimulates growth hormones. Other plants have adapted to secreting perfumes and nectars at times when their pollinators are active, increasing chances of fertilization.

Plants can send communication signals to predators and other plants. They have the ability to secrete foul-tasting substances, so herbivores will avoid eating them. Even leaves damaged by an herbivore can secrete the chemical warning to other plants. The other plants then produce the chemical substance. The plants only secrete the protective substance when needed.

Flower blooming follows a photoperiodic trend. **Photoperiodism** is the response of plant processes to the amount of daylight. Photoperiodism explains why plants bloom in different seasons. The amount of daylight in fall and winter is less than the amount of daylight in spring and summer. The photoperiods of various plants are summarized in Table 9.1 below.

Table 9.1 Photoperiods

Short-Day Plants	Flowers bloom in fall and winter. Includes ragweed, goldenrod and chrysanthemums.
Long-Day Plants	Flowers bloom in spring and summer. Includes spinach, clover and iris.
Day-Neutral Plants	Flowers bloom over a range of photoperiods. Examples include roses, tomatoes and beans.

BEHAVIORS OF UNICELLULAR ORGANISMS

Bacteria, amoeba and paramecia also respond to light and chemical signals. Photosynthetic bacteria, cyanobacteria and protists gravitate toward light in a process called **phototaxis**, to ensure survival. Monerans and protists can detect chemical signals given off by food sources, ensuring their survival. Some bacteria even have magnetic crystals inside their bodies that direct their movements. One-celled organisms are also capable of avoiding negative stimuli, such as temperature and chemical changes in their environments.

ANIMAL ADAPTATIONS

Most animals have also developed special adaptations. Animals show physical, chemical and behavioral adaptations to increase their chances for survival and reproduction.

PHYSICAL ANIMAL ADAPTATIONS

Physical adaptations help animals survive and flourish in their environment. Many species living in cold climates grow thick fur during the winter and shed it during the summer months. Animals that live in cold climates typically have short extremities (limbs, ears, tails). Shorter extremities reduce heat loss from the animals body. Animals that live in dry deserts like camels, giraffes and African deer can survive for long periods without water. Some desert frogs have special adaptations that allow them to absorb water directly from the air, some frogs can change color to a pale white to reflect heat during the hottest part of the day. Animals that live in hot climates typically have large, long extremities, which allow them to cool off.

Animals also adapt in response to predator/prey interactions. Porcupines and spiny anteaters grow sharp quills for protection against predators. Turtles retreat inside a bony shell for protection. Some animals produce venom or poison for hunting or protection. Armadillos have armor-like skin that protects the animal when it flees from predators into thorny patches. The American alligator has eyes and nostrils located on the top of its head allowing the body of the animal to remain hidden. Cottonmouth snakes, and other pit vipers, have special heat-sensing organs, located on the front of their head.

Figure 9.26 Alligator

Figure 9.27 Predator

Most land-dwelling predators have eyes located close together on the front of the head. This allows the predator to focus specifically on its prey. Most prey have eyes located far apart on either side of the head. This allows the prey to see more of the area around it, perhaps helping their escape.

Figure 9.28 Prey

ANIMAL BEHAVIOR

Ethology is the study of animal behavior. Scientists evaluate animal behavior to see how their responses relate to their goals — survival and reproduction. Behavior is broadly divided into innate behavior and learned behavior. Behavior is influenced by hormones and by the nervous system. Hormones direct certain behaviors, and the nervous system allows an animal to respond to stimuli.

INNATE BEHAVIOR

Innate behaviors are those that are under genetic control and are inherited like physical traits. Innate behaviors are animals' instincts and are performed perfectly without any learning. A baby is behaving on instinct when he or she sees a human face and smiles. Innate behavior causes a baby cuckoo bird to push an unhatched egg out of the nest so it does not have to share food and space. Instinct allows a female digger wasp to emerge from her pupa, make a nest, mate, hunt and lay eggs all within her short life span of only a few weeks. Some examples of innate behavior are territoriality, protective behaviors, courting behavior, hibernation and migration.

BEHAVIORAL ANIMAL ADAPTATIONS

Animals use behavioral adaptations for survival and reproduction. **Territoriality** is a behavioral adaptation that ensures adequate space and resources for reproduction. For example, male elephant seals battle for specific beach territories during the breeding season. When female seals arrive, they remain on the beach within the territory of a single male seal. Large, strong males typically have the largest territories, and the most females. In this way, he is assured to pass along his genes to a large portion of the next generation of elephant seal

Figure 9.29 Territorial Elephant Seals

pups will survive to adulthood. Fathering many offspring is one way males ensure reproductive success.

Many animals have adapted behaviors that protect them from predators. Birds flock together, fish school together and insects form swarms to increase their chances for survival.

Some animals help others of their kind by giving a signal that a predator is near. For instance, the whitetail deer signals alarm to other nearby deer by raising its characteristic white tail while fleeing from danger.

Figure 9.30 Flock of Birds

Figure 9.31 Bird of Paradise

Courting behavior is a behavioral adaptation that helps to ensure beneficial genes are passed along to offspring. Mates that can build the best nests, sing exuberant mating calls or have the brightest colors are healthy and strong and will likely produce the strongest offspring. The courting behavior of insects, birds, amphibians, mammals or fish can be complex visual or auditory displays. Lightening bugs display bright lights to attract mates. Birds build nests, do dances, sing songs or grow specialized feathers to attract mates. Birds of the genus Paridisaeidae are commonly called birds of paradise; males of this genus are renowned for their ornamental plumage. Frogs, alligators and whales call for a mate with elaborate songs.

Hormones organize and activate specific forms of innate behavior. Mating behavior in many animals and singing behavior in some birds are activated by hormones. For example, some animals — usually males — engage in elaborate rituals to lure a mate. Many male mammals fight with other males, and some birds will decorate nests, perform dances or puff up colorful feathers. The females generally select the males with the best traits, and those genes are passed along to offspring.

Animals, like plants, follow circadian rhythms, which are innate behavior cycles. Some animals are active during the day. They are **diurnal** animals, like squirrels and blue jays. Animals active at night are **nocturnal**, like bats and racoons.

Figure 9.32 Bear

Some animals hibernate, estivate or migrate to escape extremes in weather. These activities are innate behaviors. **Hibernation** is a period of dormancy during cold months. When animals enter a period of **dormancy**, which is a period of biological rest or inactivity, food supplies are limited, and the animal lives off its fat stores. Metabolism, breathing and body temperature all drop to conserve energy. Growth and development also cease during the dormant period. Bears hibernate in winter. **Estivation** is dormancy in hot climates. Lungfish estivate. Other animals **migrate**, or move to new locations in response to weather changes to stay close to food sources. These animals, like geese, usually follow the same routes every year.

LEARNED BEHAVIOR

Learned behavior is a result of an animal's experiences. It allows animals to adapt, so survival chances are enhanced. There are several types of learned behaviors, and it is generally believed that only animals with complex nervous systems are capable of learning. Learned behaviors are related to life span and parental care. Animals with short life spans and little or no parental care have fewer learned behaviors. Table 9.2, summarizes some learned behaviors.

Table 9.2 Learned Behavior

Type of Learning	Description	Example
Imprinting	A rapid form of learning that occurs at a young age during a critical period of development.	Some birds use imprinting.
Habituation	An animal learns not to respond to repeated stimulus.	Dogs stop barking at familiar people entering the house.
Reasoning or Insight	The ability to solve unfamiliar problems in a new situation. This type of learning is limited to humans and other primates.	A chimpanzee was placed in a room with bananas hanging from the ceiling and several boxes on the floor. When he was unable to reach the bananas, he began to stack the boxes until he could reach the bananas.
Spatial or Latent	The ability of an animal to create a mental map of its environment.	Blue jays know where they have hidden food, even if food is stored in up to one hundred locations.
Classical Conditioning	An animal learns to associate a stimulus with a response that would not normally occur.	Pavlov's dogs salivated at the sound of a bell.
Operant Conditioning	An animal learns to associate an activity with a consequence.	Toads flick their tongues at flying insects, their food source. If they are stung by a bee, they learn to associate the sting with insects that have stripes, and they avoid them in the future.

Activity

Read each statement and decide if it is a learned behavior or an innate behavior. Mark L for learned and I for innate.

1. _____ humans jump when hearing a sudden loud noise

2. _____ toads avoid eating bees

3. _____ dogs no longer bark at familiar person

4. _____ humpback whales move from warm oceans to polar oceans

5. _____ squirrels know where to find their hidden food

6. _____ cat salivating at sound of can opener

7. _____ wildebeests cover thousands of mile every year in October

8. _____ chimpanzees aggressively defend their territory from rival groups

9. _____ a crow using car traffic to crack open hard nut shells

Section Review 5:   Adaptations and Behavior

A. Define the following terms.

ethology	hibernation	adaptations	estivation	innate behavior
diurnal	courting behavior	nocturnal	learned behavior	trophism
migrate	nastic movements	geotropism	phototropism	behavior
territoriality	circadian rhythms	thigmotropism	photoperiodism	photosynthetic
			migrate	dormancy

B. Choose the best answer.

1. Which of the following is true about the connection between parental care and learning?

    A. more parental care, more learned behaviors

    B. more parental care, fewer learned behaviors

    C. less parental care, more learned behaviors

    D. less parental care, all behavior is learned

2. A cat might raise the hair on its back to

    A. appear gentle.

    B. appear intimidating.

    C. attract a mate.

    D. conserve heat.

3. Milkweed, tobacco and peyote have adapted which type of measures to protect themselves?

    A. behavioral   B. physical   C. chemical   D. territorial

4. Why is it beneficial for some insects to be able to blend in with their surroundings?

    A. It protects them from predators.

    B. It allows them to regulate body temperature.

    C. It helps them find a mate.

    D. It protects their territory.

C. Complete the following exercises.

1. Name two adaptations plants have developed to disperse their seeds.

2. What are some reasons that animals emit sounds?

CHAPTER 9 REVIEW

1. What is the time required for half of a parent isotope to decay into a daughter product known as?
   - A. half-life
   - B. measurable rate
   - C. parent-to-daughter reduction
   - D. isotopic enumeration

2. How do radioactive elements change into other elements?
   - A. by molecular collision
   - B. by decay
   - C. by combustion
   - D. by reduction

3. Which statement below is believed to be true concerning radioactive decay?
   - A. It occurs at a predictable rate.
   - B. It speeds up when temperature rises.
   - C. It slows when pressure is added.
   - D. It occurs only in the sun.

4. Identify the evidence for evolution below.
   - A. cave drawings, ancient stories and ceremonial rites.
   - B. homologous structures, DNA and embryonic evidence.
   - C. eukaryotes, symbiosis and competition.
   - D. nephrons, antibodies and homeostasis.

5. Natural selection states that individuals
   - A. with adaptive traits are more likely to survive.
   - B. on the bottom level of the hierarchy have the greatest reproductive success.
   - C. demonstrating altruistic behavior are the ones with the most mutations.
   - D. remain unchanged over a period of time.

6. A mountain, ocean or ravine divides a population. After many years, the organisms show genetic differences from the original population. Which of the following explains how this change occurred?
   - A. divergent evolution
   - B. convergent evolution
   - C. co-evolution
   - D. immigration

7. Humans have an appendix, a thin tube connected to the large intestine that serves no purpose and is a threat to human health and life if it becomes infected and/or inflamed. It is believed that the appendix once had a function as part of the human digestive system. The human appendix, therefore, is

    A. a homologous structure.   C. a vital organ.

    B. a vestigial organ.   D. a mutation.

8. Biochemical similarities exist among organisms and indicate relationships. How are these biochemical characteristics studied?

    A. observations of plant and animal behavior

    B. fossil records

    C. observations of various cells under a microscope

    D. DNA sequences

9. Brown bears and polar bears are examples of

    A. co-evolution.   C. divergent evolution.

    B. convergent evolution.   D. emigration.

10. When certain insects and plants evolve in tandem, it is considered which type of evolution?

    A. co-evolution   C. divergent

    B. convergent   D. natural selection

11. Sharks and porpoises are a classic example of which concept?

    A. co-evolution   C. divergent evolution

    B. convergent evolution   D. parallel evolution

12. Increased use of antibiotics has killed off bacterial populations that were most susceptible to antibiotic treatment. Consequently, many strains of bacteria are resistant to prescription drugs. What is the mechanism by which these resistant bacteria have been allowed to thrive?

    A. natural selection   C. speciation

    B. mutation   D. germination

13. Which statement below is true concerning mixing of gene pools?

    A. It promotes diversity.   C. It reduces the number of organisms.

    B. It increases the number of organisms.   D. It reduces diversity.

Chapter 10
Interactions in the Environment

GEORGIA PERFORMANCE SCIENCE STANDARDS COVERED IN THIS CHAPTER INCLUDE:

SB4 a – c	Students will assess the dependence of all organisms on one another and the flow of energy and matter within their ecosystems.

ORGANIZATION OF ECOSYSTEMS

ECOSYSTEM

An **ecosystem** is the interdependence of plant and animal communities and the physical environment in which they live. The **biosphere** is the zone around the Earth that contains self-sustaining systems composed of biotic and abiotic factors. **Biotic** factors include all living things, such as birds, insects, trees and flowers. **Abiotic** factors are those components of the ecosystem that are not living, but are integral in determining the number and types of organisms that are present. Examples of abiotic factors include soil, water, temperature and amount of light. In order for an ecosystem to succeed, its biotic factors must obtain and store energy. In addition, the biotic and abiotic factors of the ecosystem must recycle water, oxygen, carbon and nitrogen.

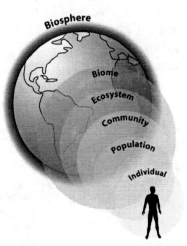

Figure 10.1 Organization of Life

COMMUNITY

A **community** is a collection of the different biotic factors in a particular ecosystem. Communities include many different species of plants and animals that live in close proximity to one another. For example, in a marine ecosystem a coral reef supports a large community of plants and animals. In this example the community of fishes, shrimps, mammals, algae, sharks, corals, urchins, sea stars and clams all live together and interact with one another. A community might have very different types of plants and animals living in one area. The members of a community interrelate with each other. Deer grazing in a clearing in the forest may be alert to the activity or movement of birds that warn them

Figure 10.2 A Forest Community

of approaching danger. In turn, the birds may depend on the deer grazing in a clearing to disturb insects hiding in the grass, thus causing them to become visible.

Each member of a community has its own **habitat**. A habitat is the dwelling place where an organism seeks food and shelter. A woodpecker lives in a hole in a tree. It eats the insects that live in the bark of the tree. A robin builds its nest and raises its young in the same tree. A mouse lives in a burrow at the base of the tree. An owl sleeps on a branch of the same tree. The tree supports a whole community of organisms and becomes their habitat. The habitat provides food and shelter for the members of the community. In turn, each species of the tree community has its own **niche**. A niche is the role that an organism plays in its community, such as what it eats and where it lives.

POPULATION

A community of living things is composed of populations. **Populations** are made up of the individual species in a community. For example, in a forest community ecosystem, there are populations of various plant and animal species such as deer, squirrels, birds, insects and trees.

Figure 10.3 A Population of Deer

SPECIES

A species is a group of similar organisms that can breed with one another to produce fertile offspring. Organisms of the same species share similar characteristics common to all organisms within the population. For example, all domestic cats can breed to produce kittens. All domestic cats have whiskers, retractable claws, canine teeth, eat meat and can land on their feet.

Some natural variation exists within all members of a species. Not all cats have whiskers of the same length or bodies of the same size. However, all domestic cats can breed to produce offspring.

Two organisms are part of a different species when they cannot breed and produce fertile offspring. A horse and a donkey can breed, but they produce a mule, which is almost always infertile. Therefore, a horse and a donkey are different species.

Figure 10.4 Cat Species

	Activity	
	Read the following text and determine which component of ecosystems each description illustrates. The first one is done for you.	
1	In a freshwater ecosystem, plants like bald Cyprus, pitcher plants and water lily can be found. Animals like black bear, river otter, crane and white-tailed deer can also be found.	Community
2	A large school of Atlantic cod	
3	A polar bear resides in the area of the Arctic that is frozen by annual ice packs.	
4	The grey bat is an endangered bat found in Georgia.	
5	The spotted Hyena (*Crocuta crocuta*) is a wild animal living in South African savanna. This animal sometimes scavenges kills from other large carnivores. The hyena lives in a clan with other hyenas and has been known to hunt and kill large herbivores like wildebeest, zebra, Thomson's gazelle, Grant's gazelle, topi and buffalo.	
6	In a terrestrial ecosystem, plants like saguaro, cardon, ironwood and ocotillo abound. Animals like coyotes, mountain lions, rodents, lizards, iguanas, Gila monsters and owls can be found living together.	
7	A large geographic area that contains many self-sustaining systems.	
8	In a forest ecosystem, squirrels live an arboreal lifestyle and eat plant matter, insects, eggs and fungi. In the fall it buries stores of tree seeds and nuts in the ground, helping to propagate many tree species.	
9	Annually millions of wildebeests migrate 500 to 1,000 miles.	
10	The three toed sloth is a mammal that is usually found in the middle or upper layer of the rainforest canopy.	

Section Review 1: Organization of Ecosystems

A. **Define the following terms.**

ecosystem	abiotic	niche
biosphere	community	population
biotic	habitat	

B. **Choose the best answer.**

1. The area in which certain types of plants or animals can be found living in close proximity to each other is called a

    A. habitat.   B. community.   C. niche.   D. kingdom.

2. A British ecologist stated the importance of realizing an organism's role in the ecosystem as follows: "When an ecologist sees a badger, they should include in their thoughts some definitive idea of the animal's place in the community to which it belongs." What does this statement describe?

    A. an animal's habitat   C. an animal's community

    B. an animal's niche   D. an animal's ecosystem

3. The giant noctule bat (*Nyctalus lasiopterus*) preys mainly upon insects during the summer months, and on migrating songbirds during the autumn and spring. The bat attacks the birds at night from several hundred meters in the air. During the day, the bat roosts in trees. What do these sentences describe?

    A. community   B. habitat   C. biome   D. niche

4. Nitrogen, oxygen and carbon dioxide are among the MOST biologically important atmospheric gases. What are these called?

    A. abiotic factors   C. biospheric factors

    B. biotic factors   D. habitat factors

5. A hinny is the offspring of a male horse and a female donkey. Like mules, hinnies are ALMOST ALWAYS sterile (unable to breed). This confirms that

    A. a mule and a donkey are different species.

    B. a mule and a hinny are different species.

    C. a horse and a donkey are different species.

    D. a horse and a hinny are different species.

C. **Complete the following exercise.**

1. Name four abiotic conditions that might determine the kind of ecosystem in an area.

Earth's Major Ecological Systems

How Climate Relates to Biome

Plants comprise the ecological foundation for most ecosystems. Plants are the main pathway by which energy enters the ecosystems. Because plants are generally stationary organisms, they cannot respond to rapidly changing environmental conditions. If the amount of rainfall or sunlight received in an area changed suddenly and permanently, most plant species would become extinct. The general climate found in an area determines the plant species that will grow under those conditions. A hot, humid and rainy climate will be favorable to jungle-like plants. The plant types found in an area will determine the animal species that live there. There are six major terrestrial ecological systems and three major aquatic ecological systems.

Terrestrial Ecosystems

Large land areas characterized by a dominant form of plant life and climate type that make up large ecosystems are called **biomes**. Organisms living in biomes have adapted to the climate of the geographic region. Distinct boundaries between biomes are not apparent; instead, one area gradually merges into the next. The six major biomes are shown in Figure 10.5.

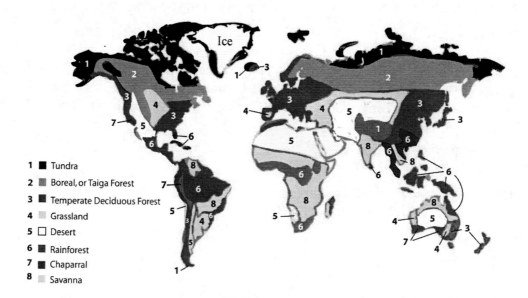

1 ■ Tundra
2 ▨ Boreal, or Taiga Forest
3 ■ Temperate Deciduous Forest
4 ▨ Grassland
5 ☐ Desert
6 ■ Rainforest
7 ■ Chaparral
8 ▨ Savanna

Figure 10.5 Biomes of Earth

Figure 10.6 Tundra Biome

The **tundra** biome is located near the north and south poles. Rainfall is light and summer temperatures average only 1° C (34°F). The land in the tundra has gently rolling plains with subsoil that is permanently frozen. There are many lakes, ponds and bogs. Grasses are present, but only a very few small trees grow there. The small plants mostly consist of *mosses, lichens* and *reindeer moss*. Examples of animals found in tundra areas are *reindeer, caribou, polar bears, arctic wolves, foxes, hares, lemmings, birds* and *insects*.

The **coniferous forest** biomes are found above 60°N latitude. Rainfall is medium and the average summer temperature is around 12°C (54°F). In the coniferous forest, the subsoil thaws for a few weeks in summer. The land is dotted with lakes, ponds and bogs. The trees are mostly *coniferous*, such as *spruce, fir* and *pine*. There are only a few deciduous trees, which shed or lose their leaves at the end of the growing season. Examples of animals living in coniferous forest areas are *moose, black bears, wolves, lynx, wolverines, martens, porcupines* and *birds*.

Figure 10.7 Coniferous Forest Biome

The **deciduous forest** biomes are found in the middle latitudes between 20° and 60°N latitude. The deciduous forest has variations in rainfall, but in general, the rainfall is medium. The average summer temperature is around 24°C (75°F). The deciduous forest has trees that are broad-leaved with foliage that changes color in autumn. Trees such as *oak, maple, red bud, tulip popular* and *dogwood* can be found in this biome. The animals consist of *squirrels, deer, foxes* and *bears*. The state of Georgia falls into this biome.

Figure 10.8 Deciduous Forest Biome

Figure 10.9 The Grasslands

The **grasslands** are located in mid-continent areas of middle latitudes. They are found in regions that have warm and cold cycles as well as in the tropic regions on the savannas with wet and dry cycles. In general, the rainfall is low, and the average summer temperature is 20°C (68°F). As the name implies, the dominant form of plant life found in this biome is grass. Other types of fleshy stemmed herbs are also found in the grassland. Plants like *buffalo grass, sunflower, coneflowers, goldenrods,* and *clover* thrive in this biome. There are large herbivores on the savannas such as *bison, pronghorn antelope* and *zebras*, as well as smaller ones such as *burrowing rodents* and *prairie dogs*.

The **tropical rain forest** biomes are found near the equator and near mountain ranges. They have abundant rainfall and are very humid. The average summer temperature is 25°C (77°F). The trees are very tall with dense canopies. The floor of the tropical rain forest does not get much sunlight, but it does keep a fairly constant temperature. There is a great diversity of species of both the plants and animals. Many different types of plants like *vines*, *trees* and *orchids* live in the rainforest. Animals like *orangutans*, *insects*, *sloths* and *jaguars* live in the rainforest.

The **deserts** are found on either side of the equator between 0° and 20° latitudes. They get little rain and have extreme temperature fluctuations. The average summer temperature is 30°C (86°F). There is not much grass in the desert, but what is there is very drought resistant. Other plants, like *sage- brush*, *mesquite* and *cacti*, have also adapted to desert conditions. Animals common to the desert are the *kangaroo rat*, *snakes*, *lizards*, some *birds*, *spiders* and *insects*.

Figure 10.10 Desert

AQUATIC ECOSYSTEMS

Aquatic ecosystems depend on a number of different factors such as amount of light, oxygen and the **salinity** (salt) level of the water. The amount of salt in the water is the most important factor in determining the type of organisms in the ecosystem. Light and oxygen are important for photosynthesis. Temperature is less important in aquatic systems since water temperatures do not fluctuate a great deal. Aquatic ecosystems include **marine areas**, **freshwater areas** and **estuaries**, all of which are determined by the salinity of the area.

Freshwater ecosystems consist of streams, rivers, lakes, marshes and swamps. All have a low salinity level. Fresh water is important in recycling the earth's water supply through the water cycle. Freshwater ecosystems are found in areas with differing temperatures and support a wide variety of animal and plant life.

Figure 10.11 Georgia Freshwater Ecosystem

Marine ecosystems are divided into the intertidal, pelagic and benthic zones. All have a high salinity level.

The intertidal zone is the area of shore that can be seen between low and high tides. It is the most biologically active area in a marine ecosystem, with a high level of light and nutrients. Because of the high tides and shifting sand, this area is also under the most stress. Animals like sand crabs often move to find protection. Rocky shores provide good places for kelp and invertebrates to attach themselves, but these organisms also have to deal with changing water levels and extreme temperature variations.

Figure 10.12 Marine Ecosystem

The largest ocean area is the **pelagic** zone, which is further divided into two areas. The more shallow area is closer to shore and has a maximum depth of 200 meters (600 feet). There is good light for photosynthetic organisms in this relatively shallow area. Many types of fish like *tuna, herring, sardines, sharks* and *rays* live in this area along with *whales* and *porpoises*. The deeper part of the pelagic zone comprises most of the oceans in the world. This area is deeper than 200 meters. It receives little light, has cold water temperatures and high pressure. Many different organisms are adapted to the various characteristics of the ocean depths. Some fish have no eyes or have developed luminescent organs. *Lantern fish, eels* and *grenadier fish* live in this area.

Shore-dwelling organisms like *seals, walrus* and *penguins* often split their time between the intertidal and pelagic areas.

The **benthic** zone is the ocean floor. Animals like *worms, clams, hagfish* and *crabs* can be found in deep benthic areas, in addition to bacteria. In deep benthic areas, hydrothermal vents can form the basis of a complex food web supporting a variety of animals. Coral reefs are commonly found in warm, shallow benthic areas. The reefs prevent erosion and provide habitats for many organisms like *sea stars, plankton, sponges* and a variety of fish.

Figure 10.13 An Estuary

An **estuary** is where fresh and saltwater meet in a coastal area. The salinity level in an estuary fluctuates, but is generally not as high as in the ocean ecosystems. The water is partly surrounded by land with access to open ocean and rivers. Estuaries contain salt marshes and swampy areas and are among the most biologically diverse locations on earth. The diversity is attributed to the large amount of nutrients, the tides that circulate the nutrients and remove waste and the abundance of different types of plants.

Activity

Get into groups of 2 or 3 students. Select a biome from one of the nine described in this chapter. Create a travel flyer or pamphlet about your biome. Use the Internet or other reference books to include at least 10 facts about your biome.

Activity

Examine the pictures below and determine the native biome of the organism.

1.

4.

7.

8.

5.

2.

9.

6.

3.

10.

Section Review 2:   Earth's Major Ecological Systems

A. Define the following terms.

biome	grasslands	freshwater ecosystem	pelagic zone
tundra	tropical rain forest	estuary	benthic zone
coniferous forest	desert	marine ecosystems	
deciduous forest	salinity	intertidal zone	

B. Choose the best answer.

1. Tundra biomes generally occur near which latitudes?

    A. equatorial

    B. polar

    C. middle

    D. mid-continent

2. What biome is predominantly represented on the east coast of the U.S?

    A. grassland biome

    B. desert biome

    C. coniferous forest biome

    D. deciduous forest biome

3. Which of the following is a correct statement about tropical rain forests?

    A. They have little to no rainfall.

    B. They have a diversity of species.

    C. They fluctuate greatly in yearly temperatures.

    D. They are found between the 0° and 20° latitudes.

4. What is the most biologically active area in a marine ecosystem?

    A. benthic zone   B. intertidal zone   C. pelagic zone   D. estuarial zone

5. Andrea travels to the rain forests of the Amazon River Basin. When she returns to Tennessee, she brings back an orchid native to Brazil. What will happen to the orchid?

    A. If kept warm, it could co-evolve with a hummingbird.

    B. If kept warm, it will survive and propagate a new species.

    C. It will likely die because the abiotic factors in Tennessee are so different than those present in the rainforest biome.

    D. It will likely die because of mutations brought on by the shift in biome.

C. Complete the following exercises.

1. Compare and contrast marine and freshwater biomes.

2. Why is climate important to biotic factors in a biome?

RELATIONSHIPS AMONG ORGANISMS

Each organism in an ecosystem interrelates with the other members. These relationships fall into one of three categories: symbiosis, competition or predation.

SYMBIOSIS

A **symbiotic relationship** is a long-term association between two members of a community in which one or both parties benefit. There are three types of symbiotic relationships: commensalism, mutualism and parasitism.

- **Commensalism** is a symbiotic relationship in which one member benefits, and the other is unaffected. Hermit crabs that live in snail shells are one example of this type of relationship. Some argue that one member in most commensalistic relationships is harmed in some way by the relationship. For example, orchids are a type of epiphytic plant that grows on top of the branches of rainforest trees. Having a *few* orchids in its branches does not harm the tree. However, the accumulation of many epiphytic plants could cause the tree to loose limbs, sunlight or nutrients. For this reason, true commensalistic relationships are rare in nature.

Figure 10.14
A Commensalistic Relationship

- **Mutualism** is a symbiotic relationship that is beneficial to both organisms. In South America, the tree *Acacia cornigera* and a species of ant (*Pseudomyrmex ferruginea*) are one example of mutualism. The acacia tree provides a home for the ants by growing specialized hollow thorns. The tree also provides food for the ants in the form of a protein-lipid and a carbohydrate-rich nectar from structures on the leaf stalk called nodules. The ants in turn, protect the tree from predators by biting or stinging them and other plant competitors by killing all plant life that comes into contact with the branches. There are many examples of mutualism in nature including: remoras and sharks and clown fish and sea anemones.

Figure 10.15 A Mutualistic Relationship

- **Parasitism** is a symbiotic relationship that benefits one organism (the parasite), but harms the other (the host). For example, heartworms in dogs (and humans) are parasites. The heartworm benefits by getting its nutrition from the bloodstream of its animal host. The host, however, is harmed because blood flow is restricted and nutrients are lost to the parasite.

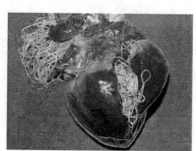

Figure 10.16 A Parasitic Relationship

COMPETITION

When two or more organisms seek the same resource that is in limited supply, they **compete** with each other. A **resource** could be food, water, light or space. Competition can be intraspecific or interspecific. **Intraspecies competition** occurs between members of the same species, whereas **interspecies competition** occurs between members of different species. Competition is one of the main driving forces behind natural selection.

PREDATION

Predators and prey help maintain an ecological balance within their ecosystem. This balance benefits the community as a whole, but can be helpful or harmful to the members that make up the community, depending upon whether they are the predator or the prey. A **predator** is an organism that feeds on other living things. The organism it feeds on is the **prey**. For instance, wild dogs will hunt down and kill zebra, separating out weak and sick animals from the herd. The predator/prey relationship is the way energy passes up the food chain of the ecosystem, and is the main driving force behind natural selection.

Figure 10.17 Predator-Prey Relationship Between a Wild Dog and Zebra

---

Activity

Collect pictures from magazines, newspapers, or the Internet of different plants and animals. Identify competitive, predator/prey, parasitic, mutualistic or commensalistic relationships. Group together the plants and animals according to their relationship to make a poster.

Section Review 3: Relationships among Organisms

A. Define the following terms.

symbiotic relationship	parasite	interspecific competition
commensalism	host	predation
mutualism	competition	predator
parasitism	intraspecific competition	prey

B. Choose the best answer.

1. The relationship between two members of a community in which one member harms another by its presence is

   A. parasitism.

   B. commensalism.

   C. mutualism.

   D. dependency.

2. A bee goes from flower to flower, gathering nectar. At each stop, the furry body and legs accumulate pollen from the flower, which the bee transfers as it moves. The flower needs pollen to reproduce and the bee needs nectar to eat. What kind of relationship is this?

   A. parasitism

   B. mutualism

   C. commensalism

   D. predation

3. Tapeworms are long, flat parasites that can live in the intestines of animals, including humans. The tapeworm feeds off the food that the host animal consumes, and the host animal loses nutrition as a result. What kind of relationship is this?

   A. parasitism

   B. mutualism

   C. commensalism

   D. predation

4. A mother cuckoo lays her egg in the nest of a warbler, then flies away. The warbler raises the baby cuckoo along with her own babies. The cuckoo baby grows quickly, becoming massive compared to the warbler babies. At some point, the baby cuckoo pushes the warbler babies out of the nest in order to make more room for itself. What does this scenario describe?

   A. parasitism

   B. predation

   C. intraspecies competition

   D. interspecies competition

5. Which of the following is NOT true regarding predation?

   A. Predation helps maintain an ecological balance.

   B. Predators keep the numbers of prey animals under control.

   C. Predators choose the sick and weak prey because they are easier to catch.

   D. Predators choose the sick and weak prey because they are trying to maintain ecological balance.

POPULATION DYNAMICS

A population is a group of organisms of the same species living in the same geographic area. Important characteristics of populations include the growth rate, density and distribution of a population. The study of these characteristics is called population dynamics.

GROWTH

The **growth rate** of a population is the change in population size per unit time. Growth rates are typically reported as the increase in the number of organisms per unit time per number of organisms present. The size of a population depends on the number of organisms entering and exiting it. Organisms can enter the population through birth or immigration. Organisms can leave the population by death or emigration. Immigration occurs when organisms move into a population. Emigration occurs when organisms move out of a population. If a population has more births than deaths and immigration and emigration rates are equal, then the population will grow. Ecologists observe the growth rate of a population over a number of hours, years or decades. It can be zero, positive or negative. Growth rate graphs often plot the number of individuals against time.

A population will grow exponentially if the birth and death rates are constant and the birth rate is greater than the death rate. **Exponential growth** occurs when the population growth starts out slowly and then increases rapidly as the number of reproducing individuals increase. Exponential growth is also sometimes called a **J-shaped curve**. In most cases, the population cannot continue to grow exponentially without reaching some environmental limit such as lack of nutrients, energy, living space and other resources. These environmental limits will cause the population size to stabilize, which we will discuss shortly.

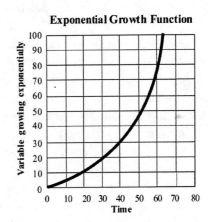

Figure 10.18 Population Growth vs. Time

J-shaped Curve

DENSITY AND DISTRIBUTION

The **density** of a population refers to the number of organisms per unit area. For example, there could be an average distribution of 100 maple trees per square kilometer in the eastern United States. However, population density does not reveal how organisms are distributed in space.

The **distribution** of a population refers to the pattern of where the organisms live. The areas in which populations are found can range in size from a few millimeters in the case of bacteria cells, to a few thousand kilometers in the case of African wildebeests. Organisms within the population can have random, clumped or even distribution within the ecosystem.

Several factors, including the location of resources and the social behavior of animals, affect the dispersion of a population. A **random distribution** is one in which there is no set pattern of individuals within the ecosystem. This pattern is rare in nature. A **clumped distribution** is one in which individuals are found in close-knit groups, usually located near a resource. Clumped distributions frequently form among highly social animals like baboons. This distribution pattern is common in nature. **Even**

distribution occurs when a set pattern or even spacing is seen between individuals. This distribution sometimes occurs with highly territorial animals. However, even distribution, like random distribution, is also rare in nature. Dispersion patterns can vary seasonally or throughout the life cycle.

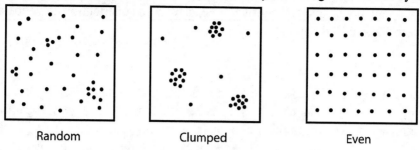

Random   Clumped   Even

Figure 10.19 Possible Population Distributions

CARRYING CAPACITY

As the population uses up available resources, the overall growth of the population will slow or stop. Population growth will slow or decrease when the birth rate decreases or the death rate increases. Eventually, the number of births will equal the number of deaths. The **carrying capacity** is the number of individuals the environment can support in a given area. A thriving population will fluctuate around the carrying capacity. When the population size exceeds the carrying capacity, the number of births will *decrease* and the number of deaths will *increase*, thus bringing the population back down to the carrying capacity. This type of growth curve is

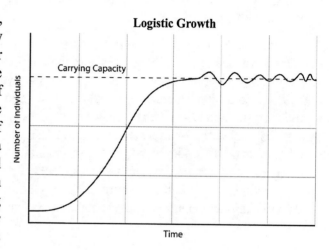

Figure 10.20 Carrying Capacity Curve

known as **logistic growth**. Logistic growth is sometimes called an **S-shaped curve** because it levels out at a certain point.

Figure 10.21 Frogs

For example, let's say a specific pond has a carrying capacity of 40 frogs. If more than 40 frogs are in the pond, then food and space become limited. Some frogs will need to move to another pond or members of the population will die. If fewer than 40 frogs are present in the pond, more frogs may move into the pond or more offspring will survive.

A decrease in environmental quality will decrease the carrying capacity of that environment. In the example above, if the pond becomes polluted, it will likely not be able to support 40 frogs. Its carrying capacity will be reduced to a population of less than 40.

An increase in the environmental quality will increase the environmental carrying capacity. For instance, if the pond is cleared of some or all of its pollution, it will again be able to support 40 or more frogs.

REGULATION OF POPULATION SIZE

Availability of resources is not the only factor that limits population growth. A **limiting factor** is anything in a population that restricts the population size. Remember that resources in an ecosystem are limited, and the availability of matter, space and energy is finite. There are two main categories of limiting factors: **density-dependent factors** and **density-independent factors**. Density-independent factors are limiting no matter the size of the population, and include unusual weather, natural disasters and seasonal cycles. Density-dependent factors are *phenomenon*, such as competition, disease and predation, which only become limiting when a population in a given area reaches a certain size. Density-dependent factors usually only affect large, dense populations.

SUCCESSION

Over time, an ecosystem goes through a series of changes known as **ecological succession**. Succession occurs when one community slowly replaces another as the environment changes. There are two types of succession: primary succession and secondary succession.

Primary succession occurs in areas that are barren of life because of a complete lack of soil. Examples are new volcanic islands and areas of lava flows such as those on the islands of Hawaii. Areas of rock left behind by retreating glaciers are another site for primary succession. In these areas, there is a natural reintroduction of progressively more complex organisms. Usually, lichens are the first organisms to begin to grow in the barren area. Lichens hold onto moisture and help to erode rock into soil components. The second group of organisms to move into an area, bacteria, protists, mosses and fungi, continue the erosion process. The chemical processes of these pioneer organisms, coupled with the decomposing matter

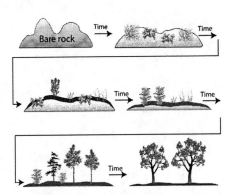

Figure 10.22 Primary Succession

created when they die, begins to create substantial amounts of soil. Once there is a sufficient number of organisms to support them, the insects and other arthropods inhabit the area. Grasses, herbs and weeds begin to grow once there is a sufficient amount of soil; eventually, trees and shrubs can be supported by the newly formed soil.

In habitats where the community of living things has been partially or completely destroyed, **secondary succession** occurs. In these areas, soil and seeds are already present. For example, at one time prairie grasslands were cleared and crops planted. When those farmlands were abandoned, they once again became inhabited by the native plants. Trees grew where there were once roads. Animals returned to the area and reclaimed their natural living spaces. Eventually, there was very little evidence that farms ever existed in those parts of the prairies.

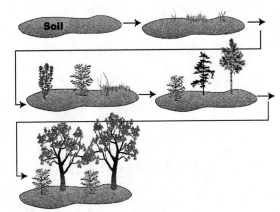

Figure 10.23 Secondary Succession

Section Review 4:   Population Dynamics

A. Define the following terms.

growth rate	carrying capacity	density-independent factor
immigration	logistic growth	ecological succession
emigration	limiting factor	primary succession
exponential growth	density-dependent factor	secondary succession

B. Choose the best answer.

1. A density-dependent factor

    A. limits a population in a given area regardless of size.

    B. limits the population when the population reaches a certain size.

    C. may include weather or a natural disaster.

    D. often affects small, sparse populations.

2. Orangutans are highly territorial primates. What is the MOST LIKELY population distribution pattern for them to maintain?

    A. clumped   B. communal   C. random   D. even

3. A population will tend to grow if

    A. it has a random population distribution.

    B. the number of births exceeds the number of deaths.

    C. the number of deaths exceeds the number of births.

    D. it is at carrying capacity.

4. An active volcano under the ocean erupts, and the build-up of cooled lava eventually forms a new island. What type of succession will immediately occur on the newly formed island?

    A. primary succession

    B. secondary succession

    C. both primary and secondary succession

    D. no succession

C. Answer the following questions.

1. How is the carrying capacity of a population determined?

2. Why do you think it is important for a population to have limiting factors?

ENERGY FLOW THROUGH THE ECOSYSTEM

Matter within an ecosystem is recycled over and over again. Earth has the same amount of abiotic matter today as it did one hundred years ago. Elements, chemical compounds and other sources of matter pass from one state to another through the ecosystem.

As a deer eats grass, the nutrients contained in the grass are broken down into their chemical components and then rearranged to become living deer tissues. Waste products are produced in the deer's digestive system and pass from the deer's body back into the ecosystem. Organisms break down this waste into simpler chemical components. The grass growing close by is able to take up those components and rearrange them back into grass tissues. Then, the energy cycle begins again.

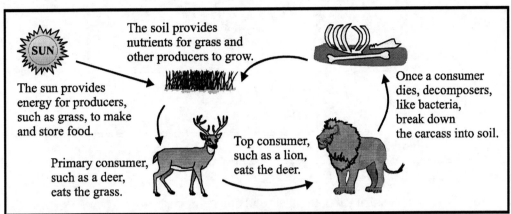

Figure 10.24 The Energy Cycle

Energy can be added, stored, transferred and lost throughout an ecosystem. **Energy flow** is the transfer of energy within an ecosystem. Inorganic nutrients are recycled through the ecosystem, but energy cannot be recycled. Ultimately, energy is lost as heat. Remember, however, that energy cannot be destroyed; although it may be lost from one system as heat, it is gained somewhere else. In this way, energy within any given system is conserved.

FOOD CHAINS AND FOOD WEBS

One way to graphically illustrate the transfer of energy within an ecosystem is a **food chain**. A food chain shows the connections between organisms, using arrows that point in the direction of biomass transfer. Another way to say this is that the arrows show who eats what (or whom)! Here we will look more closely at the interaction between producers, consumers and decomposers. From energy's point of view, we can say that energy generally transfers from producers to consumers to decomposers.

The **producers** of an ecosystem use abiotic (not living) factors to obtain and store energy for themselves or the consumers that eat them. In a forest ecosystem, the producers are trees, bushes, shrubs, small plants, grass and moss.

The **consumers** are members of the ecosystem that depend on other members for food. Each time a plant or animal consumes another organism, energy transfers to the consumer. Deer, foxes, rabbits, raccoons, owls, hawks, snakes, mice, spiders and insects are examples of consumers in a forest ecosystem. There are three types of consumers: **herbivores**, **carnivores** and **omnivores**. Table 10.1 lists characteristics of the three different types of consumers.

The **decomposers** are members of the ecosystem that live on dead or decaying organisms and reduce them to their simplest forms. They use the decomposition products as a source of energy. Decomposers include fungi and bacteria. They are also called **saprophytes**.

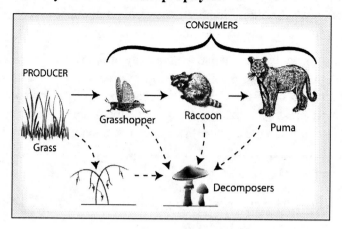

Figure 10.25 A Food Chain

Table 10.1 Types of Consumers

Consumer	Food Supply
Herbivore	animals that eat only plants
Omnivore	animals that eat both plants and other animals.
Carnivore	animals that eat only other animals.
Saprophytes	organisms that obtain food from dead organisms or from the waste products of living organisms

There can be many food chains in an ecosystem. Food webs are used to illustrate the interaction between food chains. Sometimes their paths cross directly, and sometimes they do not. A food web helps one understand that the presence of any one species nearly always affects others. Look at the food web in Figure 10.26. What impact would a disease in the rabbit population have on the other organisms in the community? A reduction in the rabbit population would affect both the snake and the owl since both of these animals are predators of the rabbit.

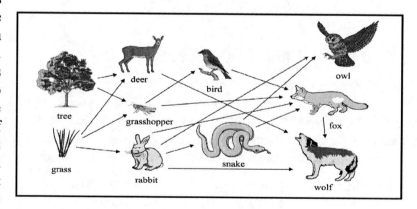

Figure 10.26 A Food Web

How about the grass? You can see by looking at the food web that the grass and trees (producers) feed everything to the right of them, either directly or indirectly. What if the grass were gone? Well, it has happened before. Decades of overproduction and inappropriate farming techniques stripped the fertile soil from the Great Plains in the early 1930s. This was an ecological disaster. Not only did the area become the Dust Bowl, there was also no food for primary consumers to eat. The consumers (both people and animals) were forced to move, leaving the barren wasteland behind.

Figure 10.27 The Dust Bowl

A **trophic level** is the position occupied by an organism in a food chain. Organisms that share a trophic level get their energy from the same source. Producers are found at the base of the energy pyramid and comprise the first trophic level of the food chain. Producers capture energy as sunlight and convert it into usable forms. Above them are the primary consumers that make up the second trophic level. Above the primary consumers are the secondary consumers that occupy the third trophic level. Finally, there are

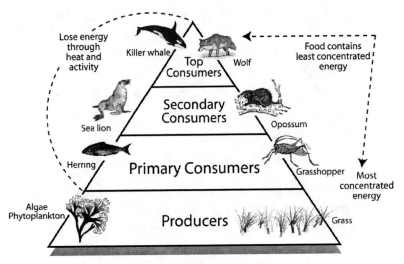

Figure 10.28 Energy Pyramid

the tertiary consumers at the top trophic level. The tertiary consumers are the so-called "top" of the food chain. They are generally omnivores, like humans, or carnivores, like wolves. Different ecosystems will have different tertiary consumers.

Activity

Make your own food chain. Use at least four organisms. Choose your own unique plants and animals. Now use your food chain to make a food web.

Section Review 5: Food Chains and Food Webs

A. Define the following terms.

food chain	decomposer	carnivore	trophic level	omnivore
producer	herbivore	food web	consumer	saprophytes

B. Choose the best answer.

1. Identify two organisms below that share the same trophic level.

    A. elephants and lions

    B. cheetahs and giraffes

    C. chipmunks and squirrels

    D. wolves and sparrows

2. The owl is a nocturnal hunter of small mammals, insects and other birds. An owl is an example of a/an

    A. producer.   B. omnivore.   C. carnivore.   D. decomposer.

3. Which food would an herbivore always avoid?

    A. worms   B. clover   C. pine nuts   D. grass

4. Emperor penguins feed mostly on crustaceans, such as krill. They are prey to orca whales and leopard seals. What ecological role does the Emperor penguin play? (HINT: Krill are zooplankton, tiny sea organisms that feed on plankton.)

    A. It is a producer.

    B. It is a primary consumer.

    C. It is a secondary consumer.

    D. It is a top consumer.

5. Which trophic level contains the LEAST amount of biomass?

    A. producer

    B. primary consumer

    C. secondary consumer

    D. top consumer

6. Snakes are ALWAYS carnivores. At what trophic level do snakes belong?

    A. producer

    B. primary consumer

    C. secondary consumer

    D. decomposer

C. Fill in the blanks.

1. Animals that eat both plants and other animals are called _____.

2. Organisms that obtain food from dead organisms or waste material are called _____.

THE NUTRIENT CYCLES

The process of recycling substances necessary for life is called a **nutrient cycle**. Nutrient cycles include the **carbon cycle**, the **nitrogen cycle**, the **phosphorous cycle** and the **water cycle**. When examining these cycles, it is important to remember that the elements are cycled in the real world. The nutrients shown in these images are not cycled as solo elements but rather, they often combine with other elements during their cycle. That is to say, when carbon, nitrogen and phosphorous cycle through the lithosphere, atmosphere or hydrosphere, they often carry other nutrients, like hydrogen or oxygen, along with them as ions that form salts. The images here show the cycles as stand alone nutrient cycles for your learning benefit.

CARBON CYCLE

The **carbon cycle** is the cycling of carbon between carbon dioxide (CO_2) and organic molecules. Organic molecules contain carbon – hydrogen bonds (C–H bonds). Inorganic carbon makes up 0.03% of the atmosphere as CO_2. Plants use CO_2 and energy from the Sun to perform photosynthesis. When animals eat plants, carbon passes into their tissues. Through food chains, carbon passes from one organism to another, as shown in Figure 10.29. It returns to Earth through respiration, excretion or decomposition after death. Some animals do not decompose after death; instead, their bodies become buried and compressed underground. Over long periods of time, fossil fuels such as coal, oil and natural gas develop from decomposing organic matter. When fossil fuels burn, carbon dioxide returns to the atmosphere.

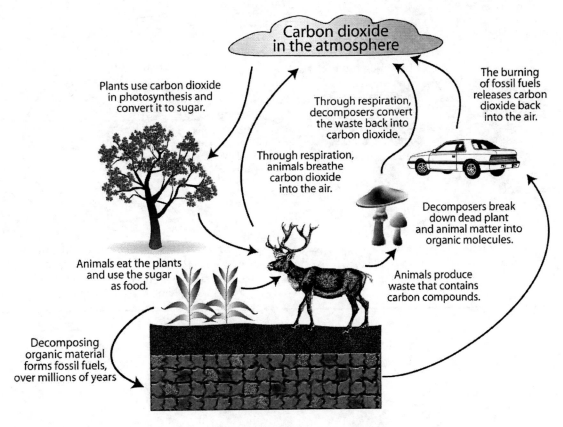

Figure 10.29 The Carbon Cycle

NITROGEN CYCLE

Nitrogen is the most abundant atmospheric gas, comprising 78% of the Earth's atmosphere. However, nitrogen gas is not in a form that is usable by most organisms. The **nitrogen cycle** transforms nitrogen into ammonia, nitrite and finally nitrate, so that it is usable by plants and animals. Refer to Figure 10.28 to see the nitrogen cycle.

Nitrogen fixation is the conversion of nitrogen gas into nitrate by several types of bacteria. Nitrogen fixation occurs in three major steps. First, nitrogen is converted into ammonia (NH_3) by bacteria called **nitrogen fixers**. Some plants can use ammonia directly, but most require nitrate. **Nitrifying bacteria** convert ammonia into nitrite (NO_2^-) and finally into nitrate (NO_3^-). The bacteria live on the roots of legumes (pea and bean plants). This process increases the amount of usable nitrogen in soil. The plants use the nitrogen, in the form of nitrate, to synthesize nucleic acids and proteins. The nitrogen then passes along through food chains. Decomposers release ammonia as they break down plant and animal remains, which may then undergo the conversion into nitrite and nitrate by nitrifying bacteria. Other types of bacteria convert nitrate and nitrite into nitrogen gas that then returns to the atmosphere. The nitrogen cycle keeps the level of usable nitrogen in the soil fairly constant. A small amount of nitrate cycles through the atmosphere; this is created when lightning converts atmospheric nitrogen into nitrate.

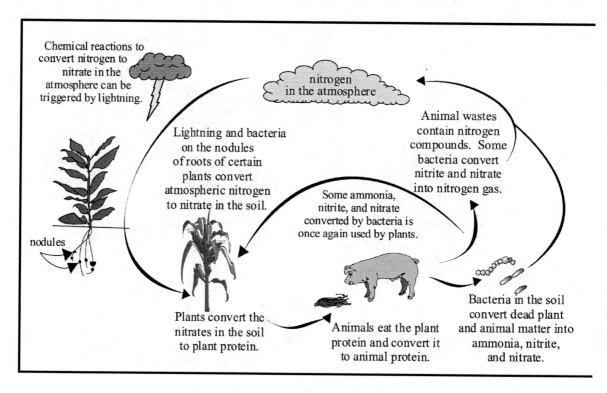

Figure 10.30 The Nitrogen Cycle

PHOSPHOROUS CYCLE

Phosphorous is an element that is essential to life. Unlike nitrogen and carbon, phosphorous is not found in the atmosphere. Phosphorous exists only as part of an organism, dissolved in water, or as an element in rock. Phosphorous, like nitrogen, is a water pollutant in excess quantities. The **phosphorous cycle** begins with the introduction of phosphates (PO_4^{3-}) into the soil from weathering, or breakdown, of sedimentary rocks. Plants then absorb phosphate ions from the soil, which introduces phosphorous into living ecosystems. Fungi can also directly absorb phosphates from the soil. All other organisms obtain phosphorous through the consumption of the fungi or plant producers. The phosphorous then passes to the consumers of the plants before returning to the soil as waste or decomposed material. Figure 10.31 diagrams the phosphorous cycle.

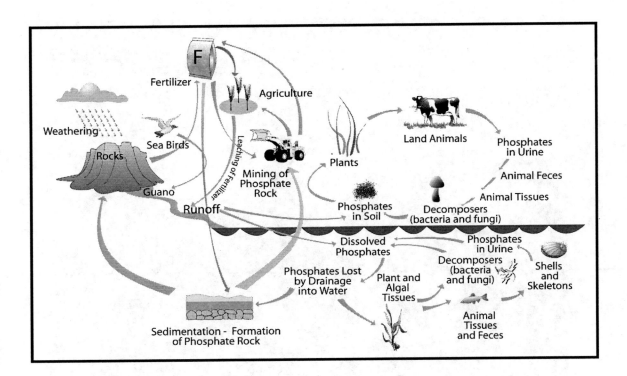

Figure 10.31 The Phosphorous Cycle

WATER CYCLE

The **water cycle** circulates fresh water between the atmosphere and the Earth as seen in Figure 10.30. Even though water covers the majority of Earth, about 95% of it is saltwater. Most of the freshwater is in the form of glaciers, leaving a very small amount of freshwater available for land organisms. Freshwater is vital for carrying out metabolic processes. The water cycle ensures that the supply of freshwater is replenished. Precipitation in the form of rain, ice, snow, hail or dew falls to the Earth and ends up in lakes, rivers and oceans through the precipitation itself or through runoff. The Sun provides energy in the form of heat, thus driving evaporation that sends water vapor into the atmosphere from bodies of water. Energy from the Sun also powers winds and ocean currents. Respiration from people and animals and transpiration from plants also sends water vapor to the atmosphere. The water vapor cools to form clouds. The clouds cool, become saturated and form precipitation. Without this cycle of precipitation, runoff and evaporation, a fresh water supply would not be available.

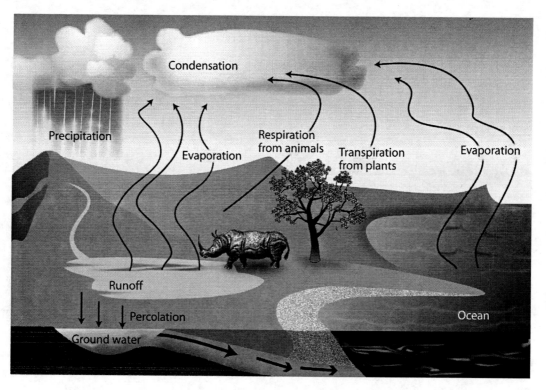

Figure 10.32 The Water Cycle

Section Review 6: The Nutrient Cycles

A. Define the following terms.

nutrient cycle   nitrogen cycle   nitrogen fixers   phosphorous cycle

carbon cycle   nitrogen fixation nitrifying bacteria water cycle

B. Choose the best answer.

1. Nitrogen-fixing bacteria perform which task?

 A. They convert nitrogen to ammonia.

 B. They convert nitrogen to animal protein.

 C. They convert ammonia to plant protein.

 D. They convert nitrogen to plant protein.

2. Metabolic processes depend on which factor listed below?

 A. carbon   B. nitrogen   C. fresh water   D. phosphorous

3. What is the main component of organic molecules?

 A. phosphorous   C. nitrogen

 B. carbon   D. carbon dioxide

4. How do plants use nitrogen?

 A. to make sugar   C. to make proteins and nucleic acids

 B. to attract pollinators   D. to transport water to their leaves

5. What is the process by which water is transferred to the atmosphere by plants and trees called?

 A. evaporation   B. respiration   C. condensation   D. transpiration

6. Which of the following compounds is an organic compound?

 A. CO_2 B. CH_4 C. NO_3^- D. H_2O

CHAPTER 10 REVIEW

Choose the best answer.

1. What are biotic factors?

   A. living factors

   B. lipids factors

   C. non-living factors

   D. always unicellular

2. What are abiotic factors?

   A. decomposers

   B. living factors

   C. non-living factors

   D. photosynthetic factors

3. What is a place where a member of a community lives and finds food called?

   A. pond   B. biome   C. habitat   D. residence

4. How will unusual weather affect populations?

   A. It will affect all populations regardless of size.

   B. It will only affect small populations of organisms.

   C. It will only affect large populations of organisms.

   D. It will have no affect on populations.

5. Which terrestrial ecological system has the greatest diversity of plants and animals?

   A. tundra

   B. grassland

   C. rain forest

   D. deciduous forest

6. What type of ecological system can include rivers, lakes, streams, marshes and swamps?

   A. freshwater   B. estuary   C. marine   D. ocean

7. Lions are carnivores and are considered a _____ in the energy cycle.

   A. primary consumer

   B. top consumer

   C. provider

   D. decomposer

8. Which of the following MOST LIKELY would be a part of the first community on a newly formed volcanic island?

   A. pine trees   B. oak trees   C. lichen   D. sea gulls

9. Many types of bacteria obtain their nutrition from dead plants and animals and, in turn, recycle elements such as carbon and nitrogen. These bacteria are considered which type of factor in an ecosystem?

    A. decomposers   B. producers   C. carnivores   D. viruses

10. During which process do producers use carbon dioxide?

    A. respiration   C. decomposition
    B. recycling   D. photosynthesis

11. Nitrogen makes up _____ of the atmosphere.

    A. 25%   B. 33%   C. 78%   D. 92%

12. During the first part of the nitrogen cycle, a plant converts the nitrogen in the soil to what other compound?

    A. plant protein   B. ammonia   C. fertilizer   D. nitrites

13. Red foxes are nocturnal and live in meadows and forest edges. They are predators to small mammals, amphibians and insects. The scraps that red foxes leave behind provide food for scavengers and decomposers. The preceding sentences describe the red fox's

    A. community.   B. prey.   C. niche.   D. food web.

14. Man-of-war fish cluster around the venomous tentacles of jellyfish to escape larger predators. The presence of the man-of-war fish does not harm or benefit the jellyfish. What is this type of relationship called?

    A. parasitism   C. succession
    B. commensalism   D. mutualism

15. In nature, why might organisms have the distribution shown to the right?

    A. They are greedy and like to compete for space.

    B. They want to be located near a resource.

    C. An organism secretes a hormone that causes individuals close by to move away.

    D. They want to learn to live in close knit communal groups.

For Questions 16 – 19 examine the diagram below.

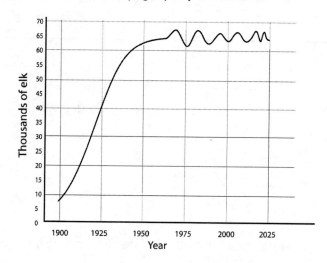

Carrying Capacity of Elk in Alaska

16. This graph shows _____ growth for the population.
   A. exponential   C. logistic
   B. linear   D. M-shaped

17. What is the carrying capacity for elk in this environment?
   A. 65   C. 75,000
   B. 6,500   D. 65,000

18. If a large oil company enters this environment and begins drilling for oil, building structures and polluting the land, what will probably happen to the carrying capacity of the elk?
   A. It will be more than 65,000.
   B. It will be less than 65,000.
   C. Nothing; it will remain the same.
   D. The elk will all leave and move into a new environment.

19. The United States government established this ecosystem as a native tribal reserve. Hunting is not permitted on native lands by anyone other than the native peoples. Based on the graph above, at what time was this ecosystem likely to have become a protected land?
   A. 1962   B. 1950   C. 1925   D. 1890

20. A symbiotic relationship means
   A. the energy cycle is not involved.   C. the solar system is involved.
   B. no one benefits.   D. one or both parties benefit.

Chapter 11
Humans and the Environment

GEORGIA PERFORMANCE SCIENCE STANDARDS COVERED IN THIS CHAPTER INCLUDE:

SB4 d	Students will assess the dependence of all organisms on one another and the flow of energy and matter within their ecosystems.
SB5 e	Students will evaluate the role of natural selection in the development of the theory of evolution.

HUMANS AND THE ENVIRONMENT

Humans are perhaps, the single most influential force affecting planet Earth today. Humans have the ability to change climate patterns, cause droughts and extinctions and alter the flow of energy through ecosystems. The global human population is growing exponentially, and shows no signs of slowing. Humans, along with a select few other animals, have the ability to modify their environment to suit their own needs. Humans modify and change the environment in many different ways. Four areas where human environmental impact is often studied are global warming, population growth, pesticide use and water and power consumption.

Humans often impact the environment in negative ways. Humans have the ability to arrest environmental degradation or cause further harm. We must work hard to stop environmental threats, after all we only have *one* planet Earth!

GLOBAL WARMING

No doubt global warming, or global climate change, is something you've heard before. From print news to television media, global warming is something many people talk about today. What most people neglect to mention is that global warming is part of a natural Earth warming process. This process is called the greenhouse effect.

The **greenhouse effect** traps solar heat within the Earth's atmosphere. Electromagnetic radiant energy provided by the Sun travels to the Earth through space. Some of this energy is trapped by bodies of water and land masses and some of this energy is reflected back into the atmosphere. Some reflected heat is lost back into space but most is trapped by atmospheric gases. Gases like water vapor, carbon dioxide, methane and chlorofluorocarbons tend to trap more heat than other types of gases. Without this heat trapping processes, the average global temperature would be around -20°C. However, like many other natural cycles, humans have altered this natural warming cycle as well.

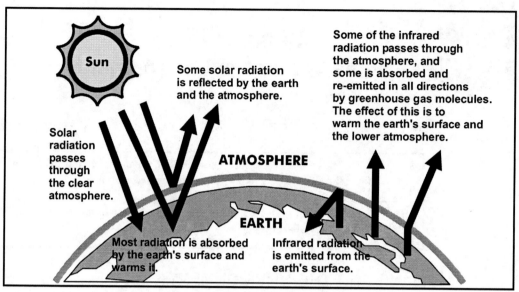

Figure 11.1 The Greenhouse Effect

Global warming is a term that describes the measured rise in the Earth's atmospheric and oceanic temperatures. The temperature rise is generally attributed to the increase in greenhouse gases in the atmosphere. This is one of the many ways that human activity is changing our planet. The degree of human impact on climate and the best way to fix the problem are still hotly debated topics. You as an active, inquiring member of the global community must examine the facts and decide where you stand. Figure 11.2 and 11.3 are just the "tip of the iceberg."

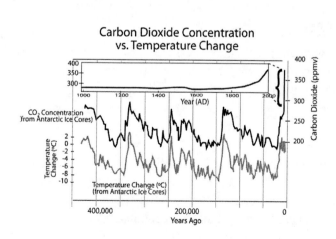

Figure 11.2 CO₂ Global Temp

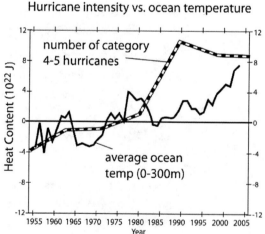

Figure 11.3 Ocean Temp and Hurricane Frequency

Figure 11.4 Arctic Ice Minimum 1979

Figure 11.5 Arctic Ice Minimum 2005

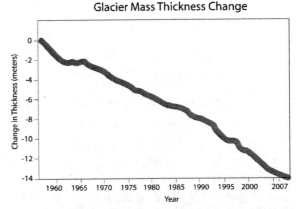

Glacier Mass Thickness Change

Figure 11.6 Average Global Glacier Mass Thickness

Figure 11.8 Grinnell Glacier 2005

Figure 11.7 Grinnell Glacier 1938

Other facts associated with global warming include increased incidence of regular tidal flooding in areas like Tuvalu (a tiny Polynesian island nation), average global temperature increase of 1°C and average polar temperature increase of 5°C.

Recall that inferring and concluding are two important aspects in scientific inquiry. The information displayed above can be interpreted in several different ways by several different people. The observations listed above are plugged into advanced weather forecasting computer models. As more data is collected, the computer models become more accurate at forecasting future events. Based on the observations and computer models many scientific minds the world over agree that human caused climate change is a real threat to the Earth. The release of CO_2, pollution and other harmful chemicals into the atmosphere is increasing the overall Earth's temperature and melting the polar ice sheets faster than ever thought possible. One reason for the accelerated melting is the fact that water absorbs more heat than ice, and as a result causes more ice to melt, in an ever accelerating process. Scientists expect to see increased temperatures, frequent intense storms and rising sea levels to impact human populations in the near future. The changes caused by global warming are predicted to cause the next global ice age.

It is theorized that as polar ice melts, ocean currents will slow causing a dramatic drop in global temperatures, thus beginning the next ice age. After examining the facts above and reading this section, what can you infer about global warming? The Earth will survive the next ice age, will we?

HUMAN POPULATION GROWTH

In the past decade, the human population reached 6 billion. The positive growth rate has continued unabated since the Industrial Revolution in the early 1900s. In fact, the human population is experiencing an explosive exponential growth curve. Advances in agriculture, medicine and sanitation have allowed the human population to grow so quickly. Along with this explosive growth comes increased pressure on the environment. Humans use lots of space for housing and food production. Examine Figure 11.9 showing the human population for the past 10,000 years. At some point in the future, the carrying capacity for the planet will be reached and humans will experience a net global negative population growth of zero.

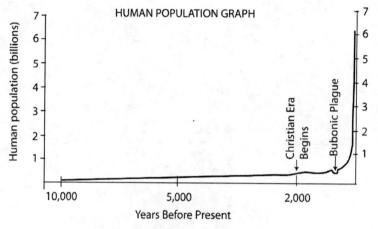

Figure 11.9 Human Population Graph

Because many world governments are concerned about population growth, they aggressively encourage population control methods, both voluntary (Western nations) and forced (China's One Child policy) among their people. However, this promotion has led to a new, emerging problem, particularly in Europe at this point: underpopulation, especially of the youth. As a result of falling birthrates, an aging and retiring workforce has fewer youth and working age populations to support the elderly in the population. European governments are finding it increasingly difficult to support the masses of elderly given the current workforce available.

The UN currently projects the population to grow to 9.1 billion by 2050, but also shows the growth in population as slowing. Both government promotion of population control and voluntary changes on an individual basis have changed the level of the growth, for better or worse. At some point in the future, the carrying capacity for planet Earth will be reached and the human population will have a growth rate of zero.

Activity

Divide the class in half and debate the validity of the global warming issue or government sponsored population controls (like China's 1 child policy).

Section Review 1: Humans in the Environment

A. Define the following terms.

greenhouse effect   global warming

B. Choose the best answer.

1. What factor listed below has NOT contributed to the explosive human growth seen in the last 100 years?

    A. advancements in medicine

    B. improved sanitation

    C. more available jobs

    D. global warming

2. Which factor listed below is NOT considered scientific evidence for global warming?

    A. data from retreating glaciers

    B. average increase in global temperatures

    C. increase in storm intensities

    D. increased rate of extinctions

3. How many people currently live on planet Earth?

    A. 1 million

    B. 1 billion

    C. 6 billion

    D. 100 billion

4. What is the carrying capacity for humans on planet Earth?

    A. 1 million

    B. 6 billion

    C. 100 billion

    D. unknown

5. How are human populations NOT likely to be impacted by global warming?

    A. frequent intense storms   C. rising sea levels

    B. rising power costs   D. increased temperatures

PESTICIDE USE

Figure 11.10 Crop Dusting Plane

Humans use pesticides for many reasons. A **pesticide** is a chemical agent used to kill damaging or harmful organisms, usually animals. Examples of organisms controlled using pesticides include termites, fire ants, grasshoppers, snails, beetles, snakes and even other mammals. Pesticides are used on a commercial scale in agriculture. Many homeowners also use pesticides to keep animals out of their homes and off their lawns.

When a pesticide is applied to an area, a certain percentage (usually 95 – 99%) of the target organism is killed, along with other non-target organisms. Only a small fraction of the original population is left intact. However, this small surviving fraction of the population passes along its immunity to future generations. Let's say, for example, a tomato farmer has a problem with snails. He estimates his field has a population of about 1,000,000 snails. He applies metaldehyde, a type of mollusk pesticide, to his field. This chemical is 97.1% effective, and kills 971,000 of the snails on his field. The remaining 29,000 snails have a resistance to the pesticide. These snails reproduce, passing along their resistance to the next generation. Over time, more potent chemicals, and more volumes of chemicals, are necessary to control the same percentage of organisms. Examine Figure 11.11, showing five hypothetical years on the tomato farm.

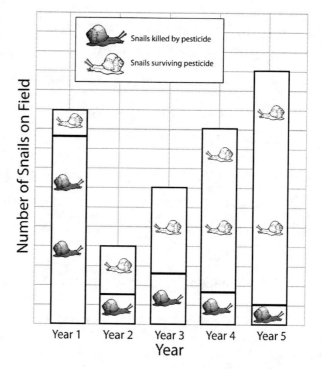

Figure 11.11 Snails in the Tomato Garden

A pesticide is a poison and after it is applied to a farmer's field it often washes into watersheds. Sometimes pesticides persist in the soil for decades after application. Toxic levels of chemicals are found in virtually every watershed in the United States. These chemicals are dangerous to amphibians (natural insect controllers), birds, fish, reptiles and humans. Sometimes the mixing of non-harmful chemicals leads to other deadly chemical cocktails. Pesticide residue is often found on foods and even penetrates the skins of many fruits and vegetables. Some people suffer from chemical toxicity disorders where they have increased sensitivity to *any* chemical agent in the environment. Pesticides have been linked to many cancers, endocrine system disorders, infertility, personality disorders, skin conditions, memory disorders and birth defects.

HUMAN CONSUMPTION

Figure 11.12 Water Consumption

As human technology has advanced, so too has our ability to modify our environment to suit our needs. Humans need **natural resources** such as water, soil and air for survival. Humans dam rivers to prevent flooding and provide a consistent, reliable source of fresh water. Dams create lakes and increase the rate at which water evaporates, thereby speeding up the water cycle. Careless water consumption like running the water while you brush your teeth or having leaky pipes further increases the rate at which this precious natural resource is used.

Along with the need for natural resources humans also have a need for power, and lots of it. Humans use power to heat and cool homes, store and prepare foods and run electronic equipment. Humans can obtain power from natural resources like fossil fuels, water, sunlight and wind. The growing human population places increased demands on ecosystems to produce energy at ever increasing rates. In reality, humans are using up many natural resources much faster than they are recycled by ecosystems. Fossil fuels, a nonrenewable energy source, produce over 60% of the electrical power used in the United States.

Figure 11.13 Power Production

Careless power consumption, like leaving lights or television sets turned on when not in use, reduces the amount of energy available in the future and increases the amount of carbon released into the atmosphere (accelerating global warming trends). Non-renewable resources are finite and are in limited supply on Earth. Once used, fossil fuels cannot be replaced in a human lifetime, or even in several human lifetimes.

Activity

Think of activities that consume power and water in your home. Come up with ways to reduce your consumption of these resources, and begin using one or two each week. Record your experiences while attempting to implement your plan. After a month write a paper or put on a play about your most meaningful moment during the "consumption reduction month."

Activity

Make a concept map about how human activities impact the environment.

Section Review 2:   Pesticide Use and Human Consumption

A. Define the following terms.

pesticide   natural resource

B. Choose the best answer.

1. Why do humans need more potent pesticides over time?

    A. because the target population soon develops a resistance to the chemical

    B. because pesticide salesman need to make more money

    C. because plants begin to eat the pesticides

    D. because the explosive growth of the human population places increased demands on current farmers

2. Where are pesticides found in the environment?

    A. in the soil only

    B. in the water only

    C. in the air only

    D. everywhere

3. Which of the following activities requires the most commercially produced power?

    A. heating a new home

    B. heating an old home

    C. heating a car

    D. building a fire

4. Which of the following is an environmentally responsible water consumption technique?

    A. washing your favorite outfit by itself in the washing machine

    B. watering your garden between 10pm and 10am

    C. leaving the hose running the entire time you wash your car

    D. taking 2 showers/baths a day

5. How much power in the US is produced by fossil fuels?

    A. under 40%   C. over 60%

    B. about 50%   D. 100%

ALTERATIONS TO THE ENVIRONMENT

ALTERATION OF NUTRIENT CYCLES

Recall that elements and nutrients cycle through the biotechnological pathways in natural processes. Humans impact many of these processes in harmful ways.

THE CARBON CYCLE

The activities of humans have greatly impacted the carbon cycle. The carbon cycle examined earlier in the chapter was somewhat incomplete. There is another component to the cycle not discussed earlier. The long-term carbon cycle relies on processes of the Earth that take hundreds, thousands or even millions of years to complete. Humans alter this cycle by digging up stored carbon, in the form of oil and coal, from the Earth and then burning it. This releases the carbon into the atmosphere millions of years before it would have happened naturally. Scientists speculate that if humans stopped burning and drilling all carbon, the cycle would stabilize in about 300 years.

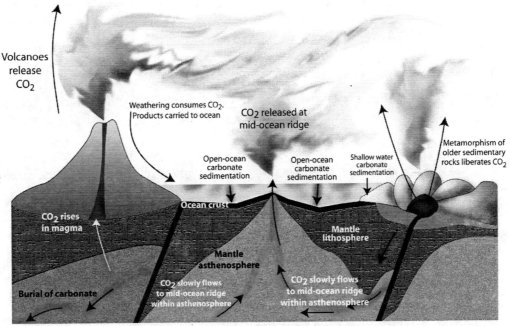

Figure 11.14 The Long-Term Carbon Cycle

THE NITROGEN CYCLE

Human activities have also impacted the nitrogen cycle. Humans have doubled the rate of land-based nitrogen released into the environment through the use of fertilizers and pesticides. This has affected natural systems in many ways. Nitrogen is the key to controlling plant diversity and productivity. Large amounts of nitrogen can become a pollutant in land and water systems. Nitrogen can acidify watersheds and coastal waters, as well as cause soil to lose nutrients like calcium and potassium. This can create a loss of biodiversity and cause declines in coastal fisheries. Increased nitrogen has also been linked to increased concentrations of nitrous oxide, which is an air pollutant. Humans can reduce the amount of nitrogen entering the ecosystem through sustainable agriculture.

PHOSPHOROUS CYCLE

Humans have also altered the phosphorous cycle. Mining of phosphorous from sedimentary rock accelerates the phosphorous cycle. Humans mine phosphorous to produce fertilizers and detergents. Excess phosphorous is added to aquatic ecosystems by runoff, improper disposal of animal wastes and discharge from municipal sewage.

THE WATER CYCLE

Humans, like most other living things, need a constant supply of water to survive. As a result, most humans live near water or bring water to where they live. Humans dam rivers to create lakes. This increases the rate at which water evaporates, thereby speeding up the water cycle. This increases rainfall amounts which, in turn, increases weathering and soil erosion.

Section Review 3: Alteration of the Nutrient Cycles

A. Describe the activity that most alters each of the following nutrient cycles.

carbon   nitrogen   water   phosphorous

B. Choose the best answer.

1. Humans have interrupted the nitrogen cycle by

    A. digging up the stored nutrient resources and combusting them during industrial processes.

    B. damming rivers and lakes.

    C. increasing the rate at which land-based nitrogen is released into the environment.

    D. all of the above

2. Humans have altered the water cycle by

    A. digging up the stored nutrient resources and combusting them during industrial processes.

    B. damming rivers and lakes.

    C. increasing the rate at which land based nitrogen is released into the environment.

    D. all of the above

3. Humans have altered the carbon cycle by

    A. digging up the stored nutrient resources and combusting them during industrial processes.

    B. damming rivers and lakes.

    C. increasing the rate at which land based nitrogen is released into the environment.

    D. all of the above

CHAPTER 11 REVIEW

1. The greenhouse effect is responsible for which environmental condition listed below?

    A. global warming

    B. thermal pollution

    C. photosynthesis

    D. clear cutting of rain forests

2. How do humans increase the rate of the water cycle?

    A. burning fossil fuels

    B. clearing farmland

    C. growing food in gardens

    D. damming rivers

3. Which of the following activities is an environmentally responsible use of power?

    A. leaving your TV on when you are not home

    B. run your furnace at 72°F year round

    C. drying your clothes on an outdoor clothing line

    D. leaving the refrigerator door open as you slowly assess your snack options

4. What will happen when the global carrying capacity for humans is reached?

    A. animals will go extinct

    B. humans will go extinct

    C. humans will not continue reproducing

    D. human populations will shrink

5. A landscaper sprays a lawn with a pesticide that is 96% effective. If there are around 50 grasshoppers living on the lawn before the pesticide application, how many are likely to survive the pesticide?

    A. 0   B. 2   C. 5   D. 10

6. What is the proposed ultimate result of global warming?

    A. space exploration   C. volcanic activity

    B. ice age   D. increased shark attacks

7. In the past 10,000 years, when did the human population experience negative growth? (Hint: look back at Figure 11.9)

    A. during the Christian era

    B. during the Industrial Revolution

    C. during the Bubonic plague

    D. near the Grinnell glacier

8. How can you combat global warming?

    A. keep the air condition on

    B. move to a cooler climate

    C. avoid eating fish

    D. turn off lights when you leave a room

9. Which of the following is a fossil fuel?

    A. water

    B. gasoline

    C. carbon dioxide

    D. ice

10. How do humans get phosphorous from the environment?

    A. precipitation

    B. evaporation

    C. mining

    D. agriculture

Section I
Practice Test 1

Use this information to answer question 1.

Karen wants to win a blue ribbon at the fair this year for the largest tomato plants. She would like to compare two new plant foods on her tomato plants to see if they really make the plants grow larger.

Karen needs to design an experiment to see which plant food induces more growth. She has three of the same type of tomato plants, and they all receive the same amount of sunlight, water, and temperature. Karen adds plant food A to plant A, she adds plant food B to plant B, and she lets plant C grow without any plant food. She measures the growth of the plants every week.

1   Plant C is part of which group?   SCSh3b

    A   control

    B   variable

    C   data

    D   experimental

2   A plant has a thick waxy cuticle to prevent moisture loss. The interior of the   SB4e plant is hollow and is used to store large quantities of water. The leaves of the plant have evolved into sharp spines, which protect the flesh of the plant from water-seeking animals. Which environment is most suited to this organism?

A   Tundra
C   Desert
B   River
D   Deciduous Forest

Go On

3 Using the SI system, what unit of measure would be used to determine the distance from Atlanta, Georgia to Detroit, Michigan?   SCSh5e

A   miles

B   kilometers

C   kilograms

D   seconds

4 A salamander, raised away from water until long after its siblings, will swim every bit as well as them the very first time it is placed in the water. For salamanders, swimming is a(n)   SB4f

A   learned behavior.

B   innate behavior.

C   diurnal behavior.

D   reflex behavior.

5 In the lab, which piece of equipment would you use to measure 15 g of NaCl?   SCSh2a

A   equipment piece W, graduated cylinder

B   equipment piece X, beaker

C   equipment piece Y, triple beam balance

D   equipment piece Z, meter stick

6 Mistletoe extracts water and nutrients from several types of trees, harming the tree. What type of symbiotic relationship is illustrated by the action of mistletoe?   SB4a

A   mutualism

B   predation

C   parasitism

D   commensalism

Go On

In a given area of the Serengeti National Park, the following distribution of animals occurs.

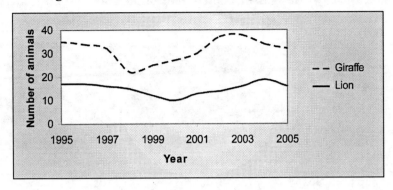

7   **Which of the following correctly explains the population changes shown in the graph?**   SB4a

A   The giraffe and lion population reached carrying capacity in 1997.

B   A sudden decrease in the giraffe population immediately reduces the lion population.

C   The lion population increases in response to a decrease in the giraffe population.

D   A change in the giraffe population is met with a corresponding change in the lion population after a 1 – 2 year lag time.

Go On

The diagram below shows the classification of four organisms. Use the information to answer question 8.

Organism	1	2	3	4
Common Name	Goats–beard	Serviceberry	Prostrate Bluets	Purple Bluets
Phylum	Anthophyta	Anthophyta	Anthophyta	Anthophyta
Family	Rose	Rose	Madder	Madder
Genus	*Aruncus*	*Amelanchier*	*Houstonia*	*Houstonia*
Species	*dioicus*	*laevis*	*serpyllifolia*	*purpurea*

8 According to the diagram, which two organisms are the most related?   SB3c

   A   organisms 1 & 2

   B   organisms 2 & 3

   C   organisms 3 & 4

   D   organisms 2 & 4

9 Which organelle helps to maintain homeostasis within a multicellular organism through the exchange of materials with other nearby cells?   SB1a

   A   cell membrane

   B   nucleus

   C   mitochondria

   D   vacuole

10 The organelle indicated by an arrow in the diagram contains a pigment responsible for capturing sunlight needed for the process of   SB3a

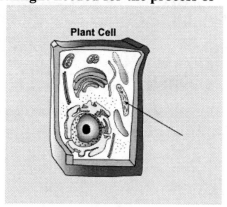

Plant Cell

   A   photosynthesis.

   B   aerobic respiration.

   C   nutrient absorption.

   D   cellular transport.

11 One octopus unscrews a jar lid and receives a food reward. Another octopus observes this occurrence and, upon receiving a jar, proceeds to quickly unscrew the lid. What type of behavior is the octopus exhibiting? SB4f

A innate behavior

B learned behavior

C diurnal behavior

D territorial behavior

12 Mass extinction is an event in which many types of living things become extinct at the same time. Which of the following statements is the most likely description of the aftermath of a mass extinction? SB5b

A A mass extinction results in gradual extinction of all other species presently alive on the Earth.

B The survivors of a mass extinction have available to them a great deal of ecological opportunity. Many habitats are opened, and an abundance of new species may evolve.

C With less demands on resources, surviving species tend to stay unchanged for a long period of time following a mass extinction.

D After a mass extinction, the occurrence of genetic mutations in surviving species will significantly increase.

13 Prokaryotic cells differ from eukaryotic cells in that SB1a

A prokaryotic cells are living and eukaryotic cells are non-living.

B prokaryotic cells lack a true nucleus and membrane bound organelles.

C prokaryotic cells are much larger than eukaryotic cells.

D prokaryotic cells require oxygen and eukaryotic cells do not.

14 An animal cell is placed in a solution of distilled water. If left overnight, this cell will SB1a

A shrivel and die.

B undergo chemosynthesis.

C swell and burst.

D remain the same, since it has a cell wall to protect it.

15 Diffusion takes place SB1d

A only in liquids

B only through a lipid bilayer

C from an area of high concentration to an area of low concentration

D from an area of low concentration to an area of high concentration

Go On

16 What is the ultimate goal of the process shown in the diagram below? SB2b

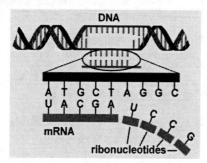

DNA

A T G C T A G G C
U A C G A U C C G
mRNA
ribonucleotides—

A to store cellular energy

B to maintain homeostasis

C to replicate DNA

D to make protein

17 What is the correct order of the stages of mitosis? SB2b

A prophase, metaphase, anaphase, telophase

B metaphase, anaphase, telophase, prophase

C prophase, telophase, metaphase, anaphase

D anaphase, metaphase, prophase, telophase

18 This molecule carries information from the DNA in the nucleus out into the cytoplasm of the cell SB2b

A tRNA

B rRNA

C ATP

D mRNA

19 Quin and Roseanna collected various samples of the flora in their backyard. Of the three samples shown below, which is/are non-vascular plants? SB4e

| Sample 1 | Sample 2 | Sample 3 |
| Magnolia | Norway Spruce | Moss |

A Sample 1

B Sample 2

C Samples 1 & 2

D Sample 3

20 A cabbage farmer has a five acre field of cabbage. Each year, his crop is attacked by cabbage eating beetles. To combat the problem, the farmer sprays his field with a mild pesticide. The pesticide kills 85% of the beetles on his field. In 1995, the farmer used 25 gallons to kill the beetles; however, by 2005, the farmer needed 40 gallons of pesticide to kill the same percentage of beetles. Why did the farmer need to use more pesticide to kill the same percentage of insects over the ten year period? SB4d, SB5e

A Because the beetles that had already been exposed to the pesticide were weaker.

B Because the surviving 15% of beetles were the only beetles reproducing each year, thus creating a population of beetles resistant to the pesticide.

C Because the farmer wants to buy lots of pesticide from his friend, the pesticide salesman.

D Because in 2005, more beetles attacked the fields than in 1995.

Go On

21 Every year people are hospitalized with simple bacterial infections. These infections can result in amputation of the infected area to save the person from death. The pervasive use of what modern technology has caused the rise in resistant bacteria? `SB4b`

- **A** vaccines
- **B** antibiotics
- **C** fertilizers
- **D** solar panels

22 The spines of a cactus are modified leaves. The thorn of a rose is a modified branch. What does this suggest about the evolution of these two families of plants? `SB5b`

- **A** The spine and the thorn are homologous structures, and are proof of common ancestry.
- **B** The spine and the thorn are analogous structures, and are not proof of common ancestry.
- **C** The spine and the thorn have separate functions, so they are not homologous and provide no evidence to support a common ancestor.
- **D** The spine and the thorn are vestigial structures that have not evolved.

23 During meiosis, only one chromosome from each homologue is passed on to the offspring. This helps increase `SB2c`

- **A** genetic variation.
- **B** genetic mutations.
- **C** fertilization rates.
- **D** the rate of evolution.

24 A microorganism is found in the lining of the human stomach. It has a flexible cell wall, no organelles and flagella. What is this organism? `SB1a, SB3b`

- **A** plant cell
- **B** animal cell
- **C** virus
- **D** bacteria

25 The figure below shows the pelvic bones of a sperm whale. What is the best description of this structure? `SB5c, SB5d`

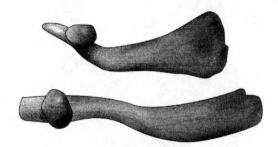

15 CM

- **A** The structure is homologous to a human's foot.
- **B** The structure is homologous to a bird's wing.
- **C** The structure is evidence of mutation.
- **D** The structure is vestigial.

Go On

26 Recall that an ecosystem is the interdependence of plant and animal communities and the physical environment in which they live. Which of the following is an accurate description of an ecosystem in that it includes all components of an ecosystem?   SB4a

A   The tropical rainforest is found near the equator. It has abundant rainfall, stays very humid, and experiences an average summer temperature of 25°C. The floor of the tropical rain forest does not get much sunlight.

B   The desert does not have much grass. Plants like sage brush, mesquite, and cacti have adapted well to desert conditions. Animals common to the desert are kangaroo rats, snakes, lizards, birds, spiders and insects.

C   The tundra is located near the north and south poles and experiences light rainfall. Summer temperatures average only 1°C. The subsoil of the tundra is permanently frozen. Grasses, mosses, and lichens are present. Animals such as polar bears, caribou, hares, arctic wolves and birds live in the tundra.

D   Freshwater systems include streams, rivers, lakes, marshes and swamps. Freshwater is important in recycling the earth's water supply. The Sun's heat does not warm water as quickly as it warms land. All organisms require freshwater for survival.

Go On

27 A particular type of   SCSh3d
    swamp- dwelling frog produces
    many offspring every spring.
    Thousands of tadpoles hatch from eggs.
    Within moments of hatching, predators
    arrive to feed on the tadpoles. The
    longer the tadpoles live, the more adept
    they become at evading predators.
    Nevertheless, only a small fraction of
    the tadpoles survive to reach adulthood.
    Which graph to the right best summa-
    rizes this information?

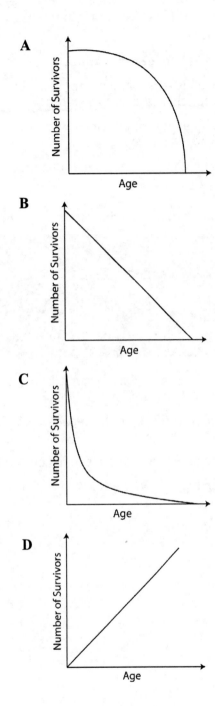

Go On

28 Which of the following actions will have a positive effect on the natural environment? SB4d

   A   overuse of garden fertilizers

   B   placing grass clippings in plastic bags and sending them to a landfill

   C   carpooling with three co-workers who live nearby

   D   voting in favor of a local referendum to fill in marshland

29 The illustration best shows SB4b

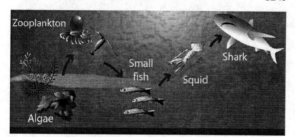

   A   how much food a shark needs to eat in order to survive

   B   the flow of energy from one organism to the next

   C   the diversity of species in the ocean

   D   the type of foods a shark likes to eat

30 An environment has cold, harsh winters with temperatures often far below freezing and cool summers with temperatures just above 45°F. This environment receives a moderate amount of precipitation. Which organism would most likely live in this environment? SB4e

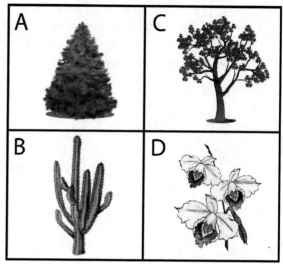

Go On

31 Which of the following correctly describes the individual shown in the karyotype? SB2f

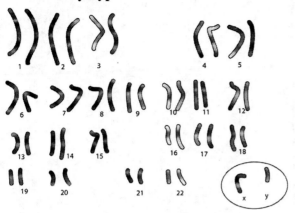

A   The individual has Down's syndrome.

B   The individual is male.

C   The individual is female.

D   The individual is a carrier for hemophilia.

32 How are transpiration and evaporation related? SB4b

A   Evaporation puts water into the water cycle, and transpiration removes water from the water cycle.

B   Evaporation is the first step in the water cycle and transpiration is the final step.

C   They both represent ways in which water enters the atmosphere in the water cycle.

D   They both represent ways in which water is removed from the atmosphere in the water cycle.

33 What does the graph shown below illustrate? SB4a

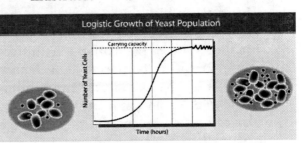

A   The exponential decline of a population.

B   The death rate of the population was much larger than the birth rate.

C   At carrying capacity, the population size never increases.

D   The growth of a population which slows after a period of exponential growth.

34 Industrial emissions of nitrogen oxides and sulfur dioxides eventually result in all of the following except SB4d

A   an increase of the pH in stream water samples taken from industrial areas.

B   acid rain that damages the leaves of plants.

C   precipitation that changes the chemistry of standing water and soil.

D   global warming.

Go On

35 The ancestors of polar bears became separated from brown bears when they moved from the mainland to the Arctic ice. The traits selected in the Arctic ice population were different than the traits selected in the land population. Eventually, the two populations could no longer interbreed. Today, we call the descendants of the Arctic ice population "polar bears" and the descendants of the mainland population "brown bears." What pattern of evolution is described? SB5d

A divergent evolution

B extinction

C co-evolution

D convergent evolution

36 Change is to evolution as lack of change is to SB5b, SB5c

A polygenic traits.

B genetic variation.

C genetic equilibrium.

D gene pool.

Go On

Use the information below and the image to answer question 37.

37 According to the classification key, to which genus and species does this member of the family Canidae belong? SB3b, SB3c

1.a. Has a pointed muzzle...go to 2.
  b. Has a stout, blocky muzzle..go to 3.

2.a. Weighs 10 – 20 pounds...*Vulpes vulpes*
  b. Weighs 20 – 50 pounds..*Canis latrans*

3.a. Has yellow eyes and large teeth; undomesticated ....*Canis lupus*
  b. Has white eyes and smaller teeth; domesticated.....................*Canis lupus familiaris*

A *Vulpes vulpes*

B *Canis latrans*

C *Canis lupus*

D *Canis lupus familiaris*

Go On

38 What does the S-shaped curve in the graph below represent? SB4a

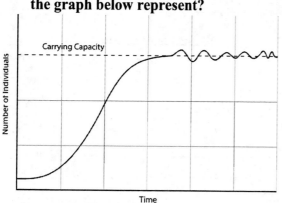

A As resources become less available, the population growth slows or stops.

B The number of births in the population continues to increase beyond carrying capacity.

C Abundant resources will continue to support the population.

D The population is now becoming extinct.

39 A unicellular organism reproduces asexually through binary fission. If the parent cell contains 28 chromosomes, how many chromosomes are contained within the daughter cell?   SB2b, SB2c, SB2e

A 7   **C** 28

B 14   **D** 56

40 During what phase of mitosis are duplicated chromosomes pulled to opposite ends of the cell?   SB2e

A metaphase

B prophase

C anaphase

D telophase

STOP

236

Section II

41 Sweating is a process by which excess water and salts and a small amount of urea are removed from the human body. Sweating involves the skin and the excretory system. This ability of an organism to maintain a stable internal environment is called

SB1a

- **A** homeostasis.
- **B** respiration.
- **C** meiosis.
- **D** fixation.

42 Which Web site listed below would be LEAST appropriate to use in a scientific research paper?

SCSh6c, SCSh8b, SCSh8c

- **A** www.highmountian/biology/cloning.edu
- **B** www.clonepets.com
- **C** www.nationalinstituteofhealth.gov
- **D** www.badscollage/biotechnology.edu

43 The equation below summarizes what biological process?

SB3a

$$\text{Light energy} + 6H_2O + 6CO_2 \rightarrow C_6H_{12}O_6 + 6O_2 + ATP$$

- **A** hemophotosynthesis
- **B** fermentation
- **C** photosynthesis
- **D** cellular respiration

44 Organism Y has an internal salt concentration of 3g/L. Solution A has a salt concentration of 5g/L. What will most likely happen to the organism if it is placed in solution A?

SB1a

- **A** the organism will swell
- **B** the organism will shrink
- **C** the organism will autolyse
- **D** the organism will do nothing

45 Which two nutrient cycles are MOST directly impacted by the fertilizers used in large-scale agricultural?

SB4b, SB4d

- **A** carbon and water cycles
- **B** carbon and nitrogen cycles
- **C** nitrogen and phosphorous cycles
- **D** phosphorous and water cycles

Go On

46 Which property of water allows many different substances to be dissolved?   SB1d

   A   adhesive

   B   cohesive

   C   polarity

   D   translucent

47 ATP stands for   SB3a

   A   adenosine diphosphate.

   B   adenosine triple phosphorous.

   C   adenosine triphosphate.

   D   adenosine tryphosphorous.

48 *Orcinus orca* **is the scientific name for the killer whale. These names represent the _____ and _____ of this organism.**   SB3c

   A   kingdom and phylum

   B   class and order

   C   genus and species

   D   family and genus

Go On

Use this information to answer question 49.

A species of bird lives in a canyon. This bird is reproductively isolated from other bird species in the area. The males of this type of bird species produce colorful red and blue iridescent feathers. During warmer years (greater than 78°F), more food is available and males can produce more vivid coloration. Females will only mate with males that have vivid coloration. During the warmer years, there are more successful breeding pairs of birds and more offspring. The graph below summarizes the number of offspring born each year.

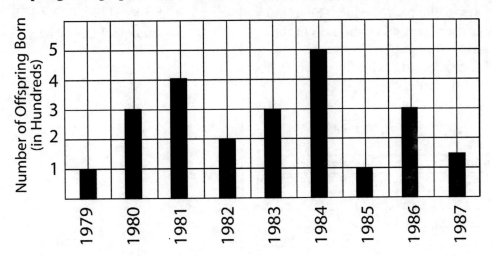

49 If the average breeding season temperature is greater than 80°F for the next five years, what trend(s) will be observed?

SB4f,
SB5d

   A   Bird coloration will become more dull.

   B   Bird coloration will stay the same.

   C   More offspring will be produced.

   D   Only female birds will be produced.

Go On

Use the information about cheetahs to answer question 50.

Cheetahs have very large territories, so family members are often separated by great distances. A scientist studying the cheetahs of a particular region observes an older male cheetah for a year and collects a DNA sample from him. He calls this cheetah the patriarch and decides to find his offspring. The scientist compiles a list of four other cheetahs in the region that are geographically likely to descend from the patriarch and collects DNA samples from those individuals. The patriarch's DNA sequence is

AAT TAT CCG CTC

Individual	DNA sequence
1	AAT TAT CCG CAG
2	TAG GAG ATC CAG
3	AAA TAC GGC CGG
4	TTA CAT CCG CTC

50 The DNA segments of possible offspring are shown in the table below. List the individuals in order from MOST related to LEAST related.

SB5c, SB5d, SB2b, SB2d

A   1, 4, 2, 3

B   1, 4, 3, 2

C   1, 2, 3, 4

D   2, 3, 4, 1

51 Around 60% of electricity produced in the United States is produced by burning coal or natural gas. The combustion of these fossil fuels does NOT lead to which consequence below?

SB4d

A   global climate change

B   increased air pollution

C   increased rates of human illness

D   alteration of the nitrogen cycle

Go On

Use this information to answer question 52.

Water chestnuts, or *Trapa natans*, are aquatic plants that live in slow-moving warm shallow water. The plant is native to warm areas of Eurasia and Africa. Water chestnuts have been eaten by humans for thousands of years. The seeds of this plant are a large starchy seed that can be boiled or roasted. Archeological evidence suggests the seeds from *T. natans* were an important dietary supplement for many humans when crops failed.

This plant was brought to the United States in the late 1850s and cultivated. Water chestnuts soon escaped human cultivation attempts, resulting in wild populations developing as early as 1879. Wild water chestnut populations exist in New York, Maryland, Vermont, Massachusetts, Arizona, New Hampshire, North Carolina and South Carolina. In several states and in Australia and Canada, this plant is considered dangerously invasive.

Around 1925, the plants covered 10,000 acres of the Potomac River basin reaching as far south as Quantico, Virginia. In 1939, the Army Corps of Engineers began a project to remove some of the plants from the river system.

During June and July, water chestnuts produce a round white flower with four petals. The flowers, also called rosettes, are pollinated by insects and take about one month to produce a nut. Each plant can produce 15 – 20 rosettes and each rosette can create up to 20 seeds. Seeds usually germinate within the next two years, but have been known to remain viable for up to 12 years.

One plant can easily colonize a new ecosystem. The surface leaves can block sunlight from entering the body of water, reducing other natural plant vegetation levels and interrupting the energy cycles in the ecosystem. Plants can grow into dense mats and block waterways for humans and animals alike.

52 **Why did the water chestnut grow so rapidly in the Northeastern US?**   SB4a, SB4d, SCSh9a

    A   because it found a favorable climate

    B   because it has seeds that can survive for 12 years

    C   because it was not native to the US and lacked predatory controls

    D   because humans continued cultivation and intentional release of plants into water ways

Go On

The DNA strand below is one half of a complementary pair.

TACCCATTCGAT

53 Which of the following correctly shows the complementary DNA strands with a duplication mutation? *SB2d*

A   TACCCATTCGATGAT

B   TACCCATTCTAG

C   UACCCAUUCGAUGAU

D   ATGGGTAAGCTACTA

54 A mother is homozygous recessive for a trait. The father is homozygous dominant for the same trait. What are the genotypes of the offspring for that trait? *SB2b, SB2c*

A   100% heterozygous

B   25% homozygous dominant, 25% homozygous recessive, and 50% heterozygous

C   100% homozygous dominant

D   50% homozygous dominant, 50% homozygous recessive

55 The snowshoe rabbit is a primary consumer. In summer, it feeds on plants like grass, ferns and leaves; in winter, it eats twigs, the bark from trees and buds from flowers and plants. The fox is both a secondary consumer and an omnivore, eating rabbits and other small prey, as well as a wide variety of vegetation. During the summer months, the rabbit has a brown coat to camouflage with the forest floor. Then, during the winter months, the rabbit grows a white coat to camouflage with the snow. This chromatic camouflage hides it from the fox. If unusually warm winter conditions cause premature melting of the snow, what would you expect to happen to the rabbit population? *SB4f, SB5d*

A   It would increase greatly, due to the increased food supply.

B   It would decrease greatly, due to the increased predation.

C   It would not change.

D   It would probably decrease somewhat, with increased predation outweighing the effect of greater food supply.

56 Crossing over occurs regularly during meiosis. Why is crossing over advantageous to species? *SB2c*

A   It destroys damaging genes.

B   It ensures that equal numbers of males and females are born into a population.

C   It increases genetic variation.

D   It decreases the possibility of mutations.

Go On

57 The DNA code eventually directs the cell to manufacture SB2b

A various proteins.

B amino acids.

C hydrogen bonds.

D sugars.

58 The development of seeds allows plants to reproduce SB4e

A away from water.

B using flowers only.

C only in freshwater.

D only in saltwater.

59 Which of the following statements about mutations is NOT true? SB2d

A Mutations can be spontaneous.

B Mutations can be caused by environmental factors.

C Mutations can occur in sex cells.

D Most mutations have extremely negative effects on an organism.

60 The tropical rain forest is found near the equator. It has abundant rainfall, stays very humid, and experiences an average summer temperature of 25 degrees Celsius. The floor of the tropical rain forest does not get much sunlight. This is a description of the ecosystem's SB4a

A biotic factors.

B abiotic factors.

C both biotic and abiotic factors.

D succession pattern.

61 Differences that exist among members of the same species are known as SB5d

A natural variation.

B artificial selection.

C natural selection.

D genetic drift.

62 An organism that lives in the water and makes all of its food from sunlight is SB3a, SB4b

A algae, a producer.

B algae, a decomposer.

C moss, a decomposer.

D moss, a producer.

Go On

63 A team of researchers announces that they have cloned a human! They refuse to explain their exact method, stating that they do not want anyone to copy their work. Which represents the MOST likely response from the *scientific* community?

SCSh1c, SCSh8c

A   Their work will be accepted because scientists can usually tell from the results whether or not the method was sound.

B   It is impossible to clone a human being, so no one will ever believe the new research.

C   Judgement will be suspended until their method and results are confirmed in identical trials by other scientists.

D   Scientists will believe the new research until it is disproved by other scientists.

64 The diagram below shows DNA fingerprints from several people.

SB2f

Brother's DNA   Individual 1   Individual 2   Individual 3

A mother and father die in a car accident. The three offspring, a brother and two sisters, are placed in foster homes. Many years later, the brother begins looking for his sisters. After a long and exhaustive search, three women claim that they are his sisters. Use the DNA fingerprints above to determine which two individuals are MOST likely his sisters?

A   Individuals 1 and 2 may be his sisters.

B   Individuals 1 and 3 may be his sisters.

C   Individuals 2 and 3 may be his sisters.

D   None of the individuals is a sibling.

Go On

Use the information below to answer question 65.

Each morning, Tamara brushes her teeth to get ready for the day. She begins by turning on the faucet to rinse her tooth brush. She then leaves the water running at full blast the entire three minutes she is brushing her teeth. She then rinses her brush and mouth for about 30 seconds and turns the faucet off.

65 How can Tamara brush her teeth in a more eco-friendly way? SB4d

    A   Tamara could brush her teeth in a more eco-friendly way by turning the water down while she is brushing her teeth.

    B   Tamara could brush her teeth in a more eco-friendly way by turning on the warm water while she is brushing her teeth.

    C   Tamara could brush her teeth in a more eco-friendly way by turning off the water while she is brushing her teeth.

    D   Tamara could brush her teeth in a more eco-friendly way by turning on the radio while she is brushing her teeth.

66 A mother and father are both heterozygous for a trait. What percentage of their offspring will show the dominant phenotype? SB2c

    A   25%

    B   50%

    C   75%

    D   100%

67 What type of metamorphosis is indicated by the cricket life cycle shown below? SB3b

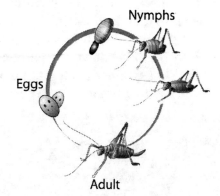

    A   complete metamorphosis

    B   incomplete metamorphosis

    C   true metamorphosis

    D   total metamorphosis

Go On

68 Bacteria inhabit the intestines of cows, and both benefit from the relationship. Cows eat plants but cannot digest the cellulose. The bacteria derive their nutrition from the plants the cows eat and make available nutrients for the cow by breaking down the plant cellulose. What symbiotic interaction is illustrated by the cows and bacteria? SB4a

- A   mutualism
- B   predation
- C   parasitism
- D   commensalism

69 An adaptation known as camouflage may aid in some salamanders' SB4f

- A   mutations.
- B   geographic isolation.
- C   convergent evolution.
- D   survival.

70 A raisin was left in a solution overnight and was swollen by morning. The solution that the raisin was placed in was SB1a

- A   hypertonic.
- B   hypotonic.
- C   isotonic.
- D   acidic.

71 Which of the following describes the role of the abalone in this system? SB4b

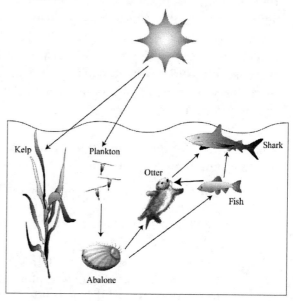

- A   parasite
- B   decomposer
- C   consumer
- D   producer

72 Enzymes are one kind of protein. What are proteins made up of? SB2a, SB2b

- A   nucleic acids
- B   amino acids
- C   carbohydrates
- D   lipids

73 The process that involves mRNA and tRNA and results in the formation of proteins is SB2a, SB2b

- A   transcription.
- B   translation.
- C   replication.
- D   cytokinesis

Go On

74 Homeostasis is the term for the relatively stable internal environment maintained by an organism. During physical exertion, animals begin to respire (breathe) heavily. What is the purpose of the heavy breathing?   SB1a

A To decrease heat loss.

B To increase the amount of oxygen available to cells and remove excess water.

C To increase the amount of oxygen available to cells and remove excess carbon dioxide.

D To increase the amount of carbon dioxide available to cells and remove excess oxygen.

Use the information in the Punnett square to answer question 75.

	BF	Bf	bF	bf
BF	BBFF	BBFf	BbFF	BbFf
Bf	BBFf	BBff	BbFf	Bbff
bF	BbFF	BbFf	bbFF	bbFf
bf	BbFf	Bbff	bbFf	bbff

75 In orchids, flower color and fragrance are two genetic traits. Each trait is located on a separate chromosome. In orchids, the allele for producing blue flowers (B) is dominant to the allele for producing white flowers (b). The allele for producing strong fragrance (F) is dominant to the allele for producing little fragrance (f). Two orchids that have genotypes that are heterozygous blue flowers and strong fragrance (BbFf) were crossed. Use the completed Punnett square to determine the probability of offspring that have blue flowers and strong fragrance.   SB2c

A 1/16   **C** 6/16

B 3/16   **D** 9/16

Go On

76 The cellular component indicated is

SB1a

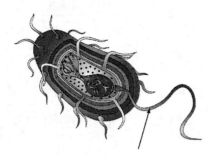

A   pilia.

B   flagellum.

C   cell membrane.

D   pili.

77 In the table below the data given is

SCSh3c

Bird observed	Bird Color
Bird 1	Blue
Bird 2	Red
Bird 3	Brown
Bird 4	Black

A   qualitative.

B   quantitative.

C   exact.

D   none of these

78 One important way to control the spread of viruses is through

SB3d

A   the use of vaccines.

B   proper hand washing.

C   the use of other types of bacteria.

D   the use of antibiotics.

79 Which group of organisms recycles organic matter?

SB4a, SB4b

A   ferns

B   moss

C   mushrooms

D   sponges

80 Which of the following are possible sources of pollution?

SB4d

A   inorganic chemicals

B   organic chemicals

C   volcanoes

D   Inorganic chemicals, organic chemicals, and volcanoes are all possible sources of pollution.

STOP

Section I

1 Which of the following comparison would give a scientist the MOST information about the relatedness of two organisms?   SB5b, SB5d

   A   comparing the fins of a dolphin with those of a tadpole

   B   comparing the tail feather of a penguin with the fins of a fish

   C   comparing the tail feathers of a peacock and a pheasant

   D   comparing the teeth of an alligator with the beak of a toucan

2 An organism has short arms, legs and ears. This animal is covered   SB4f
   with fur that is several layers thick. The animal is white with blue
   eyes. Which environment is most suited to this organism?

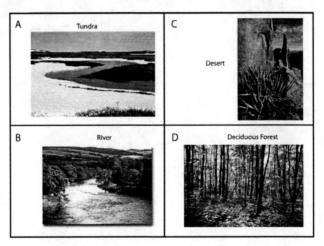

Go On

3   The fly *Ormia ochracea* is   SB4a
    attracted to the song of the male
    cricket, using it to locate the male in
    order to deposit her young on him. The
    larvae promptly burrow into the cricket
    and eat him. What symbiotic relation-
    ship does this illustrate?

    A   mutualism
    B   predation
    C   parasitism
    D   commensalism

4   If a cell is placed in a highly con-   SB1a
    centrated glucose solution, water
    will leave the cell by which process
    listed below?

    A   osmosis
    B   diffusion
    C   active transport
    D   facilitated diffusion

5   A single strand of DNA with   SB2a, SB2b
    the base pairing sequence
    C-G-A-T-T-G is compatible
    only with the sequence

    A   T-A-G-C-C-T.
    B   G-C-T-A-A-G.
    C   G-C-T-A-A-C.
    D   C-G-A-T-T-G.

6   The biomass of *Akobia quinata*,   SCSh5d
    an invasive weed removed from
    a forest plot, totaled 9.2 kg. How many
    grams were removed?

    A   20.3 g   C   920 g
    B   92.0 g   D   9200 g

Go On

7 As red blood cells pick up carbon   SB1b
dioxide from tissues to be moved
to the lungs, the carbon dioxide reacts
with water to form carbonic acid. Carbonic acid is transported to the lungs
where it is converted back to carbon
dioxide and water, and the carbon dioxide can then be exhaled.

Carbonic anhydrase increases the rate of
production of carbonic acid from only 200
molecules of carbonic acid being formed
per hour to 600,000 molecules of carbonic
acid being formed per hour. This increase
in reaction rate is necessary for the process
to be biologically useful. Carbonic
anhydrase is a(n)

A   substrate.

B   enzyme.

C   pigment.

D   reactant.

8 The message of the DNA code   SB1c
instructs the cell to build which
biomolecule listed below?

A   nucleic acids

B   glucose

C   proteins

D   polysaccharides

9 Each set of three nitrogen bases   SB2b
representing an amino acid is
known as

A   a codon.

B   an amino acid.

C   a protein.

D   RNA.

10 Students are performing a dis-   SCSh2c
section of a frog in biology class.
They have a dissection tray, pins, a scal-
pel and the frog, preserved in formalde-
hyde. What are some necessary safety
precautions the student should take
while performing this lab?

A   They should follow liquid waste
disposal procedures.

B   They should follow sharp instrument
safety procedures and wear safety
goggles.

C   They should follow fire and heat
safety guidelines.

D   They should follow glassware safety
procedures.

11 Ostriches and gazelles feed next to   SB4a
each other. They both watch for
predators and alert each other to danger. The visual abilities of the two species are different, so that together they
can identify threats that the individual
animal would not readily see. What
symbiotic relationship does this
illustrate?

A   commensalism

B   mutualism

C   predation

D   parasitism

12 After fertilization, an embryo goes   SB2c
through many mitotic cell divi-
sions, eventually developing into a
zygote. If the embryonic cell contains 32
chromosomes, how many chromosomes
are contained within the cells of the
zygote?

A   4

B   16

C   32

D   64

Go On

13 What is the correct term for the structures pictured below which have a similar appearance, but different functions?   SB5d

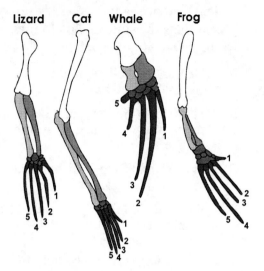

Lizard   Cat   Whale   Frog

   A   analogous structures

   B   homologous structures

   C   adaptive structures

   D   vestigial structures

Use the table below to answer question 14. Scientists were studying rock lobsters found on a coral reef.

Length	Depth Found
15.9 cm	22 m
6.2 cm	2 m
8.8 cm	12 m
19.2 cm	26 m
5.5 cm	9 m
4.9 cm	8 m
17.6 cm	26 m

14 Which graph below correctly represents the data collected by the scientists?   SCSh3c, SCSh3d

A

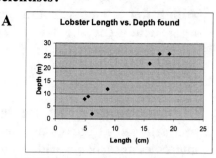

B

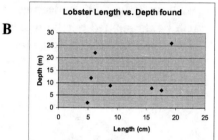

C

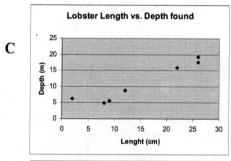

D

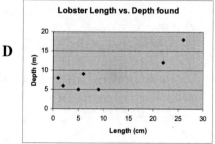

Go On

15 The amount of rainfall an ecosys-   SB4a
tem receives is considered

   A   a limiting nutrient.

   B   only when it concerns the increase in primary consumers.

   C   a limiting factor.

   D   only when it refers to drought situations.

16 Which of the following would not   SB4d
be considered a renewable
resource?

   A   trees in a forest

   B   water in the ocean

   C   grass in a pasture of grazing sheep

   D   coal buried deep in the ground

17 In biological terms, what does suc-   SB4c
cession mean?

   A   a descendent of animal breeding.

   B   the result when one species is more successful than another.

   C   the gradual change of dominant species present in an ecosystem.

   D   There is no biological term called succession.

18 Which of the following human   SB4d
activities is not associated with
global warming?

   A   over-fishing the Great Lakes

   B   burning of fossil fuels

   C   cutting down forests

   D   burning forests

19 The appearance of fins and   SB5d
streamlined bodies on diverse
groups of animals such as dolphins,
sharks and penguins is an example of

   A   coevolution.

   B   adaptive radiation.

   C   convergent evolution.

   D   macroevolution.

20 Which would a breeder use to   SB5b
produce cows which give more
milk?

   A   natural selection

   B   artificial selection

   C   gene mutation

   D   acquired characteristics

21 What type of organism lives on   SB4a,
land, cannot move and obtains all   SB4b
of its food from dead organic
matter?

   A   producer

   B   consumer

   C   decomposer

   D   lichen

Go On

22 During phase two, 3-carbon sug- SB3a
ars and oxygen enter the mitochondria to begin the "citric acid cycle."
What process is this a description of?

A   anaerobic respiration

B   aerobic respiration

C   alcoholic respiration

D   ATP respiration

Use the following scenario to answer question 23.

In rabbits, the fur color and ear
position are two genetic traits. Each
trait is located on a separate chromosome. The allele for producing
brown fur (B) is dominant to the
allele for producing white fur (b).
The allele for producing straight
ears (E) is dominant to the allele for
producing floppy ears (e).

23 What are the possible genotypes SB2b,
for a rabbit with brown fur and SB2c
floppy ears?

A   Bbee, BBee

B   Bbee, BbEe, BBee and BBEe

C   BBee and BBEE

D   BbEe, BBEe, BbEE and BBEE

24 Which of the following describes SB4a,
the correct energy flow in an SB4b
ecosystem?

A   Energy flows from heterotrophs to
autotrophs to decomposers.

B   Energy flows from decomposer to
consumers to producers.

C   Energy flows from producers to consumers to decomposers.

D   Energy flows from producers to
decomposers to consumers.

25 Opponents of genetic engineering SB2f
argue that there is no way to fore-
see the consequences of crop alterations
to the local habitat. Which of the following is a possible negative outcome of
genetic modification (GM)?

A   Pest-resistant plants may reduce the
local population of pollinating
insects.

B   Weed-resistant plants may modify to
attack other local crops.

C   GM plants may cross–pollinate with
similar plants and cause unforeseen
consequences.

D   GM plants require more resources
that non-GM plants to thrive.

26 The process by which those SB5d
organisms most suited for their
environment survive and reproduce is
known as

A   classification.

B   nondisjunction.

C   punctuated equilibrium.

D   natural selection.

27 The desert does not have much SB4a
grass. Plants like sagebrush, mesquite and cacti have adapted well to
desert conditions. Animals common to
the desert are kangaroo rats, snakes, lizards, birds, spiders and insects. This is a
description of the ecosystem's

A   biotic factors.

B   abiotic factors.

C   biotic and abiotic factors.

D   succession pattern.

Go On

28 Some groups of chimpanzees use grass like a spoon, to get and eat termites. Other groups of chimpanzees use rocks to break into termite mounds. Which type of behavior is illustrated by these examples? SB4f

A   learned behavior

B   innate behavior

C   diurnal behavior

D   nocturnal behavior

29 While it is rare, sometimes swimmers in the ocean are bitten by sharks. Which of the following is NOT a probable cause of the attacks? SCSh1b

A   Sharks swimming in areas frequented by humans cannot see well and often "test bite potential" prey.

B   Humans in the water often display behaviors like splashing or yelling that is similar to the sharks' natural prey.

C   Sharks are displaying a natural territorial behavior.

D   Sharks are afraid that humans will take their food.

30 Bacteria are being used to break-down pollutants into harmless molecules and to produce medicines. Bacteria are also cultured so that their enzymes can be extracted to make soy sauce, cheese, chewing gum and laundry detergent. Which of the following characteristics of bacteria makes them valuable in pollution cleanup, the making of medicine and industry? SB3b

A   All bacteria have exactly the same genetic code, so any type of bacteria can potentially be used for pollution cleanup, medicine making and the manufacture of industrial products.

B   Bacteria are not susceptible to threats, such as viruses, so bacterial populations will never suffer any adverse effects.

C   Bacterial populations multiply quickly, increasing the potential for pollution cleanup, medicine making and the manufacture of industrial products.

D   The chemical reactions that take place within bacterial cells do not have any by-products and, therefore, do not interfere with their roles as pollution cleaners or medicine makers.

31 *Ursus arctos* and *Ursus maritimus* are organisms that belong to the same SB3c

A   population.

B   species.

C   genus.

D   chromosome.

Go On

32 When recovering from injury, blood platelets that cover the wound are slowly replaced by newly-formed skin cells. Old skin cells, with 46 chromosomes, divide to form new skin cells with 46 chromosomes. This is classified as what sort of reproductive process?   SB2e

A   sexual

B   asexual

C   gestation

D   binary fission

33 What do the beak and claws indicate about a bird?   SB4f

A   what type of food they eat and the habitat in which they live

B   the type of nest they build

C   their migration pattern

D   their genotype

34 Scientific studies have shown that a mutation in gene p53 is present in cancerous skin tumors. It has also been shown that consistent exposure to UV radiation or high levels of UV radiation is associated with occurrences of mutations in gene p53 of skin cells. Why is it that a mother who had the mutation in gene p53 and had skin cancer and a mother who did not have either the mutation in gene p53 or skin cancer both had offspring that did not have the p53 mutation?   SB2d

A   The offspring did not have the skin cell mutation because neither of the fathers had the mutated gene, and both parents must donate the mutated p53 skin cell gene for the offspring to also have the mutation.

B   The offspring of the mother with skin cancer did not have the mutated p53 gene because the mother did not sunbathe during pregnancy.

C   The offspring did not have the skin cell mutation because only mutations in reproductive cells are able to be passed on to offspring.

D   Since there is a 1 in 4 chance of an offspring receiving a mutated gene from its parents, it is by chance that neither offspring received the mutated gene.

Go On

35 Which of the following organisms is eukaryotic, has cell walls, and is heterotrophic? SB3b

A   organism W

B   organism X

C   organism Y

D   organism Z

Use the following scenario to answer question 36.

Researchers collected information on pond size preference for several different frog species found in Georgia. Each frog species has a unique preference for a particular pond size. Within each pond, the number of frogs of each species was counted and a dominant frog species was determined. The graph below shows how pond size related to percentages of one native species, the burrowing mudhen.

Burrowing Mudhens

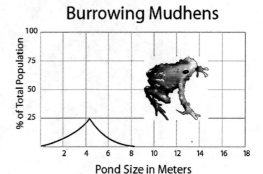

Pond Size in Meters

36 At pond sizes above 6 meters,   SB5d there are not enough burrowing mudhens to maintain genetic diversity and their numbers begin to fall. What biological force is acting upon the burrowing mudhen population?

A   natural selection

B   selective breeding

C   extinction

D   emigration

Go On

The green sea turtle lives in warm waters. This large turtle can weigh up to 200 pounds. It has a hard shell to protect its vital organs. The green sea turtle is so named because of the color of its body fat; its algae diet is responsible for the colored tissue.

The leatherback turtle spends most of its time in colder northern waters. The largest of all turtles, it can weigh up to 600 pounds. It has a black shell made of soft connective tissue, rather than the hard plates than most turtles have. The beak of the leatherback turtle is specially hooked to help it bite jellyfish and its throat has backward-facing barbs to help it swallow them

Green Sea Turtle   Leatherback Turtle

37 What best explains the differences in appearance of these two turtle species? SB4f, SB5d

A Each baby turtle adapts its features to the specific food source of its habitat and thus grows distinct adult characteristics.

B Over time, the two turtle species have adapted differences in appearance due to the differences in environment.

C Each turtle adapts a different appearance once it moves to a comfortable habitat.

D Over time, the two turtle species developed different breeding preferences, and came to look very different form each other.

Go On

A botanist is attempting to identify an unfamiliar plant collected from a local state park. Use the information to answer questions 38 and 39.

1. a. Flower pods located on radially symennetrical stacks. ....go to 2.
   b. Flower pods located along the bottom edge of the stalk ....go to 3.

2. a. Small flowers located close together ....*Smilacina racemosa.*
   b. Large flowers located far apart ....*Trillium undulatum.*

3. a. Hairs located on the underside of its leaf....................*Polygonatum pubescens.*
   b. Surface of leaf is smooth.. *Polygonatum biflorum.*

38 **Use the dichotomous key above to determine the genus and species of the unfamiliar plant.** SB3b, SB3c

   A   *Smilacina racemosa*

   B   *Trillium undulatum*

   C   *Polygonatum pubescens*

   D   *Polygonatum biflorum*

39 **Which two plants listed in the key are most related?** SB3b, SB3c

   A   *Polygonatum pubescens* and *Polygonatum biflorum*

   B   *Smilacina racemosa* and *Trillium undulatum*

   C   All the flowers are equally unrelated.

   D   All the flowers are equally related.

Go On

Use the information below to answer question 40.

Andre wanted to see if pea plant growth could be affected by the kind of musical environment they grew in. In each of 2 rooms, he placed one plant and one CD player playing one type of music. All other conditions (sunlight, water) were kept constant. In a separate control room, no music was played. Measurements were taken at the end of each week. The resulting lines below show lines of best fit for each data set. Use this information to answer question 40.

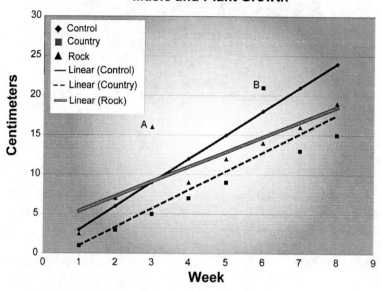

40 Based on the results, in which week was the height of the plant in the room where rock is played the same as the height of the plant in the room where country is played?

SCSh3e

A They were the same at week 1.

B They were the same at week 3.

C They were the same at week 8.

D During no week were plant heights the same, but the trends show that they might be if the experiment continued.

Session II

41 The tropical rain forest is found near the equator. It has abundant rainfall, stays very humid and experiences an average summer temperature of 25°C. Many exotic types of plants and birds make their home in the rain forest. Primates and other mammals can also be found in the rain forest. The floor of the tropical rain forest does not get much sunlight, but does still harbor many plant and insect species. What type of factors are air temperature and rainfall? *SB4a*

    A   Both are biotic factors.

    B   Both are abiotic factors.

    C   Temperature is abiotic and rainfall is biotic.

    D   Temperature is biotic and rainfall is abiotic.

42 Within the human population, humans vary greatly in height. The height of a person cannot be directly related to any one other trait, and is not attributable to any one gene. What is the most likely inheritance pattern for height in humans? *SB2b, SB2c*

    A   co-dominant

    B   polygenic trait

    C   sex-linked

    D   incomplete dominance

43 Squirrels are an arboreal rodent found in most of the eastern United States. Natural predators of the squirrel include: hawks, eagles, owls, snakes and foxes. When a squirrel encounters any perceived threat, its instinct is to flee in an erratic way. The squirrel zigs and zags in several directions, attempting to elude its pursuers. However, when a squirrel encounters a motor vehicle its natural escape method often results in the death of the squirrel. If a squirrel population resided in a mostly urban area, with few natural predators, what do you think would most likely happen to the erratic escape trait after many generations? *SB5d*

    A   It would become more pronounced.

    B   It would become less pronounced.

    C   It would not change at all.

    D   It would appear in field mice.

44 Which biome is located between 20° and 60° latitude, has an average summer temperature of 24°C, and medium rainfall? *SB4a*

    A   desert

    B   rain forest

    C   deciduous forest

    D   coniferous forest

Go On

Use the image below to answer   question 45.

45   What is the relationship between SB4a, **the caribou and the Dall sheep?** SB4b

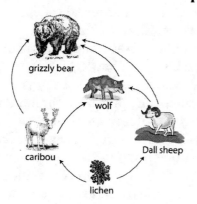

A   predator/prey

B   parasite

C   symbiotic

D   competitor

46   A scientist set up an experiment SCSh3b **to determine if eating organic carrots will cause thicker fur coats in rabbits. What is the independent variable in this experiment?**

A   type of cages the rabbits are housed in

B   the thickness of the rabbits' fur

C   the amount of water the rabbits drink

D   the type of carrots the rabbits eat

47   Amino acids are linked by pep- SB2b **tide bonds to make proteins. During what process does this occur?**

A   translation

B   transcription

C   replication

D   complimentary stranding

48   The purpose of the cycle below is SB3a **to**

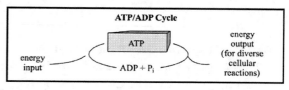

A   provide the cell with ADP molecules.

B   provide the cell with both ADP and ATP molecules.

C   provide the cell with a renewable energy source.

D   to change ATP into ADP.

49   Out of the following list of names, SB5a **determine those who had primary influence in developing the theory of evolution.**

> Albert Einstein, Francis Crick, Linus Pauling, Charles Darwin, James Watson, Edward Jenner

A   Charles Darwin

B   James Watson and Francis Crick

C   Charles Darwin, James Watson and Francis Crick

D   Charles Darwin, Albert Einstein and Edward Jenner

50   A bird in the rain forest grows to SB4f **sexual maturity. His first mating season he builds an elaborate nest with sticks and leaves. Then to attract a mate he performs an elaborate dance complete with specific calls and whistles. Attracting a mate is considered what type of behavior?**

A   learned behavior

B   innate behavior

C   diurnal behavior

D   nocturnal behavior

Go On

A botanist crossed a yellow (YY) orchid flower with a blue (BB) orchid flower. The resulting offspring had green (YB) flowers. The green flowers were then crossed as shown in the Punnett square below:

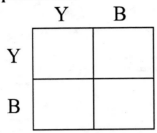

51 What is the probability that the offspring of the green flower cross will be green? SB2c

A   25%

B   50%

C   75%

D   100%

52 In January, a population of jewel beetles was around 450 individuals. By November, the population had shrunk to 220 individuals. In February of the following year, the population of beetles has once again risen to around 420 individuals. Given this information, what can you infer about the population of beetles in this environment? SB4a

A   The average yearly carrying capacity is around 335 individuals.

B   The average yearly carrying capacity is around 450 individuals.

C   The jewel beetle population is on the verge of extinction.

D   The jewel beetle population is growing exponentially.

53 Mutations in an organism's DNA can be harmful because SB2d

A   all organisms only have one copy of DNA in each cell.

B   the DNA in each cell of an organism is different.

C   a mutation can lead to the incorrect synthesis of glucose, which plays a fundamental role in regulating cell activities.

D   a mutation can lead to the incorrect synthesis of proteins, which play a fundamental role in regulating cell activities.

54 An algal bloom is a rapid increase in the population of algae in an aquatic ecosystem. Blooms may turn water green, brown or red. Increased growth of algae also increases the amount of dead organic matter produced and the amount of bacteria in the water. In consequence, oxygen levels decrease and fish die. In many cases, algal blooms are the result of nutrient-enriched runoff from fertilized agricultural areas. What nutrients are MOST responsible for algal blooms? SB4d

A   nitrogen and oxygen

B   nitrogen and phosphorous

C   nitrogen and carbon

D   phosphorous and oxygen

Go On

55 After eating a salty meal, a person feels very thirsty. This feeling of thirst is the body's way to maintain   SB1a

  A   healthy DNA.

  B   cell fractionation.

  C   homeostasis.

  D   fertility.

Use the DNA below to answer question 56.

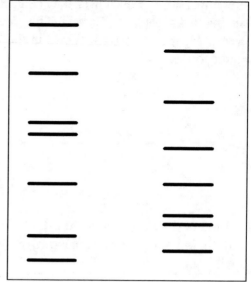

Foal's DNA   Steeplechase's DNA

56 A horse breeder must confirm the lineage of a new foal in order to submit its pedigree. The diagram above shows DNA fingerprinting from the foal and its assumed father, Steeplechase. Which conclusion can you draw?   SB2f, SCSh3e

  A   The foal definitely was not sired by Steeplechase.

  B   The foal definitely was sired by Steeplechase.

  C   It is unlikely that the foal was sired by Steeplechase, but further testing is needed to be certain.

  D   The lack of matches indicates that the test is corrupted; a new test will have to be performed.

Go On

57 Which organelle helps to provide cellular energy within a multicellular organism?

SB1a

A   cell membrane

B   nucleus

C   mitochondria

D   vacuole

58 What type of cells contain a true nucleus?

SB1a

A   bacterial cells

B   virus cells

C   prokaryotic cells

D   eukaryotic cells

59 Examine the equations below. What are the reactants in the process of respiration?

SB3a

$$6\,CO_2 + 6\,H_2O + \text{light energy} \longrightarrow C_6H_{12}O_6\ (\text{glucose}) + 6\,O_2$$

$$C_6H_{12}O_6\ (\text{glucose}) + 6\,O_2 \longrightarrow 6\,CO_2 + 6\,H_2O + \text{energy}$$

A   carbon dioxide, water and energy

B   carbon dioxide, energy and oxygen

C   oxygen and glucose

D   oxygen, glucose and water

60 Solution G has a salt concentration of 2.36 g/mL, and it is placed in one side of a U-shaped tube. Solution H has a salt concentration of 0.236 g/mL and is placed on the other side of the U-shaped tube. The semi-permeable membrane separating the two solutions will not allow passage of a solute. Predict the outcome of this experiment.

SB1d, SCSh3e

A   Water will not move through the membrane, because both sides contain salt.

B   Water will move through the membrane from solution H to solution G.

C   Water will move through the membrane form solution G to solution H.

D   Solute will accumulate at the membrane barrier and clog the passage of solvent.

61 Which of the following figures depicts the first stage of mitosis?

SB2e

A

B
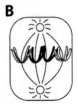

C

D
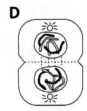

Go On

Use the following diagram to answer question 62.

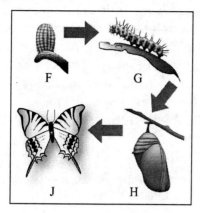

62 Butterflies belong to which kingdom? SB3b

A   Eubacteria

B   Animalia

C   Plantae

D   Protista

63 Plants must use oxygen in the process of respiration. Based on this information, which of the following is a valid conclusion? SB3a, SB3b, SCSh3f

A   Plants are likely incapable of anaerobic respiration.

B   Plants only engage in anaerobic respiration.

C   Plants must use a synthetic respiration process.

D   Plants do not respire, only animals.

Go On

Use the following diagram to answer questions 64 and 65.

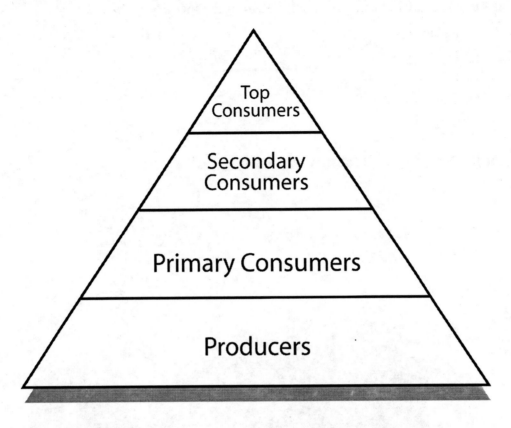

64 Which of the following groups contains organisms that belong in the first trophic level?   SB4b

A   Kingdom Fungi
B   Phylum Cnidaria
C   Class Mammalia
D   Kingdom Plantae

65 Which two organisms are top consumers?   SB4b

A   wolves and lions
B   bears and salmon
C   bears and foxes
D   chipmunks and squirrels

Go On

66 A cell contains a nucleus, mitochondria and endoplasmic reticulum. Given only this knowledge, what can you conclude about the identity of the cell?   SB1a

   A   It is a plant cell.

   B   It is an animal cell.

   C   It is a eukaryotic cell.

   D   It is a prokaryotic cell.

Use the following diagram to answer question 67.

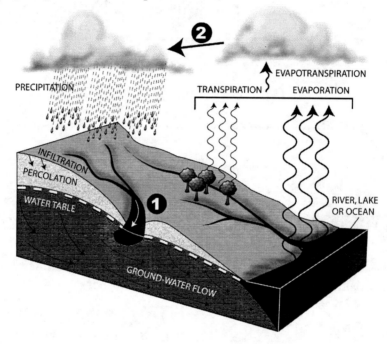

67 Which water cycle processes are labeled as (1) and (2) in the above diagram?   SB4b

   A   Condensation is depicted by arrow (1).
        Sublimation is depicted by arrow (2).

   B   Runoff is depicted by arrow (1).
        Sublimation is depicted by arrow (2).

   C   Runoff is depicted by arrow (1).
        Condensation is depicted by arrow (2).

   D   Condensation is depicted by arrow (1).
        Evaporation is depicted by arrow (2).

Go On

68 The Humboldt squid (*Dosidicus* SB3a *gigas*) lives the eastern Pacific Ocean. This squid uses its chromatophores (special skin cells) to quickly change colors and sometimes produce light. The production of light within an organism is known as bioluminescence. How do you suppose the squid obtains the energy needed to produce light?

A by breaking down light waves to make glucose

B by reflecting stored sunlight using a small shiny surface

C by breaking down glucose into ATP and ADP

D by burning fossil fuels in a way similar to humans

69 A mother homozygous dominant SB2c for the presence of freckles and a father heterozygous for freckles have a child. What is the chance that the child will be homozygous recessive for freckles?

A 0%

B 25%

C 50%

D 75%

70 Cells often store water, proteins, SB1a salts and carbohydrates in structures called

A vacuoles.

B mitochondria.

C Golgi apparatus.

D ribosomes.

71 Which eukaryotic organelle SB1a contains the genetic information?

A endoplasmic reticulum

B chloroplast

C nucleus

D cell membrane

Go On

72 Intertidal wetlands are an ecologically diverse area, containing both saline and fresh water. In fact, the primary natural stress on these areas is the daily alternation between different aquatic environments. Intertidal wetlands experience extreme salinity fluctuations, containing mainly salt water at high tide, and fresh water at low tide. At other times, water may be brackish. **SB4d**

The saline water concentration is a particularly difficult condition for plants to survive in. The grey mangrove accomplishes this by excluding salt at the root system; its especially thick root casing filters out greater than 95% of sodium salt before it is absorbed into the tree. Salt that is absorbed is concentrated and secreted at salt glands in the leaves. However, even this well-adapted plant is vulnerable to changes in salinity levels.

Changes to tidal movements through increased run-off or altered drainage can cause the roots of mangroves to be inundated for longer than normal periods, swamping their filtration system. It can also be pushed past its threshold level if water quality is changed.

One source of change is human activity. Wetlands have historically been regarded as unimportant by humans. They are often drained and filled to create parking lots and other urban structures. They may be segmented, which was theorized to prevent flooding. In other areas, flooding is desirable for agricultural or recreational purposes, so excess water is pumped into the wetland area. How have humans impacted wetlands?

A Humans have not had any major impacts on wetlands, because the wetland is able to adapt.

B Humans have filled, flooded or drained millions of acres of wetlands across the United States, causing decreased water quality, among other things.

C Humans have filled, flooded or drained millions of acres of wetlands with no adverse effects on habitats or water quality.

D Human activity has lead to an increase in wetlands throughout the United States.

73 Which of the following best describes the structure of the cell membrane? **SB1a**

A lipid bilayer

B carbohydrate bilayer

C nucleic acid bilayer

D protein bilayer

74 Which statement below is true of the cell wall? **SB1a**

A It provides support for animal cells.

B It is the site of protein synthesis.

C It provides support for plant cells.

D It is the organelle in which mitosis takes place.

Go On

75 What do prophase, metaphase, anaphase and telophase have in common? SB2e

  A They are phases of protein synthesis.

  B They are phases of cellular mitosis.

  C They are phases of cytokinesis.

  D They are phases of cellular respiration.

76 A mother who is homozygous recessive for short eyelashes and a father who is homozygous dominant for long eyelashes have a child. What are the chances that the child will have short eyelashes? SB2c

  A 100%

  B 50%

  C 25%

  D 0%

77 The main function of lipids within a cell is to SB1c

  A provide the main structural components of the cell membrane.

  B provide energy storage within the cell.

  C provide cellular energy.

  D store cellular information.

78 Which of the following is NOT a heterotroph? SB3b

  A plants

  B animals

  C fungi

  D many bacteria

79 Which cellular component is indicated by the arrow below? SB1a

  A nucleus.

  B nucleolus.

  C endoplasmic reticulum.

  D mitochondria.

80 Identify which part of the human anatomy listed below MOST resembles the xylem and phloem found in plants. SB3b

  A the reproductive system

  B the digestive system

  C the nervous system

  D the circulatory system

fungi 145, 148

G

Galapagos Islands 159
gamete 110, 149
gene 117, 119, 161
  flow 169
  frequencies 161
  types of 117
gene mutation 125
gene therapy 129
generation
  types of 119
genes 104
genetic diversity 155
genetic drift 161, 169
genetic engineering 131
genetic pollution 131
genetics 118
genotype 117
genus 145, 146
geotropism 173
gill slit 150
glassware safety 29
Global Contenders 67
global warming 212
glucose 140
glycolysis 140
Golgi bodies 87
graduated cylinder 34, 47
gram 47
graph
  types of 67
grassland 187
greenhouse effect 211
growth rate 195
GTP 140
guanine 104

H

habitat 182
half-life 164
haploid 108, 110
Hayworth representation 96
herbivore 199, 200
heterotroph 148, 149, 156
heterozygous 117
hibernate 176
homeostasis 83, 89
homologous chromosome 110
homologous pair 110
homologous structure 156, 170
homozygous 117
hormone 89, 106
hot plate 35
human population 214
hydrogen 96
hypertonic 90
hypothesis 60
hypotonic 90

I

immigration 169, 195
imprinting 177
incomplete dominance 122
index fossil 163
inference 40
innate behavior 175
inorganic molecule 96
inquire 59
interkinesis 110
interphase 108
interspecific competition 193
intertidal zone 188
intraspecific competition 193
inversion mutation 125
invertebrates 150
ionic bond 99

J

journal 62
J-shaped curve 195

K

Kelvin 48
kingdom 145
Krebs Cycle 140

L

lactic acid fermentation 141
learned behavior 176
length 47
lichen 197
life processes
  description of 84
light-dependent phase 139
light-dependent reaction 139
light-independent reaction 139
limiting factor 197
line graph 67
Linnaeus, Carl 146
lipids 97
living cell
  elements of 96
living fossil 163
living things
  characteristics of 83
logistic growth 196
lysosome 87

M

macroevolution 161
macromolecule 96
mass 47
material safety data sheet (MSDS) 32
measurement
  types of 45
mechanical pan balance 34
mechanical stress 172
mechanisms of evolution 167